Graphics in Design & Communication

One Volume Edition

David Anderson

Gill Education
Hume Avenue
Park West
Dublin 12
www.gilleducation.ie

Gill Education is an imprint of M.H. Gill & Co.

Design and print origination by www.hlstudios.eu.com
Artwork by Peter Bull Art Studio and www.hlstudios.eu.com

The paper used in this book is made from the wood pulp of managed forests. For every tree felled, at least one tree is planted, thereby renewing natural resources.

CONTENTS

PART 1

PLANE AND

DESCRIPTIVE GEOMETRY

AREA 1

PROJECTION SYSTEMS

Syllabus Outline

Areas to be studied:
- Definition of a plane.
- Principal planes of reference.
- Auxiliary views, including second and subsequent auxiliary views.
- True shapes of surfaces and true lengths of lines.

Learning Outcomes

Students should be able to:

Higher and Ordinary levels
- Represent three-dimensional objects in logically arranged two-dimensional views.
- Apply their knowledge of reference planes and auxiliary projection planes to solving problems using a first auxiliary view.
- Present drawings in first-angle orthographic conventional views.
- Determine the projections, inclinations, true length and true shape of lines and planes.

Higher Level only
- Apply their knowledge of reference planes and auxiliary projection planes to solving problems using a first auxiliary view and subsequent auxiliary views.
- Present drawings in third-angle orthographic conventional views.
- Determine the projections of lines given the angles of inclination to the principal planes of reference.

 # Plane

A plane is a flat surface with no thickness. If two points are selected on a plane and joined with a straight line, then the straight line will lie on the plane along its full length. Planes are considered to have no boundaries, to be limitless. We usually draw edges to the planes to help our visualisation of them.

Fig. 1.1 shows the principal planes of reference. Two planes, one vertical and one horizontal, intersect along the straight line xy. These planes divide space into four sections: first, second, third and fourth angles. When representing objects we generally place them in the first angle or the third angle and project their image onto the horizontal plane and the vertical plane. This gives first-angle projection and third-angle projection.

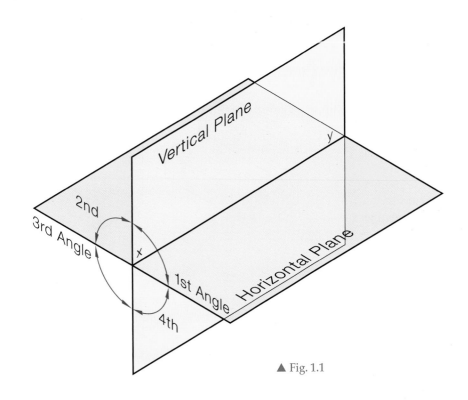

▲ Fig. 1.1

First-angle Projection

The object to be drawn is positioned in the First Angle of the intersecting vertical and horizontal planes. When we view from directly in front of the object we see the **Front Elevation**. The view that we see is projected onto the vertical plane behind. When we view from directly above the object we see the **Plan**. The view that we see is projected onto the horizontal plane below, see Fig. 1.2.

Note: The plane that we project onto must always be perpendicular to our line of sight.

▼ Fig. 1.2

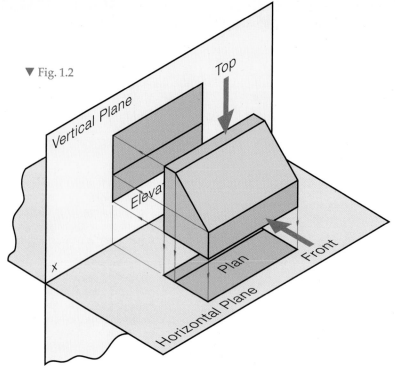

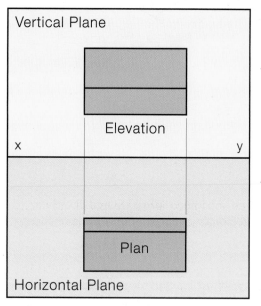

◀ Fig. 1.3   We now fold the horizontal plane down in line with the vertical plane. The plane is hinged about the xy line. This gives two views of the one object. The elevation is always directly above the plan.

The two drawings together give us a lot of information about the object but not the complete picture. This plan and elevation could represent any of the objects in Fig. 1.4. To represent the object completely we need a third view, a view from the side. When viewing from the side we need to introduce a new vertical plane onto which we project our image.

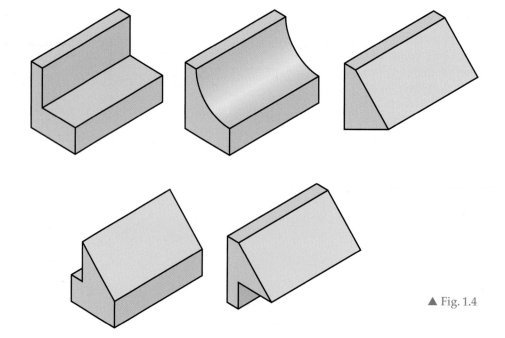

▲ Fig. 1.4

The plane must be perpendicular to the line of sight (Fig. 1.5). When we consider all three views together we have a complete representation of the object.

▼ Fig. 1.5

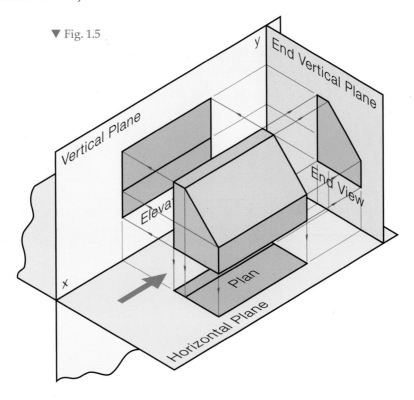

The line of intersection between the two vertical planes is called the yy line. All three planes are folded out flat as seen in Fig. 1.6. The horizontal plane is folded down, hinging along the xy line, and the end vertical plane swings back, hinging along the yy line. All three planes now lie on one plane.

As was mentioned earlier, the vertical planes and horizontal plane are limitless in size. When drawing objects in this format, **orthographic projection**, we dispense with the plane edges and just use the hinge lines, i.e. the xy line and yy line. In this example, for clarity, the object was raised up above the horizontal plane. Usually the object is placed on the horizontal plane. This means that the elevations will be on the xy line.

◀ Fig. 1.6

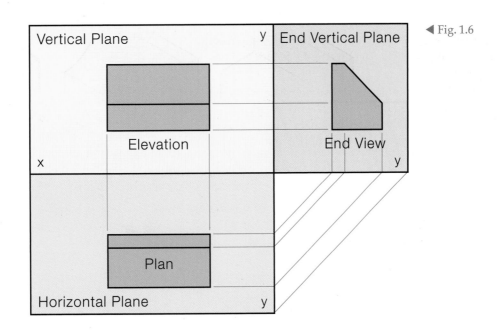

The XY Line

It is worth noting at this stage that the xy line represents several things:

(1) The line of intersection between the vertical and horizontal planes, Fig. 1.7.

(2) The xy line is the hinge line about which the horizontal plane drops down in line with the vertical plane, Fig. 1.7.

(3) When looking straight down to see the plan, the xy line represents the edge of the vertical plane, Fig. 1.8.

(4) When looking in horizontally to see the front elevation or the end elevation, the xy line represents the edge of the horizontal plane, Fig. 1.9.

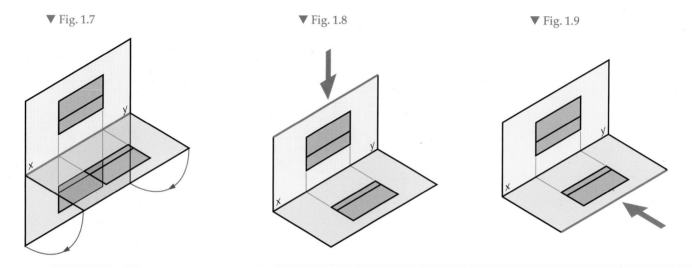

▼ Fig. 1.7   ▼ Fig. 1.8   ▼ Fig. 1.9

Fig. 1.10 shows a pictorial view of an object.
(i)   Draw a front elevation of the object looking in the direction of arrow A.
(ii) Project a plan from the front elevation.
(iii) Project an end elevation looking in the direction of arrow B.

(1) Draw the xy line first.

(2) Set up a box that will contain the front elevation on this xy line. The height will be 70 mm and the length will be 104 mm.

(3) The box for the plan is usually drawn next. The plan will be the same length and directly below the front elevation. The size of the gap between the plan and the xy line is chosen to give a good drawing layout.

▼ Fig. 1.10

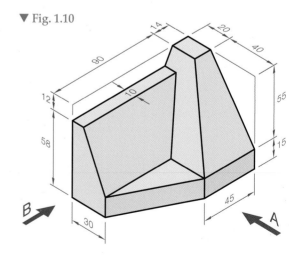

(4) The height of the box for the end elevation is projected across from the front elevation. The intersection between the xy line and the yy line gives the centre for the arcs swung up from the plan, Fig. 1.11.

These arcs represent the end vertical plane as it swings around into place.

(5) The details of the three views are built up as shown in Fig. 1.12.

▼ Fig. 1.11   ▼ Fig. 1.12

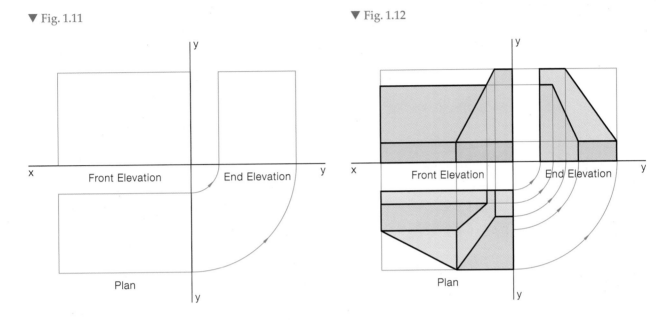

Auxiliary Elevation

The front elevation, end elevations and plan together give a huge amount of information about the object being drawn. We looked from in front of the object, from the sides and from above the object to obtain these views. The views themselves were projected onto the principal planes of reference. An object can of course be viewed from any direction and the image projected onto a new plane. Remember, the plane onto which an image is projected must be perpendicular to the line of sight. An image projected onto a vertical plane is an elevation. To see an image on a vertical plane we must view horizontally. An auxiliary elevation, therefore, is a view parallel to the horizontal plane and at an angle between 0° and 90° to the vertical plane.

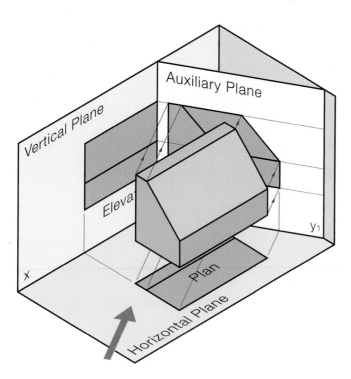

Fig. 1.13 shows the principal planes of reference. The front elevation and plan are projected in the normal way. To view in the direction of the arrow we must introduce a new vertical plane, as shown, perpendicular to the line of sight. This auxiliary plane intersects the horizontal plane along a line which we call the x_1y_1 line. The view of the object may now be projected onto this plane.

▲ Fig. 1.13

Since the line of sight is horizontal, the image is an elevation. The heights used in the auxiliary elevation will be the same heights as in all the other elevations. Fig. 1.14 shows the planes folded down flat. The projection lines are always perpendicular to the xy line. It should be noted that the auxiliary plane can be close to the object or far away from the object, it will not affect the image in any way because the projection lines are parallel.

▶ Fig. 1.14

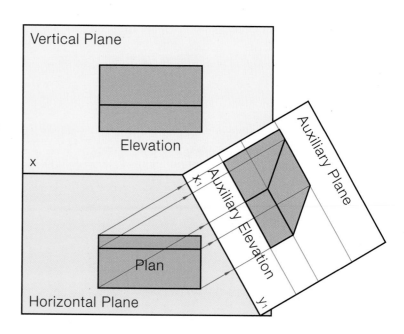

Fig. 1.15 shows the plan and elevation of an object which has been cut by a vertical plane as shown.

(i) Draw the given views.

(ii) Draw an auxiliary elevation of the object that will show the cut surface as a true shape.

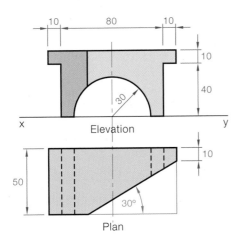

▲ Fig. 1.15

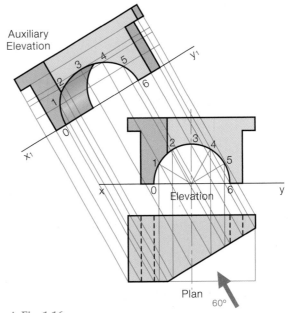

▲ Fig. 1.16

(1) Divide the semicircle into six and index the points.

(2) The cut surface is at 30° in the plan so the x_1y_1 will be at 30° and the viewing angle at 60°.

(3) Project the points from the plan and take heights from the elevation.

A pictorial drawing of a solid is shown in Fig. 1.17.

(i) Draw an elevation of the solid, viewing in the direction of arrow A.

(ii) Project a plan.

(iii) Draw an end elevation, viewing in the direction of arrow B.

(iv) Project a new elevation that will show the true shape of surface A.

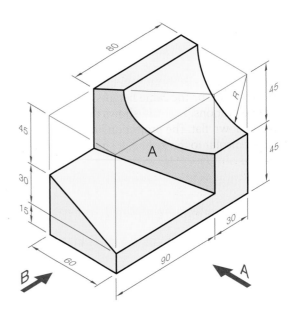

▲ Fig. 1.17

(1) Draw the xy line and set up the boxes for the views. The front elevation will be on the left and the end elevation to the right.

(2) The end elevation and the plan can be completed without difficulty.

(3) The curve in the front elevation is found by dividing the quadrant in the end elevation giving 0, 1, 2 and 3. These points are projected down to the plan and up to the front elevation. They are then projected across from the end view. Where the lines intersect gives points on the curve, Fig. 1.18.

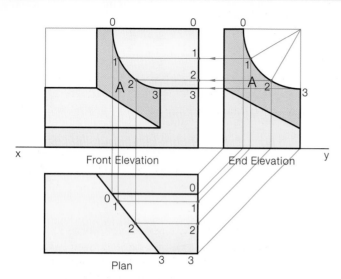

▲ Fig. 1.18

(4) In order to see the surface A as a true shape we must view it straight on. Surface A is seen as an edge view in the plan. We view perpendicular to this edge view in Fig 1.19.

(5) Draw x_1y_1 (the new vertical plane) parallel to surface A in plan and perpendicular to the line of sight.

(6) Project the points as for an ordinary elevation. Every point must be brought up including the two sets of points on the curves.

(7) The heights of all points on the auxiliary elevation will be the same as the corresponding points on the other elevations. The true shape is found in the auxiliary.

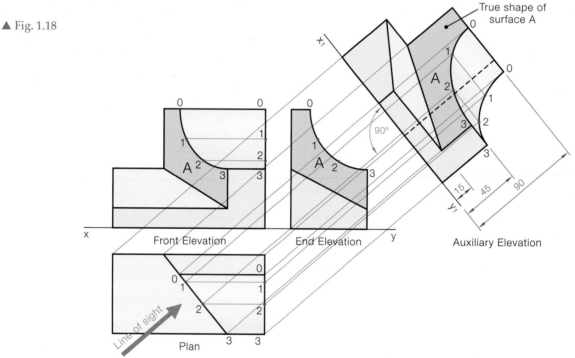

▲ Fig. 1.19

See worksheet 1.1

Auxiliary Plans

When viewing an object to see its plan we are viewing from directly above that object. The line of sight is vertical and is therefore parallel to the vertical plane. The view is projected onto the horizontal plane. When viewing an object to get an auxiliary plan we continue to view parallel to the vertical plane, but at an angle between 0° and 90° to the horizontal plane. As is always the case, the view is projected onto a plane that is perpendicular to the line of sight.

▼ . 1.20

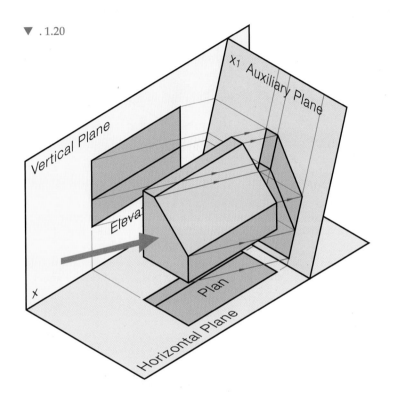

The diagram Fig.1.20 shows the principal planes of reference. The front elevation and plan of an object are shown. These are projected in the normal way. To view in the direction of the arrow we introduce a new plane perpendicular to the line of sight. The line of sight is inclined to the horizontal plane and parallel to the vertical plane. The auxiliary plane is inclined to the horizontal plane and perpendicular to the vertical plane. The x_1y_1 is the line of intersection between the auxiliary plane and the vertical plane. Since the line of sight is parallel to the vertical plane, the auxiliary plan which is produced will be the same distance from the x_1y_1 as the ordinary plan is from the xy line.

As before, the plane itself can be positioned close to, or far away from, the object as long as it is at the correct angle. Fig. 1.21 shows the planes folded back.

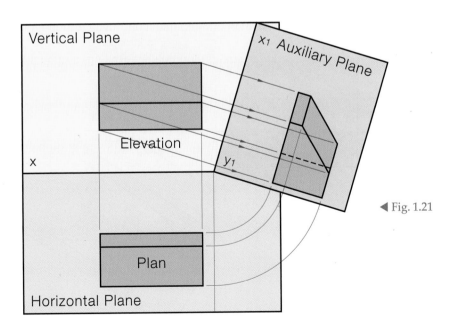

◄ Fig. 1.21

The pictorial drawing of a solid is shown in Fig. 1.22.

(i) Project a front elevation of the solid, viewing in the direction of arrow A.

(ii) Draw an end elevation, viewing in the direction of arrow B.

(iii) Project a plan.

(iv) Project a new plan of the solid showing the true shape of surface S.

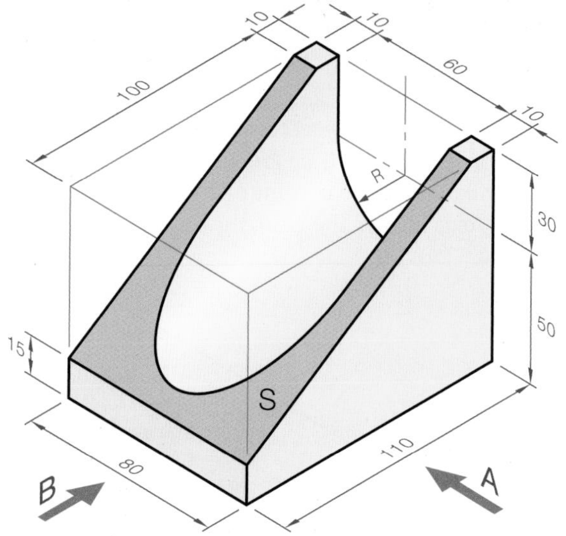

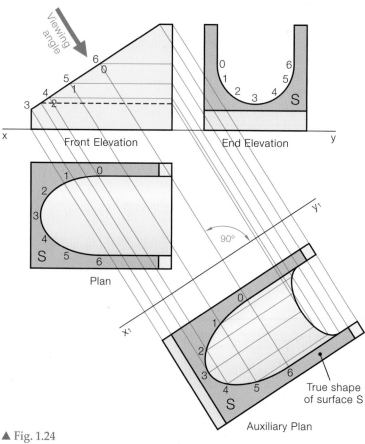

▲ Fig. 1.22

Always think through the problem before starting to plan how the various components of the solution will be positioned on the sheet.

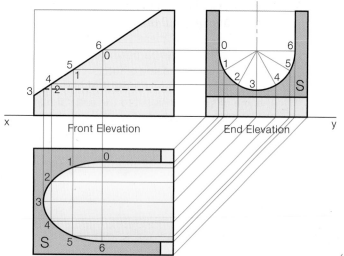

▲ Fig. 1.23

(1) Front elevation will be on the left and the end elevation to its right, Fig 1.23.

(2) Both elevations need to be completed before the plan. The curve in the plan is found in the usual way.

(3) To see the true shape of a surface we view perpendicular to the edge view.

(4) The construction is clearly shown from the illustration Fig. 1.24.

▲ Fig. 1.24

See worksheet 1.2

Further Uses of Auxiliary Views

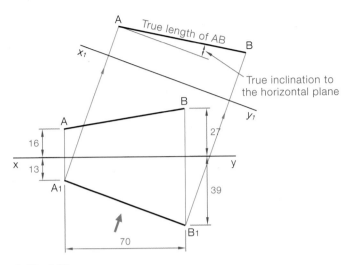

▲ Fig. 1.25

To find the true length of a line AB and to find its inclination to the horizontal plane.

(1) To see the true inclination of the line to the horizontal plane we use an auxiliary elevation. We view perpendicular to the plan of the line.

(2) Draw the x_1y_1 line parallel to the line in plan.

(3) Project the new elevation, which shows both the true length and the true inclination to the horizontal plane (HP).

To find the true length of a line AB and to find its inclination to the vertical plane.

(1) Set up the plan and elevation to the same measurements as Fig. 1.26.

(2) To see the true inclination to the vertical plane an auxiliary plan must be projected.

(3) View perpendicular to line AB in elevation.

(4) Draw x_1y_1 parallel to line AB in elevation.

(5) Project the auxiliary plan showing the true length and the required inclination.

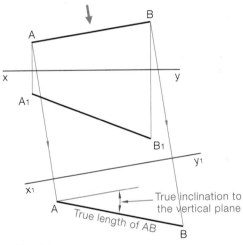

▲ Fig. 1.26

To find the inclination of a plane abcd to the horizontal plane.

Lines dc and ab are horizontal, and are therefore seen as true lengths in the plan. Project an auxiliary elevation, viewing in the direction of the true lengths. The plane abcd will appear as an edge view in the auxiliary and the angle can be seen.

Note:

(1) A line on a plane parallel to the xy line in elevation will appear as a true length in plan.

   The converse is also true.

(2) A line on a plane parallel to the xy line in plan will appear as a true length in elevation.

(3) When a line on a plane appears as a true length, viewing along the true length will show an edge view of that plane.

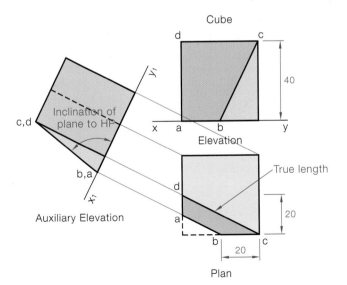

▲ Fig. 1.27

Activities

Q1. Fig. 1.28 shows the plan and elevation of an object. Make a pictorial drawing showing the planes of reference and demonstrating how the views are projected.

Q2. Make a pictorial drawing showing the planes in question one rebatted in line with the vertical plane. Show the elevation and plan in their respective positions on the planes.

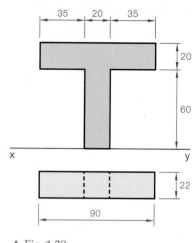

▲ Fig. 1.28

Q3. Fig. 1.29 shows the elevation and plan of a solid. Draw the given views and project an end view looking from the left.

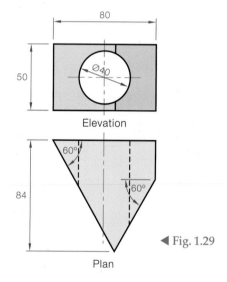

◀ Fig. 1.29

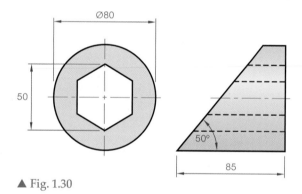

▲ Fig. 1.30

Q4. Two views of a shaped cylinder are shown in **Fig. 1.30**. Draw the given views and project a plan.

Auxiliary elevations

Q5. Given the plan and elevation in Fig. 1.31. Draw the given views and project an auxiliary elevation in the direction of arrow A.

Q6. The diagram **Fig. 1.32** shows the plan and elevation of a cylinder lying on the horizontal plane. Draw the given views and project an auxiliary elevation of the solid viewing in the direction of arrow A.

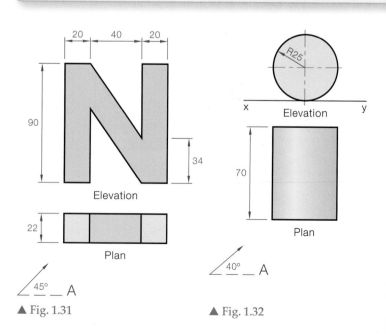

▲ Fig. 1.31   ▲ Fig. 1.32

Q7. The diagram Fig. 1.33 shows the plan, elevation and end view of a solid. Draw the given views and project an auxiliary elevation in the direction of the arrow A.

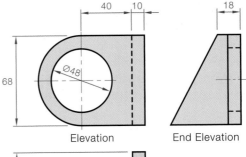

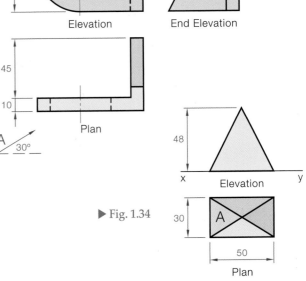

▶ Fig. 1.33

Auxiliary plans

Q8. Draw the given views, Fig. 1.34, of a rectangular-based pyramid. Project a new plan that will show the true shape of surface A.

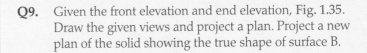

▶ Fig. 1.34

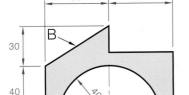
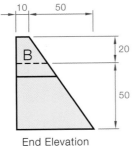

Front Elevation   End Elevation

▲ Fig. 1.35

Q9. Given the front elevation and end elevation, Fig. 1.35. Draw the given views and project a plan. Project a new plan of the solid showing the true shape of surface B.

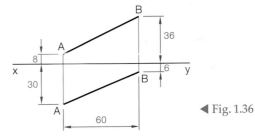

◀ Fig. 1.36

Q10. Given the plan and elevation of a line AB, Fig. 1.36. Find the true length of the line and its true inclination to the horizontal plane using an auxiliary view.

Q11. Given the plan of a line AB and the elevation of one end of the line, A, Fig. 1.37. The true inclination of this line is to be 30° to the horizontal plan. Draw the elevation.

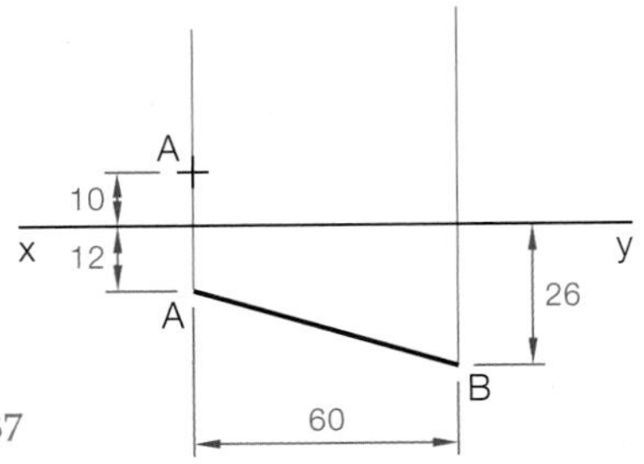

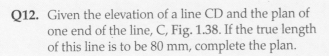

▶ Fig. 1.37

Q12. Given the elevation of a line CD and the plan of one end of the line, C, Fig. 1.38. If the true length of this line is to be 80 mm, complete the plan.

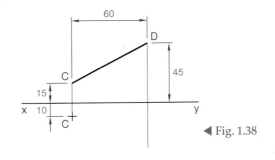

◀ Fig. 1.38

Third-angle Projection

Third-angle projection is the system of orthographic projection which is more favoured in America whereas first-angle projection is more favoured in Europe. The object to be drawn is placed in the third angle of the intersecting reference planes. The views are found by looking **through** the planes.

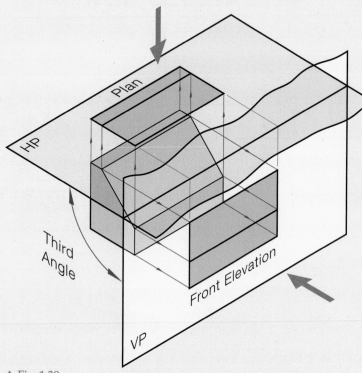

▲ Fig. 1.39

Fig. 1.39 shows the arrangement of planes and object. The front elevation is found by looking through the vertical plane. The view that is seen is what is projected onto the plane. Similarly, for the plan, we look down through the horizontal plane. The view that is seen is projected up to the horizontal plane.

The horizontal plane is hinged about the xy line until it is vertical. The plan, therefore, is above the xy line and the front elevation is below the plan and the xy line.

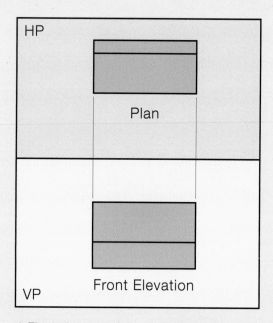

▲ Fig. 1.40

The two end views are drawn in line with the front elevation, Fig. 1.40. They can be projected in a similar way as was done in first-angle projection. It should be noted that we are viewing through the plane and then projecting the image back onto the same plane. The end elevation on the left, therefore, will be the view from the left and the end elevation to the right of the front elevation will be the view from the right of the object.

Symbol

The angle of projection must be stated on a drawing either by using text or by using the appropriate symbol, Figures 1.41a and 1.41b.

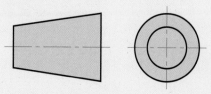

▲ Fig. 1.41a First-angle Projection

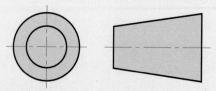

▲ Fig. 1.41b Third-angle Projection

A pictorial drawing of an object is shown in **Fig. 1.42**. Using third-angle projection draw:

(i) A front elevation looking in the direction of arrow A.

(ii) A plan.

(iii) An end elevation projected from the other two views.

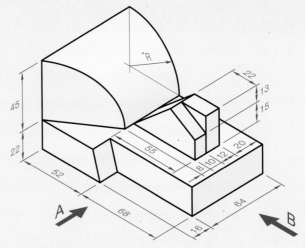

▲ Fig. 1.42

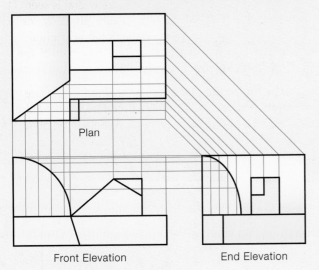

Plan

Front Elevation   End Elevation

▲ Fig. 1.43

(1) Set up the relative positions of the three views. The arrow A is pointing from the left so the front elevation will be drawn on the left.

(2) The plan is directly above the front elevation.

(3) The arrow B is viewing from the right so the end elevation will be to the right of the front elevation.

(4) The symbol must be used to indicate third-angle projection, Fig. 1.43.

Fig. 1.44 shows a pictorial view of a shaped block. Using third-angle projection draw:

(i) A front elevation viewing in the direction of arrow A.

(ii) A plan.

(iii) An end elevation viewed in the direction of arrow B.

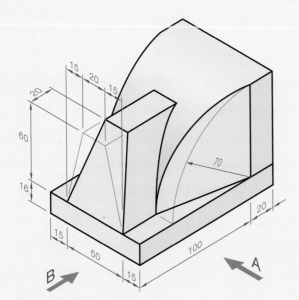

▲ Fig. 1.44

Fig.1.45 shows a possible arrangement for the xy line and the yy line. The construction of the views themselves should be straightforward.

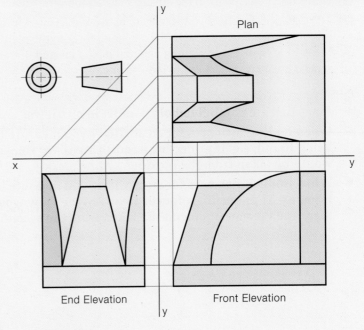

End Elevation   Front Elevation

▲ Fig. 1.45

Second Auxiliary Views

Once an auxiliary view is constructed it can be used as a basis for another auxiliary. The second auxiliary can be used to get a third auxiliary view and so on. An auxiliary plan can only be projected from an elevation or an auxiliary elevation. Similarly, an auxiliary elevation can only be projected from a plan or an auxiliary plan.

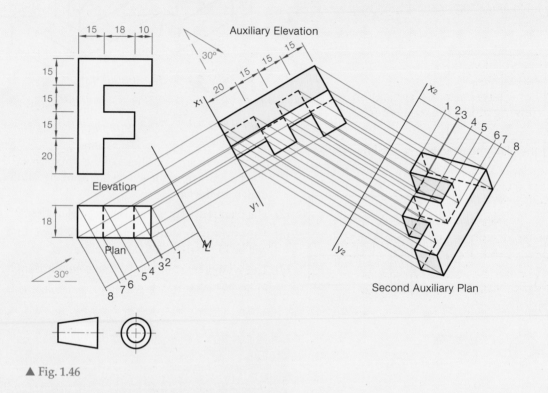

▲ Fig. 1.46

(1) Draw the elevation, plan and auxiliary elevation in the normal way, Fig. 1.46.

(2) The new line of sight is shown at 30° to the x_1y_1. Set up the x_2y_2 perpendicular to this line of sight.

(3) Points are projected from the auxiliary elevation in the direction of the line of sight.

(4) The distances for the second auxiliary plan are measured from the x_1y_1 back to the plan for each point. It is often useful to put a line, parallel to the x_1y_1 line, closer to the plan. This line is called a **measuring line** or a **datum line**. Measuring from the measuring line to the plan instead of from the x_1y_1 line to the plan has the effect of bringing the second auxiliary plan closer to the x_2y_2 line.

Note:

- **Lines that are parallel remain parallel in all views.**
- **When finding distances for an auxiliary you measure from the xy line before the one for the view being found, e.g. if projecting a fourth auxiliary we would be drawing it from x_4y_4. Measurements would be taken from the previous xy line, i.e. x_3y_3.**
- **When finding distances for an auxiliary you measure to the view before the view being projected from, e.g. if projecting a fourth auxiliary, the view would be projected from the third auxiliary, therefore the measurements are taken from the second auxiliary.**

Applications of Second Auxiliary View

> To project the point view of a line.

A point view of a line is when a view is taken down the length of the line and the whole line is only seen as a point. Only the end of the line is seen and it is a dot.

> **To obtain a point view of a line, a view is projected to show the true length of the line. A subsequent view is then taken viewing along the true length.**

(1) Project the plan and elevation of the line.

(2) Draw x_1y_1 parallel to the line in plan and project an auxiliary elevation. This auxiliary elevation shows line AB as a true length.

(3) The second auxiliary is projected from the first, viewing along the true length. The x_2y_2 is perpendicular to the true length.

(4) Both A and B end on the same point, as they are both distance d from the x_1y_1 in the plan.

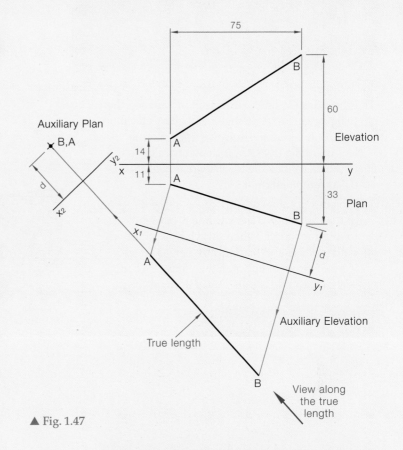

▲ Fig. 1.47

Given a tetrahedron of 75 mm side which is cut as shown in **Fig. 1.48**. Project a view of the given solid showing the true shape of the cut surface.

(1) The edge 1,2 is horizontal and is therefore seen as a true length in plan.

> **If we view along the true length of a line, the plane on which the line rests will be seen as an edge view.**

Project the auxiliary elevation with x_1y_1 perpendicular to 1,2 in plan.

(2) Project perpendicular to the edge view to show the true shape. Draw x_2y_2 parallel to the edge view. Distances for the second auxiliary plan are taken from the x_1y_1 back to the plan.

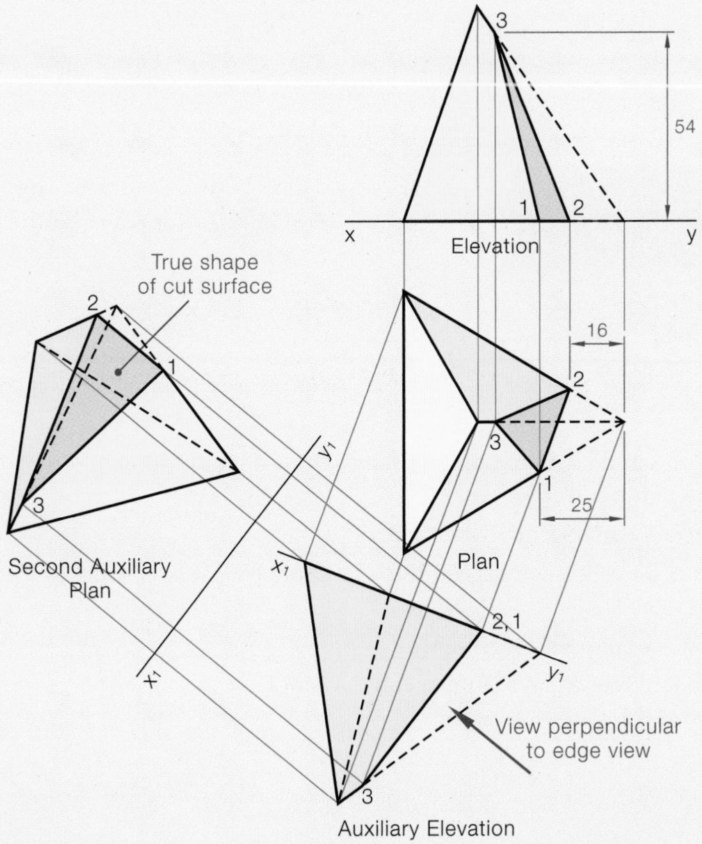

◀ Fig. 1.48

HIGHER LEVEL

> Given the solid, Fig. 1.49.
> Side 1,2 = 60 mm, side 1,3 = 75 mm, side 2,3 = 80 mm.
> Find the true angle between surfaces A and B.

(1) Line 0,3 is the line of intersection between the two planes. Project either an auxiliary elevation or auxiliary plan to show this line as a true length. In Fig. 1.49 x_1y_1 is drawn parallel to 0,3 in the elevation. The auxiliary plan will show 0,3 as a true length.

(2) Project a point view of 0,3. View in the direction of the true length. The x_2y_2 line is perpendicular to the true length. When this view is projected, both plane A and plane B are seen as edge views. The angle between the planes is clearly seen. This angle is called the **dihedral angle**.

See worksheet 1.3

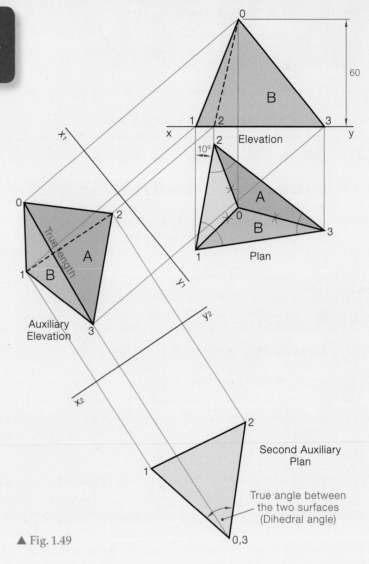

▲ Fig. 1.49

Projection of Lines Given Angles of Inclination

> Given the elevation of a line AB and its true inclination to the horizontal plane as 30°. Draw the plan of the line given one point.

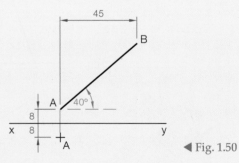

◀ Fig. 1.50

(1) The heights of A and B will remain the same. Draw a line starting at A in elevation and at the correct angle.

(2) Project B across to intersect this line at B.

(3) Project to plan. Since it is a true length in elevation it must be parallel to the xy line in plan.

(4) Rotate the line about point A in plan.

(5) Drop point B from elevation to intersect the rotation.

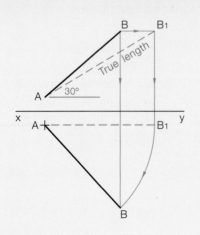

▲ Fig. 1.51

Given the elevation of a line AB and its true inclination to the vertical plane as 20°. Given one point on the plan, complete the plan.

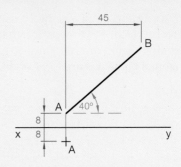

▶ Fig. 1.52

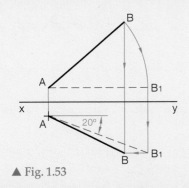

▲ Fig. 1.53

(1) Rotate line AB about A in elevation until it is horizontal.

(2) Project to plan. The line when horizontal will make an angle of 20° to the xy line. Draw the line from A at 20° to the xy line, locating point B.

(3) B1 can be projected across locating B in plan as shown in Fig.1.52.

Given the plan of a line AB and the elevation of point B. The true length of the line is 60 mm. Find the elevation of the line.

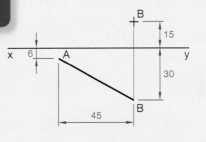

▲ Fig. 1.54

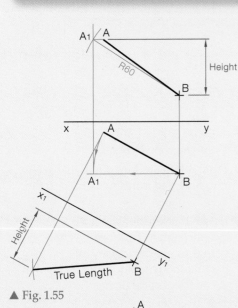

▲ Fig. 1.55

(1) Two approaches to solving this problem are shown in Fig. 1.55.

(2) The line is rotated about point B in plan until it is parallel to xy, giving A. A projection line is brought vertically from A1 to elevation. The true length of AB is swung from B in elevation finding A1. Point A is found in elevation by projection.

(3) The alternative method uses an auxiliary view. The construction is self-explanatory.

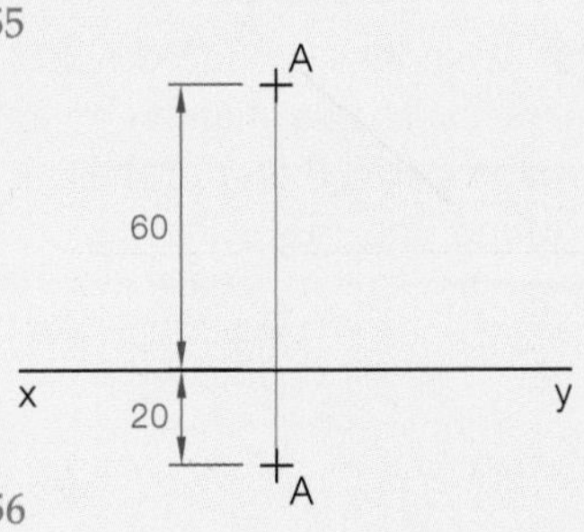

Given the true length of a line AB, its true angle to the vertical plane and its true angle to the horizontal plane. Draw a plan and elevation of the line in Fig. 1.56.

Length = 60 mm, Angle to vertical plane (VP) = 20°, Angle to HP = 40°.

▲ Fig. 1.56

(1) Locate point A in plan and elevation.

(2) From A in the elevation, draw a line that is 60 mm long and is inclined at 40° to the horizontal plane.

HIGHER LEVEL

(3) Rotate this line about a vertical axis through A. This forms a cone with A as apex having every generator 60 mm long and inclined at 40° to the horizontal plane, Figures 1.57 and 1.58.

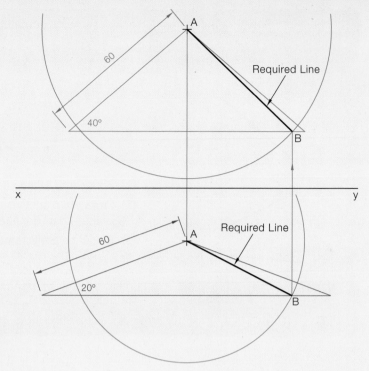

▲ Fig. 1.57

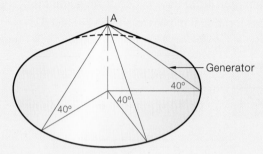

▲ Fig.1.58

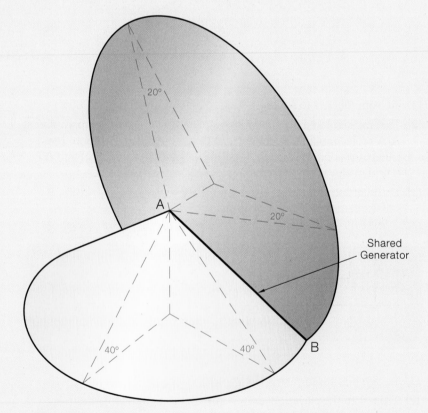

▲ Fig. 1.59

(4) Draw the cone in plan.

(5) From A in plan draw a line that is 60 mm long and is inclined at 20° to the vertical plane.

(6) Rotate this line about a horizontal axis through A. This forms a cone with A as apex having every generator 60 mm long and inclined at 20° to the vertical plane.

(7) The two cones produced will intersect along a shared generator in two locations. Either of these is the required line, Fig. 1.59.

Activities

Third-angle projection

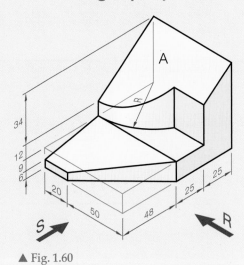

▲ Fig. 1.60

Q1. The diagram, Fig. 1.60, shows a shaped solid.

    (i) In third-angle projection draw a front elevation viewing in the direction of arrow R.

    (ii) Draw an end view looking in the direction of arrow S.

    (iii) Project a plan from these views.

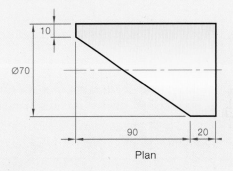

Plan

▲ Fig. 1.61

Q2. The diagram, Fig. 1.61, shows the plan of a cylinder which has been cut by a vertical plane. In third-angle projection draw:

    (i) The front elevation.

    (ii) An end elevation viewing from the left.

    (iii) An auxiliary elevation viewing perpendicular to the cut surface. Include hidden detail and the third-angle symbol.

Q3. The diagram in **Fig. 1.62** shows the elevation and plan of a letter.

    (i) Draw the given views.

    (ii) Project an auxiliary elevation onto the x_1y_1.

    (iii) Project a second auxiliary plan onto x_2y_2.

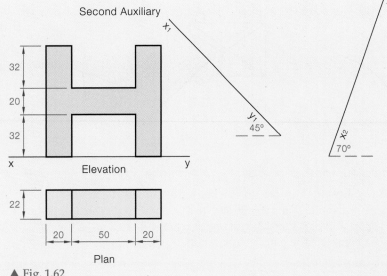

▲ Fig. 1.62

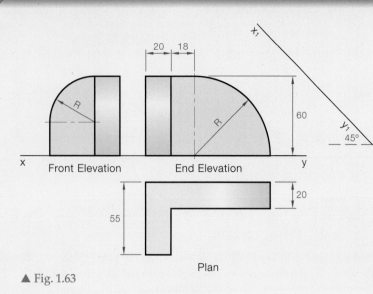

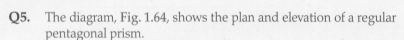

Front Elevation   End Elevation

Plan

▲ Fig. 1.63

Q4. Draw the views indicated in Fig. 1.63 and project an auxiliary elevation and a second auxiliary plan on the xy lines shown.

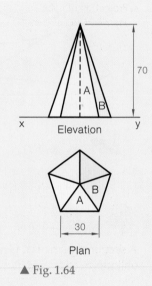

Elevation

Plan

▲ Fig. 1.64

Q5. The diagram, Fig. 1.64, shows the plan and elevation of a regular pentagonal prism.
   (i) Draw the given views.
   (ii) Project a new elevation showing the true length of the line of intersection between surfaces A and B.
   (iii) Project a second auxiliary plan showing the dihedral angle between surfaces A and B.

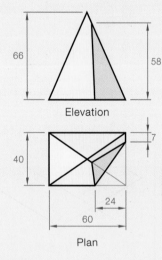

Elevation

Plan

▲ Fig. 1.65

Q6. A rectangular-based pyramid has been cut by a plane as shown in Fig. 1.65.
   (i) Draw the given views.
   (ii) Project an auxiliary elevation which will show the true angle the cutting plane makes with the horizontal plane.
   (iii) Project a second auxiliary plan showing the true shape of the cut surface.

Q7. Given the true length of a line as 70 mm, its true angle to the horizontal plane as 45° and its true angle to the vertical plane as 30°, Fig. 1.66. Given the projections of one end of the line, complete the plan and elevation.

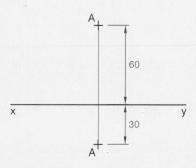

▲ Fig. 1.66

2 Sections of Solids

Syllabus Outline

Areas to be studied:
- Sectional views.
- Projection of cube and tetrahedron, *their inscribed and circumscribed spheres.*

Learning Outcomes

Students should be able to:

Higher and Ordinary levels
- Solve problems that involve the intersection of solids by simply inclined planes and obliquely inclined planes, using horizontal and vertical section planes.
- Represent in two dimensions the cube and tetrahedron from given information.

Higher Level only
- Solve problems that involve the intersection of solids by simply inclined planes and obliquely inclined planes using simply inclined section planes.
- Determine the incentre and circumcentre of cube and tetrahedron.

 Sectional Planes

A sectional plane is a plane which slices through an object. These planes can be horizontal, vertical, simply inclined or oblique. Sectional planes are used to reveal the inside of an object or can be used to help solve the interpenetration of solids. See Figures 2.1, 2.2, 2.3 and 2.4.

Horizontal Section Plane

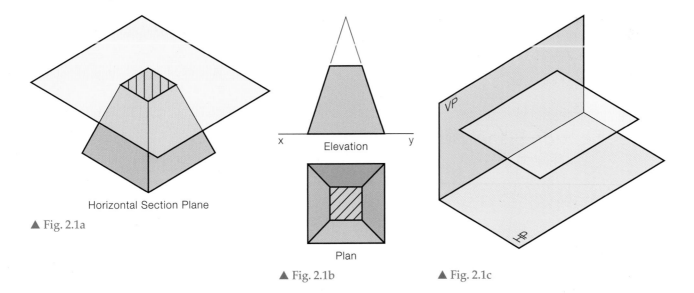

Horizontal Section Plane

▲ Fig. 2.1a

Elevation

Plan

▲ Fig. 2.1b

▲ Fig. 2.1c

Vertical Section Plane

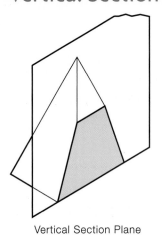

Vertical Section Plane

▲ Fig. 2.2a

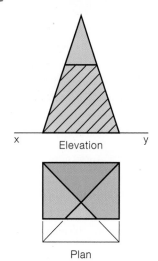

Elevation

Plan

▲ Fig. 2.2b

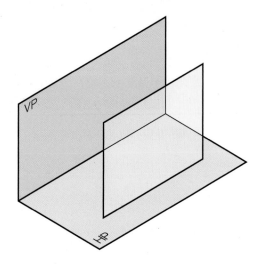

▲ Fig. 2.2c

Simply Inclined Section Plane

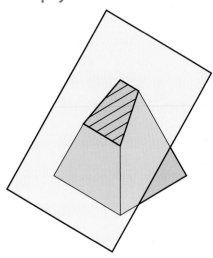

Simply Inclined Section Plane

▲ Fig. 2.3a

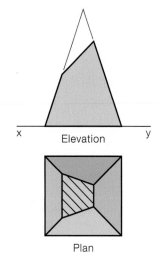

Elevation

Plan

▲ Fig. 2.3b

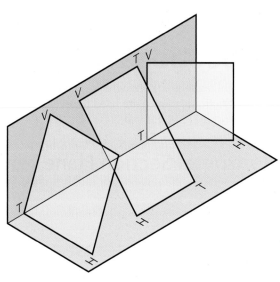

▲ Fig. 2.3c

Oblique Section Plane

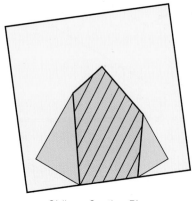

Oblique Section Plane

▲ Fig. 2.4a

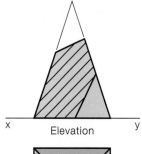

Elevation

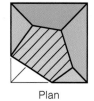

Plan

▲ Fig. 2.4b

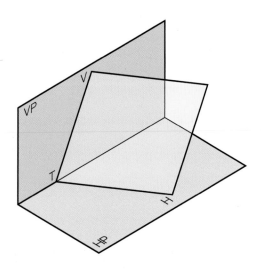

▲ Fig. 2.4c

Traces of a Plane

When a plane meets another plane the line of intersection will always be a straight line. If a plane is extended to meet the horizontal plane the straight line produced is called the horizontal trace. Similarly, if a plane is extended to meet the vertical plane the straight line produced is called the vertical trace. When the plane intersects both planes simultaneously it will have both a horizontal trace and a vertical trace. These traces will always meet on the xy line except for one type of plane shown in Fig. 2.5. In this case the traces run parallel to the xy line.

Fig. 2.5 shows the plane pictorially while Fig. 2.6 shows the representation of the same plane in orthographic projection.

All planes can be represented orthographically by their traces. Fig. 2.7 shows a number of plane types in a pictorial view while Fig. 2.8 shows the corresponding orthographic representation of the same planes.

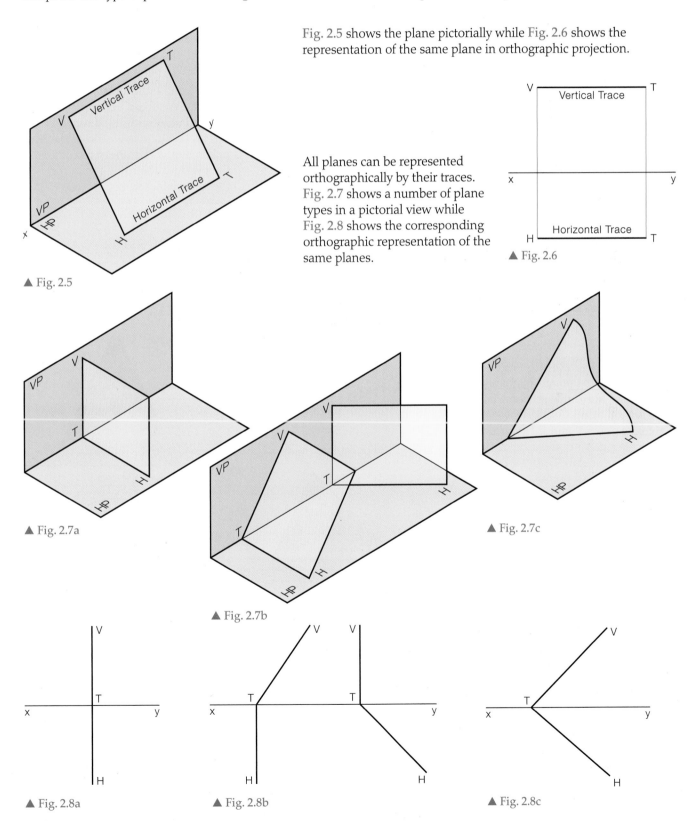

▲ Fig. 2.5

▲ Fig. 2.6

▲ Fig. 2.7a

▲ Fig. 2.7b

▲ Fig. 2.7c

▲ Fig. 2.8a

▲ Fig. 2.8b

▲ Fig. 2.8c

Projection of Solids Cut by Simply Inclined Planes

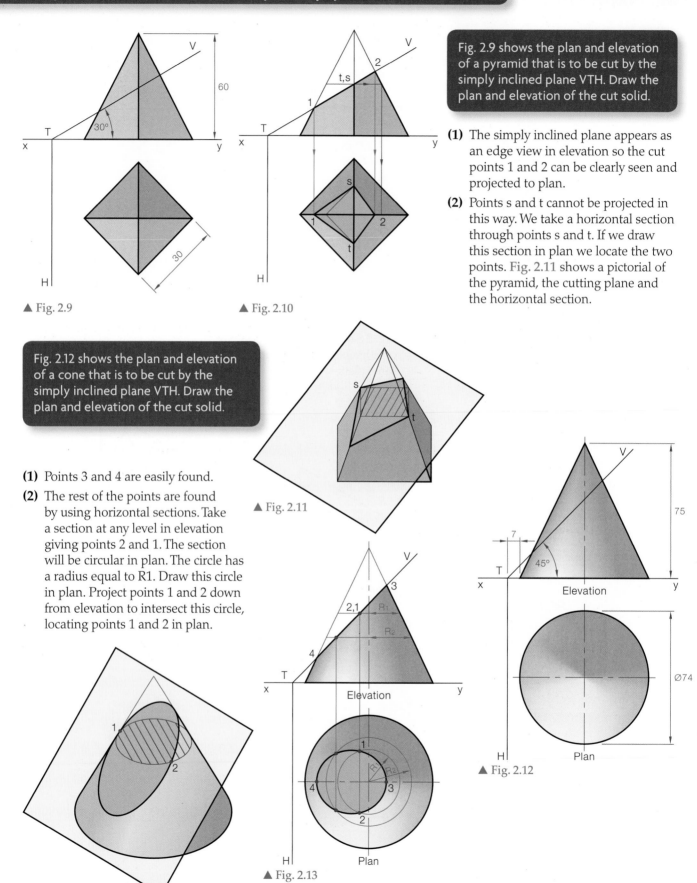

▲ Fig. 2.9

▲ Fig. 2.10

Fig. 2.9 shows the plan and elevation of a pyramid that is to be cut by the simply inclined plane VTH. Draw the plan and elevation of the cut solid.

(1) The simply inclined plane appears as an edge view in elevation so the cut points 1 and 2 can be clearly seen and projected to plan.

(2) Points s and t cannot be projected in this way. We take a horizontal section through points s and t. If we draw this section in plan we locate the two points. Fig. 2.11 shows a pictorial of the pyramid, the cutting plane and the horizontal section.

Fig. 2.12 shows the plan and elevation of a cone that is to be cut by the simply inclined plane VTH. Draw the plan and elevation of the cut solid.

(1) Points 3 and 4 are easily found.

(2) The rest of the points are found by using horizontal sections. Take a section at any level in elevation giving points 2 and 1. The section will be circular in plan. The circle has a radius equal to R1. Draw this circle in plan. Project points 1 and 2 down from elevation to intersect this circle, locating points 1 and 2 in plan.

▲ Fig. 2.11

▲ Fig. 2.12

▲ Fig. 2.13

▲ Fig. 2.14

Projection of Solids Cut by Oblique Planes

The rectangular prism shown in Fig. 2.15 is to be cut by the oblique plane VTH. Draw the plan and elevation of the cut solid.

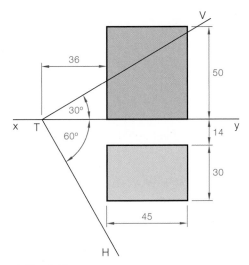

▲ Fig. 2.15

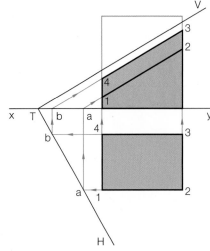

▲ Fig. 2.16

We use vertical section planes to solve this problem. A vertical plane, running parallel to the xy line in plan, will intersect the oblique plane along a line which will be parallel to the VT of the oblique plane. Construction as shown in Fig. 2.16.

A regular rectangular prism is to be cut by the oblique plane VTH, Fig. 2.17. Project the plan and elevation of the cut solid.

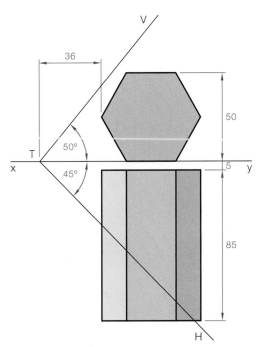

▲ Fig. 2.17

Horizontal section planes are used to produce lines of intersection with the oblique plane which are parallel to the horizontal trace. Construction as shown in Fig. 2.18.

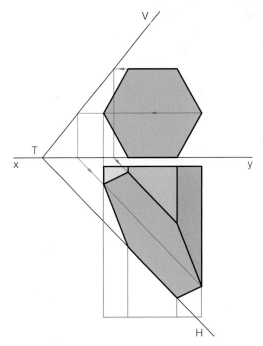

▲ Fig. 2.18

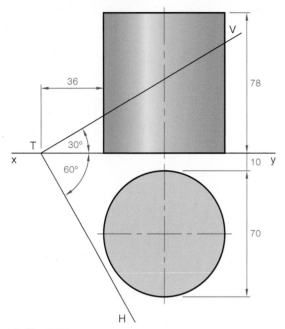

36

78

T
x   30°
      60°   10   y

                                                   70

H

▲ Fig. 2.19

The plan and elevation of a cylinder are shown in Fig. 2.19. Show the projections of this cylinder when it has been cut by the oblique plane VTH.

In this example the problem is solved using a series of vertical planes.

(1) A vertical plane is drawn to cut the cylinder in plan giving points 1 and 7.

(2) This vertical plane will intersect the oblique plane along a straight line which will run on the cut surface (see Fig. 2.21).

(3) This line of intersection is parallel to the vertical trace.

(4) Draw the line in elevation and project points 1 and 7 onto it. Repeat as necessary.

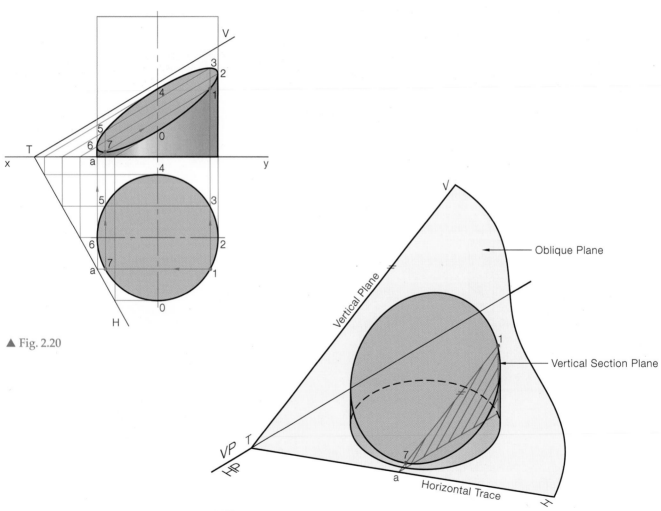

▲ Fig. 2.20

▲ Fig. 2.21

Fig. 2.22 shows a cone which is to be cut by a simply inclined plane.
Using simply inclined section planes, determine the cut surface.

If we use simply inclined section planes with each containing the apex
of the cone, the sections produced will be triangles (see Fig. 2.24).
Construction of solution is shown in Fig. 2.23.

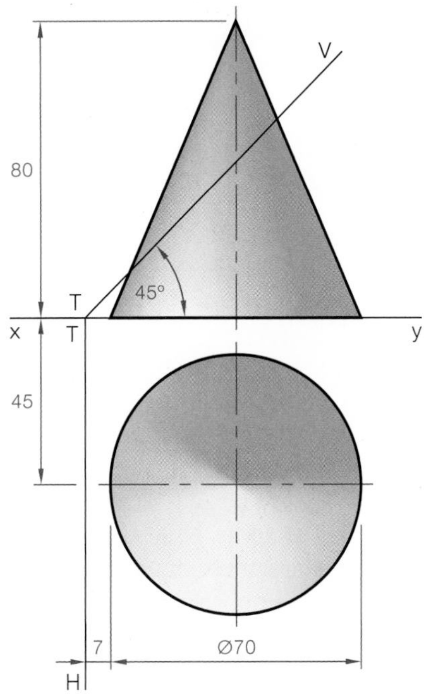

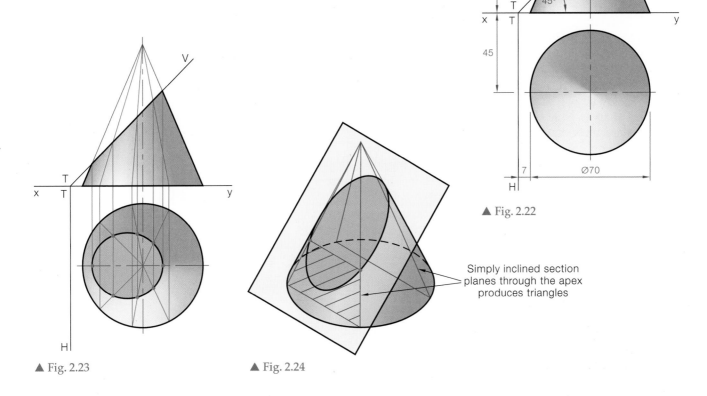

▲ Fig. 2.22

▲ Fig. 2.23

▲ Fig. 2.24

Simply inclined section
planes through the apex
produces triangles

Cube and Tetrahedron

The Cube

This is by far the most familiar of the five regular polyhedra:

- Tetrahedron
- Cube
- Octahedron
- Dodecahedron
- Icosahedron.

A cube has six faces, eight vertices and twelve edges. Each face is a square, three of which come together at each vertex. It is the only regular polyhedron that can be tiled by itself to fill three-dimensional space. A cube of unit edge is defined as the unit of volume and all other volumes are measured by the number of unit cubes they can contain. Another name for the cube is the **regular hexahedron**.

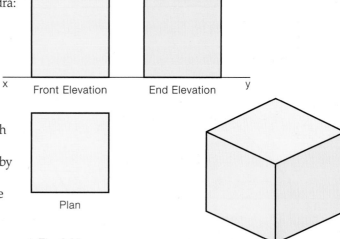

Front Elevation   End Elevation

x   y

Plan

▲ Fig. 2.25

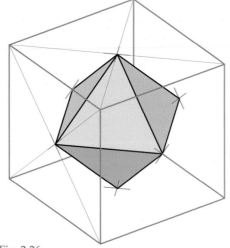

▲ Fig. 2.26
Dual of a cube is an octahedron.

Duality

For every polyhedron there exists a dual polyhedron. Just looking at the regular polyhedra, it will be shown that the tetrahedron is self-dual and the cube and the octahedron are a dual pair. (The icosahedron and the dodecahedron are another dual pair but will not be looked at here.) Find the centre of each face by joining the diagonals. This gives the six vertices of the octahedron. Join each corner to its four neighbours, Fig. 2.26.

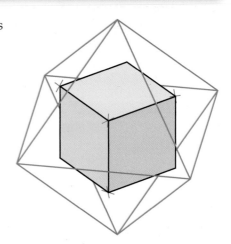

▲ Fig. 2.27
Dual of an octahedron is a cube.

What is even more interesting is that the dual of a regular octahedron is a cube. Finding the dual of the dual will give back the original solid.

Tetrahedron inside a cube

All the faces of a cube are squares of equal size. The diagonals of each square are therefore also equal. The six face diagonals in the cube in Fig. 2.28 form the edges of a tetrahedron. There are two possible arrangements of such tetrahedrons inside a cube.

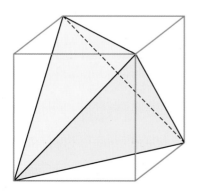

▲ Fig. 2.28

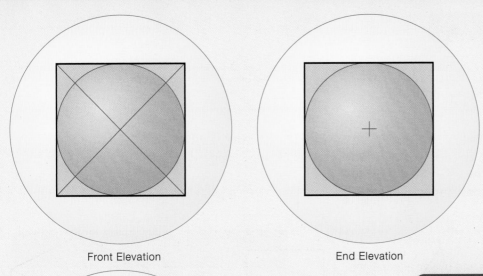

Front Elevation   End Elevation

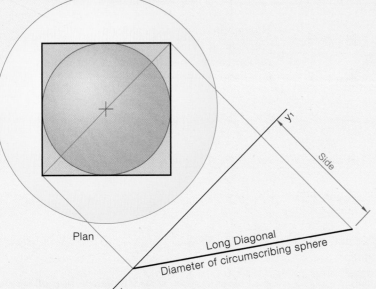

Plan

Long Diagonal
Diameter of circumscribing sphere

Side

y₁

x₁

▲ Fig. 2.29

To inscribe and circumscribe a cube

The inscribed sphere and the circumscribed sphere share the same centre point. The radius of the inscribed sphere equals half the length of the square's sides. Its centre is located by joining the diagonals of the square. For the circumscribed sphere diagonally opposite corners of the cube are in contact with the sphere so therefore this sphere's diameter equals the long diagonal of the cube. The true length of this diagonal is found by drawing an auxiliary.

HIGHER LEVEL

The Tetrahedron

A tetrahedron is the simplest possible polyhedron. It has four faces, four vertices and six edges. Each face is an equilateral triangle for a regular tetrahedron.

Construction

(1) Draw the plan which is an equilateral triangle and bisect each angle to locate point 0, Fig. 2.30.

(2) Edge 2,0 will be seen as a true length in end view. Project vertex 2 to the xy line and scribe an arc, centre at vertex 2, to intersect the line projected for the apex 0.

(3) Complete the end view and front elevation.

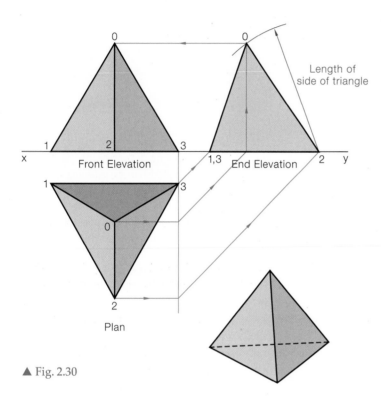

▲ Fig. 2.30

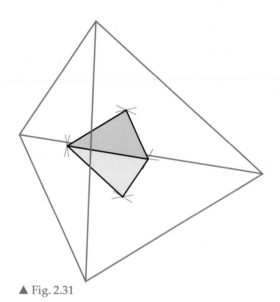

Duality

The tetrahedron stands alone as a self-dual polyhedron. When the centroid of each face is found and joined to its neighbours another tetrahedron is formed, Fig. 2.31.

▲ Fig. 2.31

To inscribe and circumscribe a tetrahedron

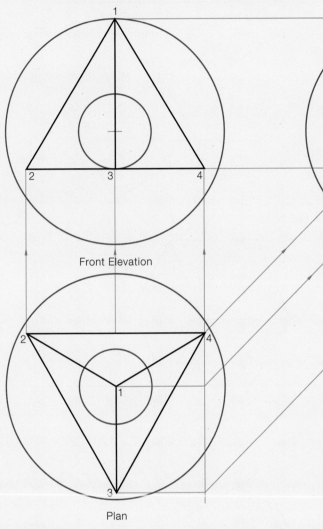

Front Elevation

End Elevation

Plan

▲ Fig. 2.32

The inscribed and circumscribed spheres share the same centre point.

(1) Draw a view of the tetrahedron that shows two faces as edge views. The end view is used in this example.

(2) Drop a perpendicular from the apex and bisect the angle 1,4,3 between the two edge view faces.

(3) With C as centre both spheres can be drawn. We have seen earlier how a tetrahedron can fit into a cube. This cube and tetrahedron will share the same circumscribing sphere.

Worked Problems

The plan of a square abcd which is inclined at 40° to the HP is shown in Fig. 2.33. The edge ab rests on the horizontal plane. The square is the base of a cube. Draw the plan and elevation of the solid.

(1) Line ab rests on the horizontal plane and is therefore a true length.

(2) Complete the square abc_1d_1. This represents the cube base resting on the horizontal plane.

(3) Project an auxiliary view showing ab as a point view. Project d_1c_1.

(4) Rotate the base in the auxiliary, about ab, to make a 40° angle with the x_1y_1.

(5) Complete the cube in auxiliary by rotating d_1c_1 onto the 40° line and completing a square.

(6) Project the corners back to plan. The points in plan move perpendicular to the hinge line ab.

(7) Heights for the elevation are found from the auxiliary.

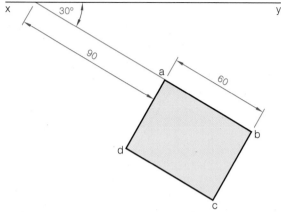

▲ Fig. 2.33

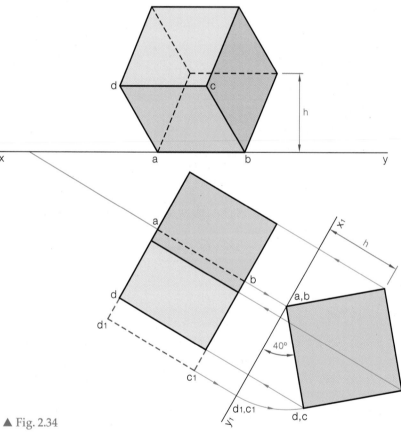

▲ Fig. 2.34

The elevation of a cube of 50 mm side is shown in Fig. 2.35. Draw the plan and elevation of the cube.

(1) Set up line ac in elevation. Project an auxiliary plan from this with x_1y_1 parallel to ac. This view will show the true shape of abcd.

(2) Construct a square of correct size, and find the length of its diagonal. Start with a point c in auxiliary plan. Swing an arc, centre c, radius equal to the diagonal, to locate point a. Complete the square in auxiliary.

(3) Project back to the front elevation and plan, similar to the previous example.

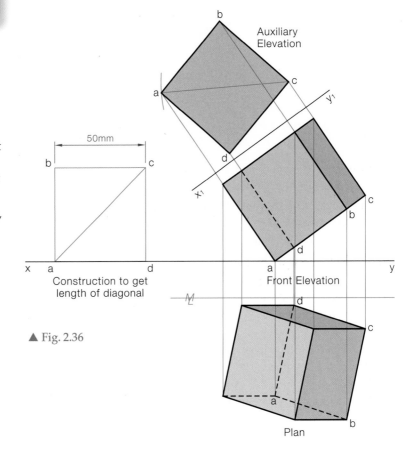

▲ Fig. 2.36

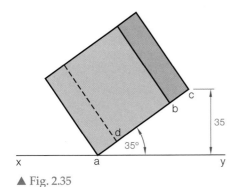

▲ Fig. 2.35

The plan of the base of a tetrahedron is shown in Fig. 2.37. Edge ab rests on the horizontal plane. Draw the plan and elevation of the solids.

◀ Fig. 2.37

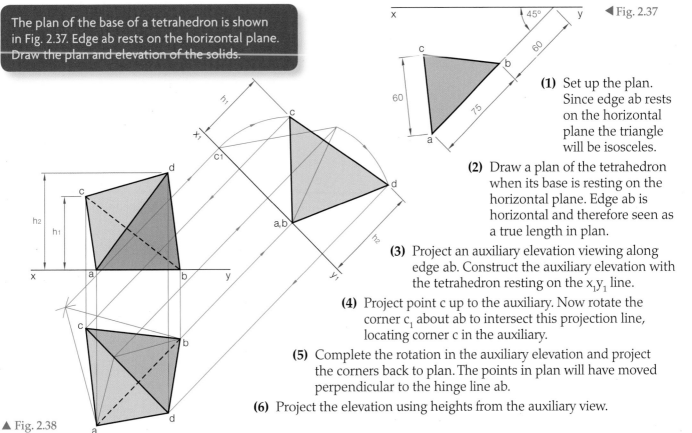

(1) Set up the plan. Since edge ab rests on the horizontal plane the triangle will be isosceles.

(2) Draw a plan of the tetrahedron when its base is resting on the horizontal plane. Edge ab is horizontal and therefore seen as a true length in plan.

(3) Project an auxiliary elevation viewing along edge ab. Construct the auxiliary elevation with the tetrahedron resting on the x_1y_1 line.

(4) Project point c up to the auxiliary. Now rotate the corner c_1 about ab to intersect this projection line, locating corner c in the auxiliary.

(5) Complete the rotation in the auxiliary elevation and project the corners back to plan. The points in plan will have moved perpendicular to the hinge line ab.

(6) Project the elevation using heights from the auxiliary view.

▲ Fig. 2.38

The plan of a sphere resting on the horizontal plane is shown in Fig. 2.39. The sphere is inscribed in a regular tetrahedron. Draw the plan and elevation of the tetrahedron.

There is only one size of tetrahedron that will fit around this sphere, but it can be positioned in an infinite number of aspects. It is simplest to place it with one face resting on the HP and another appearing edge on in elevation.

(1) Draw the sphere in plan and elevation.

(2) Draw a tetrahedron, of any size, such that the solid's apex is above the sphere centre in plan and that two faces appear as edge views.

(3) Enlarge this solid to the required size so that the two faces, seen edge on in elevation, will be tangential to the sphere.

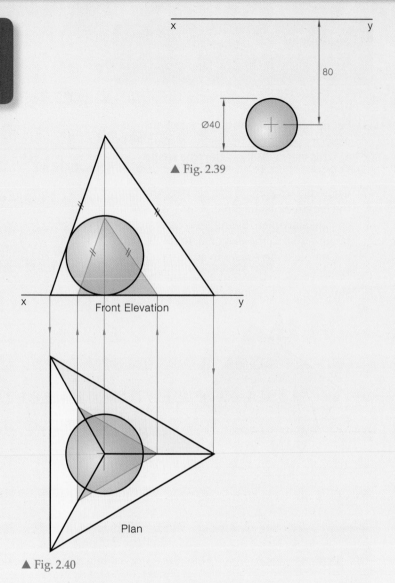

▲ Fig. 2.39

Front Elevation

Plan

▲ Fig. 2.40

Activities

Section plane types

Q1. Make neat freehand sketches of the horizontal and vertical projection planes showing the following plane types:
- Horizontal section plane,
- Vertical section plane,
- Simply inclined section plane,
- Oblique section plane.

Draw a separate diagram for each plane type.

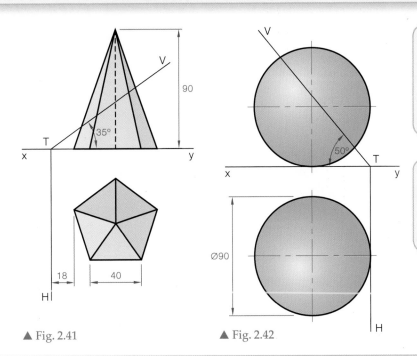

▲ Fig. 2.41

▲ Fig. 2.42

Q2. The pentagonal right pyramid shown in Fig. **2.41** is cut by the simply inclined plane VTH. Find the cut surface with the aid of horizontal section planes.

Q3. A sphere resting on the horizontal plane is to be cut by the simply inclined plane VTH, Fig. **2.42**. Find the cut surface using horizontal section planes.

Q4. Using horizontal or vertical section planes, find the cut surface of the hexagonal prism shown in Fig. **2.43**.

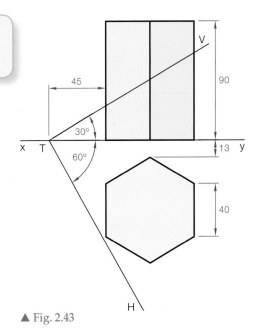

▲ Fig. 2.43

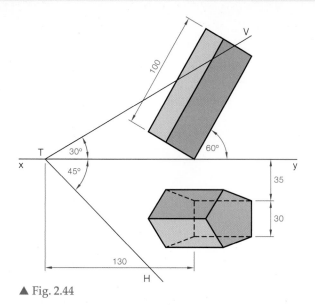

▲ Fig. 2.44

Q5. A regular, right, pentagonal prism has been tilted onto one edge as shown in **Fig. 2.44**. The prism is to be cut by the oblique plane VTH. Using vertical section planes find the cut surface of the solid.

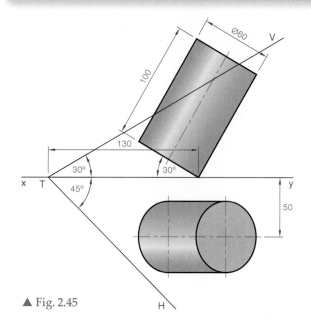

▲ Fig. 2.45

Q6. A right cylinder has been tilted to the horizontal plane as shown in **Fig. 2.45**. This cylinder is to be cut by the oblique plane VTH. Using vertical section planes find the cut surface of the cylinder.

Q7. Make a neat pictorial diagram of a cube with its dual solid, the octahedron, inside it.

Q8. Make a neat pictorial diagram of an octahedron showing its dual, the cube, inside it.

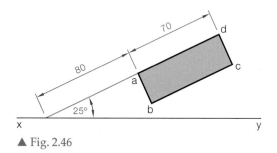

▲ Fig. 2.46

Q9. The elevation of one face of a cube, abcd, is shown in **Fig. 2.46**. Edge ad rests against the vertical plane and the surface abcd makes an angle of 70° to the vertical plane. Draw the plan and elevation of the cube.

Q10. The elevation of an equilateral triangle inclined at 20° to the VP and having edge ab on the vertical plan is shown in **Fig. 2.47**. The triangle is one face of a tetrahedron. Draw the plan and elevation of the solid.

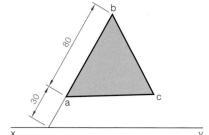

▲ Fig. 2.47

Q11. The plan of a tetrahedron is shown in **Fig. 2.48**. Corner a rests on the horizontal plane and corner b is 14 mm above the horizontal plane. The tetrahedron has sides 70 mm long and edge bc is parallel to the xy line in plan. Draw the tetrahedron in plan and elevation.

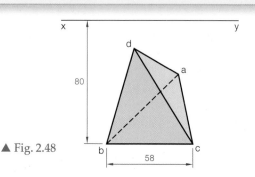

▲ Fig. 2.48

Learning Outcomes

Students should be able to:

Higher and Ordinary levels
- Construct views of up to three solids having curved surfaces and/or plane surfaces in mutual contact.
- Determine point of contact for surfaces in mutual contact.
- Construct views of solids given the point of contact.
- Depict the solutions of two-dimensional problems in three-dimensional format.

Higher Level only
- Model various problems involving solids in contact, planes of reference and auxiliary planes.

 # Solids in Contact

In this chapter you will draw the orthographic views of spheres, cones, cylinders, pyramids and prisms in contact with each other. First we must examine how to find points on the surface of cylinders, cones and spheres.

> The elevation of a cylinder is shown in Fig. 3.1 and the position of a point P on its surface. Draw the plan of the cylinder and point P.

By using an end view the location of point P in the plan can be easily found, see Fig. 3.2.

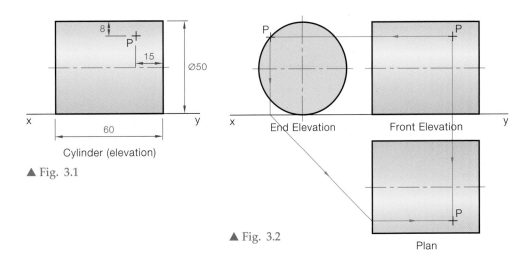

▲ Fig. 3.1

Cylinder (elevation)

▲ Fig. 3.2

The plan of a cone of altitude 60 mm is shown in Fig. 3.3. Also shown is a point P on its surface. Draw the elevation and locate point P.

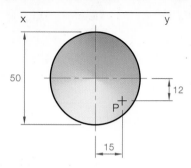

▲ Fig. 3.3

There are two methods shown to solve this problem. The horizontal section method is the preferred method.

Method 1 (Fig. 3.4a)

Rotate point P in plan horizontally. Project to the side of the cone in elevation giving the height of point P. Project the height horizontally and bring point P up from plan.

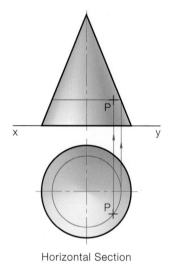

Horizontal Section

▲ Fig. 3.4a

Method 2 (Fig. 3.4b)

Draw a generator through point P in plan. Project this generator to elevation. Point P is projected onto this generator in elevation.

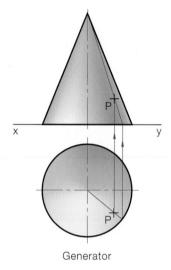

Generator

▲ Fig. 3.4b

The elevation of a sphere with a point P on its surface is shown in Fig. 3.5. Draw the plan and locate point P on it.

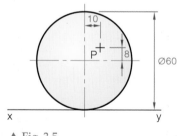

▲ Fig. 3.5

As in the previous example, a horizontal section is used. Project P horizontally to touch the side of the sphere. Project down to the horizontal axis of the plan and rotate round. Drop point P from elevation, Fig. 3.6.

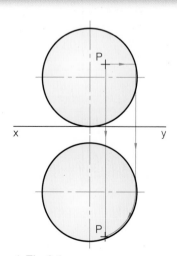

▲ Fig. 3.6

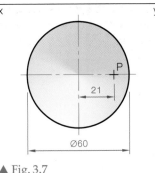

▲ Fig. 3.7

The plan of a cone of altitude 70 mm is shown in Fig. 3.7. Also shown is a point P on the cone's surface. A sphere which rests on the horizontal plane touches the cone at point P. Draw the plan and elevation of the two solids in contact.

(1) Draw the plan and project the elevation. Locate point P in elevation.

(2) Since the cone is tangential to the sphere, its edge will form a tangent to the sphere in elevation. A perpendicular to the side of the cone from point P will therefore pass through the sphere's centre.

(3) Since the sphere touches the horizontal plane and the cone edge, its centre will be on the bisector of the angle between the two, in elevation, Fig. 3.8.

(4) Draw the sphere in elevation and plan.

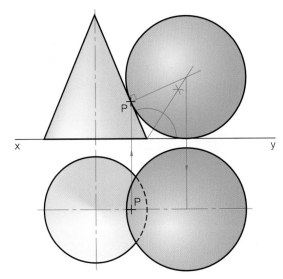

▲ Fig. 3.8

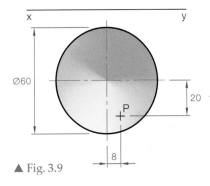

▲ Fig. 3.9

The plan of a cone of 70 mm altitude is shown in Fig. 3.9. Also shown is a point P on the cone's surface.

(i) Draw the plan and elevation of the cone and the point P.

(ii) Draw the plan and elevation of a sphere that rests on the horizontal plane and touches the cone at point P.

(1) Draw the plan and elevation of the cone.

(2) Rotate point P in plan about the cone centre onto the axis. Project up to the side of the cone in elevation and then project across horizontally. Locate point P on this horizontal.

(3) The sphere required to touch the cone at point P and touch the horizontal plane is constructed at the side of the cone. The construction is the same as in the previous example.

(4) Once the sphere centre is located, it is dropped to plan and rotated onto a line drawn from the cone centre through point P.

> **The centre of the cone, the point of contact and the sphere centre will form a straight line.**

(5) Draw the sphere in position in plan. Project the sphere centre to elevation and draw the sphere, Fig 3.10.

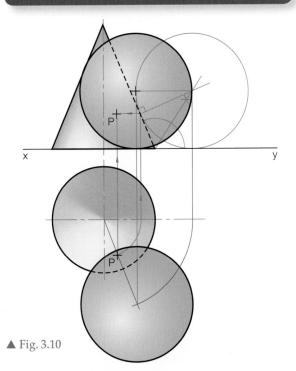

▲ Fig. 3.10

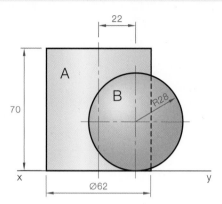

▲ Fig. 3.11

Shown in Fig. 3.11 is the elevation of a cylinder A and a sphere B. Both solids are in contact with each other and rest on the horizontal plane. Draw the elevation and plan of the solids and the point of contact.

(1) Draw the given elevation of both solids and project the plan of the cylinder.

(2) The sphere is drawn at the side of the cylinder. The point of contact (POC) can be clearly seen.

(3) Drop the centre of the sphere to the plan's horizontal axis and rotate it into the correct position. Draw the sphere in plan.

(4) Join the centres of the solid in plan thus locating the point of contact.

(5) Project the point of contact up from the plan and across from the constructional sphere, Fig. 3.12.

> When a sphere and cylinder are in contact the point of contact will be level with the sphere centre.

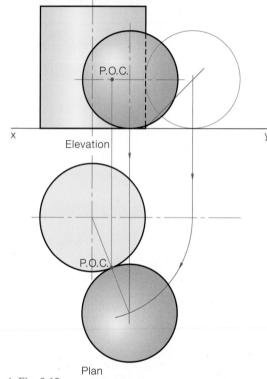

▲ Fig. 3.12

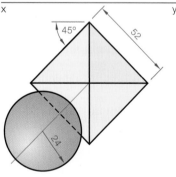

▲ Fig. 3.13

(1) Draw the plan and elevation of the pyramid.

(2) Project an auxiliary elevation to show the face that is in contact with the sphere as an edge view.

(3) Construct the sphere in the auxiliary. The radius is 24 mm so the centre is 24 mm above the x_1y_1 line. Also bisect the angle between the x_1y_1 and the side of the pyramid.

(4) Once the sphere is located in auxiliary it is projected back to plan and elevation.

(5) The point of contact is first found in the auxiliary by drawing a line from the sphere centre, perpendicular to the face of the pyramid. It is projected to plan and then elevation. The height of the POC in elevation equals the height of the POC in the auxiliary elevation, Fig. 3.14.

The plan of a square-based pyramid and a sphere, resting on the horizontal plane, are shown in Fig. 3.13. They are in contact with each other. Draw the plan and elevation of the solids showing the point of contact. The pyramid has an altitude of 58 mm.

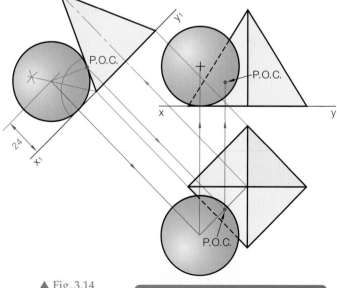

▲ Fig. 3.14

See worksheet 3.1

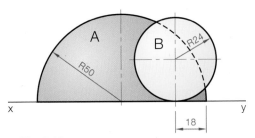

▲ Fig. 3.15

The elevation of a hemisphere A and a sphere B resting on the horizontal plane are shown in Fig. 3.15. The solids are in contact. Draw the plan and elevation of the solids and show the point of contact in both views.

(1) Draw the given elevation and draw the plan of the hemisphere A.

(2) Sphere B is drawn to the side of the hemisphere in elevation. The centre is located by projecting the centre of sphere B horizontally. This horizontal line is then cut by an arc drawn from the centre of the hemisphere and equal to the two radii added together, i.e. 50 mm + 24 mm = 74 mm.

(3) The point of contact is located between the hemisphere and the constructional sphere by joining their centres.

(4) Both point of contact and sphere centre are dropped to plan and rotated into position.

(5) The point of contact is located in elevation, Fig. 3.16.

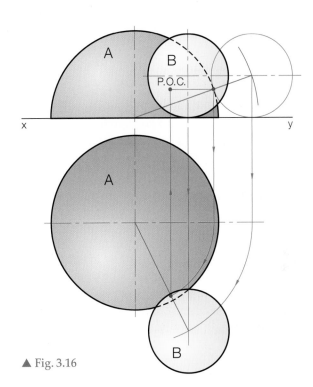

▲ Fig. 3.16

Fig. 3.17 shows the plan of a cone, resting on the horizontal plane, having an altitude of 60 mm. Also shown is a point P on the cone's surface. Draw the plan and elevation of the cone. Draw the plan and elevation of a sphere that will touch point P and also rest on the horizontal plane.

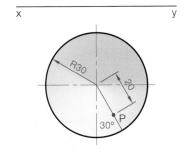

▲ Fig. 3.17

(1) Draw the given plan and project the elevation. Point P is rotated in plan onto the horizontal axis, projected to the side of the cone and then horizontally.

(2) The sphere is constructed to the side of the cone in elevation. Point P is brought horizontally to the side of the cone and a perpendicular constructed to the cone edge. The angle between the xy and the cone side is bisected. The intersection between the perpendicular and the bisector gives the sphere centre.

(3) The sphere is rolled into position and drawn in both views, Fig. 3.18.

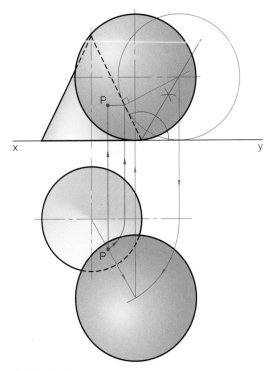

▲ Fig. 3.18

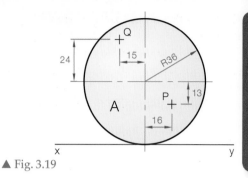

▲ Fig. 3.19

Fig. 3.19 shows the elevation of a sphere A with two points, P and Q, on its surface.

(i)   Draw the given elevation and project a plan showing points P and Q in both views.

(ii) Show the projections of a sphere of radius 15 mm that will be in contact with the sphere A at point P.

(iii) Show the projections of a sphere of radius 28 mm that will be in contact with sphere A at point Q.

(1) Draw the given elevation and project the plan of the sphere.

(2) Project point P horizontally in elevation to the side of the sphere. Project down to the plan's horizontal axis and rotate into position, vertically below point P in elevation.

(3) Similar construction for point Q.

(4) Point P is the point of contact. When it is moved horizontally to the circumference of sphere A we can construct the sphere of radius 15 mm. The centre of sphere A, the point of contact and the centre of the required sphere will be in line. The distance between the centres will be equal to the sum of the radii.

(5) Draw the sphere and project through the views.

(6) Similar construction for the sphere touching at point Q, Fig. 3.20.

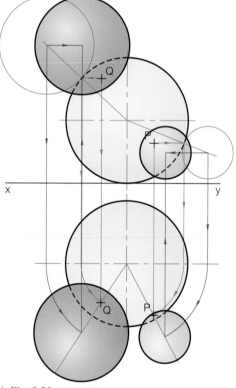

▲ Fig. 3.20

Fig. 3.21 shows the plan of a cylinder A and a cone B. Both solids rest on the horizontal plane. The cylinder has an altitude of 80 mm and the cone has an altitude of 50 mm. A sphere C of radius 18 mm is placed so that it touches both these solids and rests on the horizontal plane. Draw the plan and elevation of the solids and show the points of contact.

See worksheet 3.2

(1) Draw the elevation and plan of the cone and cylinder.

(2) Draw the sphere C touching the side of the cylinder. Project the centre to the plan and rotate it about the cylinder. Similarly for the cone, draw the sphere C touching its side in elevation.

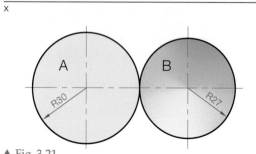

▲ Fig. 3.21

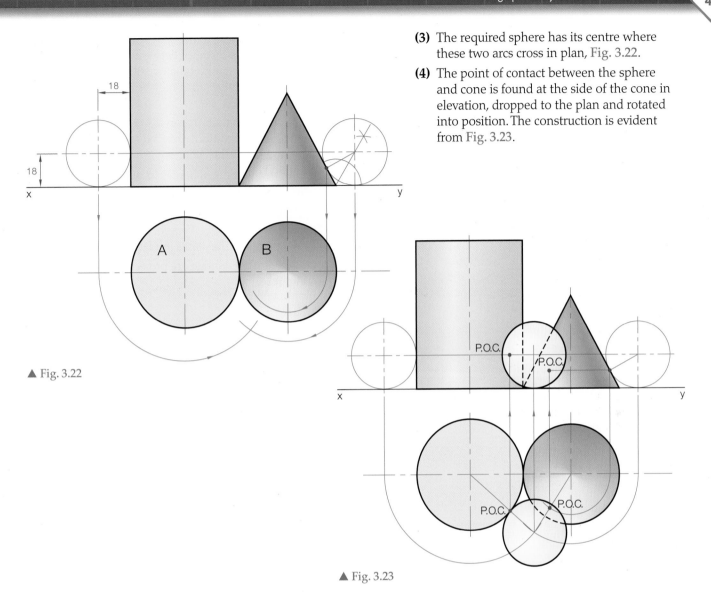

▲ Fig. 3.22

▲ Fig. 3.23

(3) The required sphere has its centre where these two arcs cross in plan, Fig. 3.22.

(4) The point of contact between the sphere and cone is found at the side of the cone in elevation, dropped to the plan and rotated into position. The construction is evident from Fig. 3.23.

Shown in Fig. 3.24 is the elevation of a cylinder A and a hemisphere B in contact with each other and resting on the horizontal plane. A sphere of 50 mm diameter is placed in position C. The sphere is to be in contact with the other two solids and the horizontal plane. Draw the plan and elevation of the solids showing all points of contact.

(1) Draw the given elevation and project the plan of the cylinder.

(2) The centre of hemisphere B is projected to plan. The distance between the centres of A and B in plan will equal the sum of their radii.

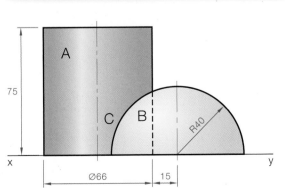

▲ Fig. 3.24

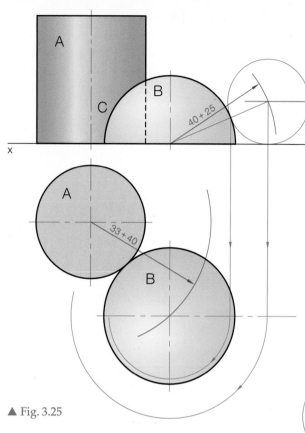

▲ Fig. 3.25

(3) Draw the sphere to the side of hemisphere B in elevation. The distance between their centres will equal the sum of their radii. The centre is dropped and rotated about the hemisphere in plan, Fig. 3.25.

(4) The sphere is then drawn to the side of the cylinder in elevation, dropped to the plan and rotated about the cylinder.

(5) The centre of the sphere is located where the arcs from steps 3 and 4 cross.

(6) Complete the elevation.

(7) The points of contact are located on lines joining the centres of the solids in plan.

(8) The points of contact are projected to elevation, Fig. 3.26.

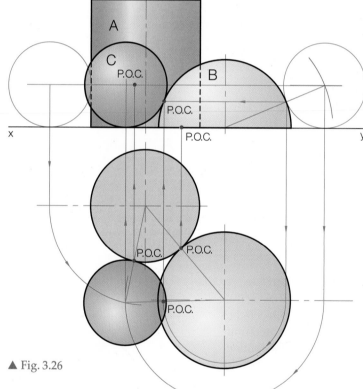

▲ Fig. 3.26

Fig. 3.27 shows the elevation of a cone A and a sphere B resting on the horizontal plane and in contact with each other.

(i)   Draw the elevation and plan of the two solids.

(ii) Draw the projections of another sphere C, of 40 mm diameter, which is in contact with the sphere and cone in position S. The centre of the sphere is to be 50 mm above the horizontal plane.

(iii) Show all points of contact.

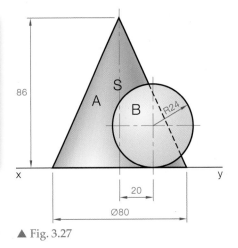

▲ Fig. 3.27

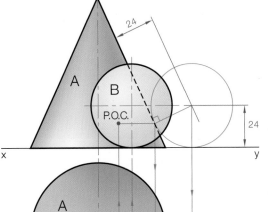

(1) Draw the given elevation and project the plan of the cone.

(2) Sphere B must be drawn to the side of the cone, touching it, projected to plan and rolled into position, Fig. 3.28.

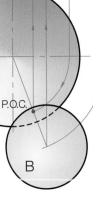

▲ Fig. 3.28

(3) The point of contact is found at the side of the elevation, projected to plan and rotated until it hits the line joining the centres. Project to elevation.

(4) Sphere C has its centre 50 mm above the horizontal plane, Fig. 3.29. Draw the sphere to the side of, and touching, the cone A. Project to plan and rotate about the cone.

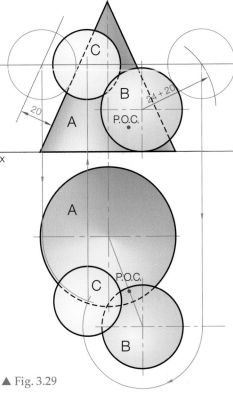

▲ Fig. 3.29

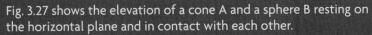

▲ Fig. 3.30

(5) Draw the sphere C to the side of, and touching, sphere B. Project to plan and rotate about sphere B.

(6) Draw the sphere C in its correct position in both views.

(7) The points of contact between the solids are found in the usual way as can be seen in Fig. 3.30.

See worksheet 3.3

Activities

Q1. The plan of a cylinder is shown in Fig. 3.31. A and B are points on its surface. Project an elevation of the cylinder and locate points A and B.

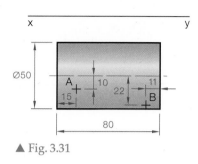

▲ Fig. 3.31

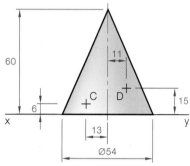

▲ Fig. 3.32

Q2. The elevation of a cone is shown in Fig. 3.32. Two points C and D are shown on the surface. Project a plan showing clearly how the two points are located.

Q3. The plan of a sphere with two points on its surface, E and F, is shown in Fig. 3.33. Project the elevation of the sphere and the two points.

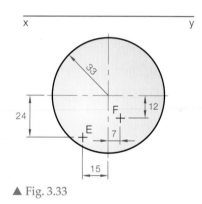

▲ Fig. 3.33

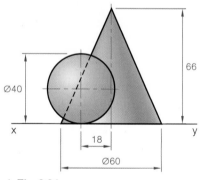

▲ Fig. 3.34

Q4. The elevation of a sphere and cone are shown in Fig. 3.34. The two solids are in contact. Draw the given view and project the plan. Show the point of contact in both views.

Q5. The plan of a cone A and a sphere B are shown in Fig. 3.35. The two solids are in contact and rest on the horizontal plane. Draw the plan and elevation of the solids and show the point of conduct in both views. The cone has an altitude of 60 mm.

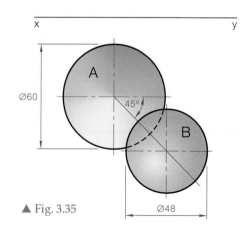

▲ Fig. 3.35

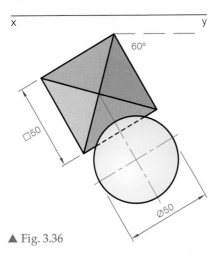

▲ Fig. 3.36

Q6. Fig. 3.36 shows the plan of a square-based pyramid of altitude 70 mm. Also shown is a sphere which is in contact with the pyramid. Both solids rest on the horizontal plane. Draw the given plan and project the elevation. The point of contact should be clearly shown in both views.

Q7. The elevation of a hemisphere is shown in Fig. 3.37. A sphere S is in contact with the hemisphere. Draw the plan and elevation of the two solids showing the point of contact clearly in both views. Also shown is a point P on the surface of the hemisphere. Draw the plan and elevation of point P.

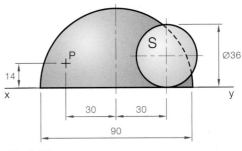

▲ Fig. 3.37

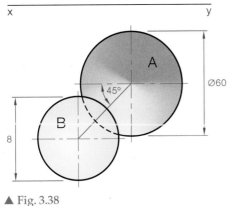

▲ Fig. 3.38

Q8. The plan of a cone A of 50 mm altitude and a sphere B are shown in Fig. 3.38. Both solids rest on the horizontal plane and are in contact with each other.

(i) Draw the plan and project the elevation of the solids.

(ii) Draw the projections of another sphere C, diameter 30 mm, whose centre is 36 mm above the horizontal plane. The sphere C is to touch the cone A and the other sphere B.

(iii) Show the points of contact in all views.

Q9. Shown in Fig. 3.39 is the elevation of a hemisphere A and a sphere B in contact with each other and resting on the horizontal plane.

(i) Draw the elevation and project the plan of the solids.

(ii) Draw the projections of a diameter 40 mm sphere which rests on the horizontal plane and touches the hemisphere A and sphere B.

(iii) Show all points of contact.

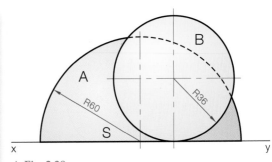

▲ Fig. 3.39

Worked Examples

Problem 1

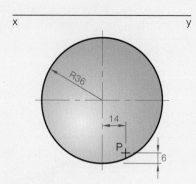

▲ Fig. 3.40

Fig. 3.40 shows the plan of a sphere with a point P on its underside.

(i)   Draw the plan and elevation of the sphere and find the projections of point P.

(ii) Find the projections of the sphere which rests on the horizontal plane and has point P as its point of contact.

(1) Draw the sphere in plan and elevation.

(2) Find point P in elevation in the usual way. Rotate point P onto the horizontal axis in plan and project to the sphere's circumference in elevation giving P_1.

(3) Draw a line from C through P_1 and extend.

(4) Draw a locus of points equidistant from the circumference and the xy line.

(5) The locus and CP_1 extended cross giving the sphere centre, Fig. 3.41.

(6) Draw the sphere and roll it into position, Fig 3.42.

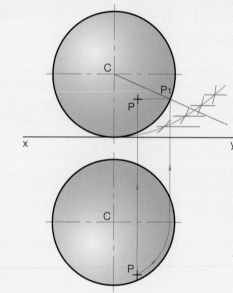

▲ Fig. 3.41

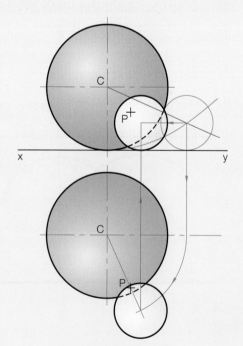

▲ Fig. 3.42

Problem 2

The diagram in Fig. 3.43 shows the elevation of two spheres and a cone in contact with one another. Draw the elevation and plan of the solids showing all points of contact.

(1) Draw the plan and elevation of the cone. The elevation of sphere A can also be drawn.

(2) The location of sphere A in plan is found by rolling the sphere to the side of the cone, dropping it to the side of the plan and rotating it into position. The centre point is brought across in elevation and intersects with the bisector of the angle formed by the cone side and the horizontal plane, Fig. 3.44.

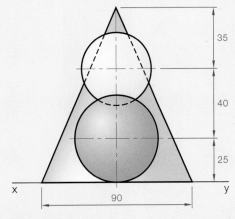

▲ Fig. 3.43

(3) The radius of sphere B is not given. It too must be brought to the side of the cone. Project the given centre point across to the side. This line intersects with the locus of points which are equidistant from the cone side and the circumference of sphere A rotated.

(4) Project the sphere centres back to the elevation and plan, Fig. 3.44.

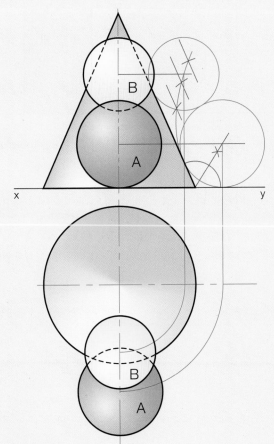

▲ Fig. 3.44

(5) The points of contact must now be found. Join the centres of the two rotated spheres giving P_1. Draw a perpendicular from the rotated spheres centres to the cone side, as shown in Fig. 3.45, thus locating P_2 and P_3. The three points of contact can then be projected back onto the plan and elevation.

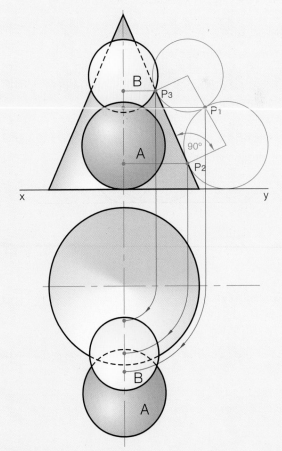

▲ Fig. 3.45

HIGHER LEVEL

Problem 3

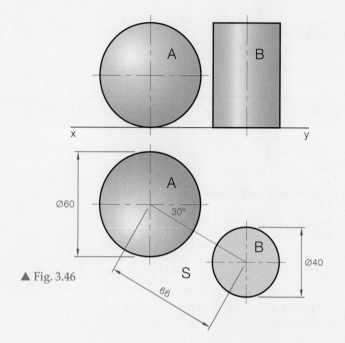

▲ Fig. 3.46

Fig. 3.46 shows the plan and elevation of a sphere A and a cylinder B.

(i)   Draw the elevation and plan of the solids.

(ii) Draw the elevation and plan of a cone of 60 mm base diameter and 60 mm height, which rests on the horizontal plane in position S and is in contact with the given solids. Show all points of contact.

(1) Draw the required cone to the side of the elevation and slide it across to come into contact with sphere A.

(2) The point of contact is located.

(3) Drop the cone centre and point of contact down to plan and rotate about the plan of sphere A, Fig. 3.47.

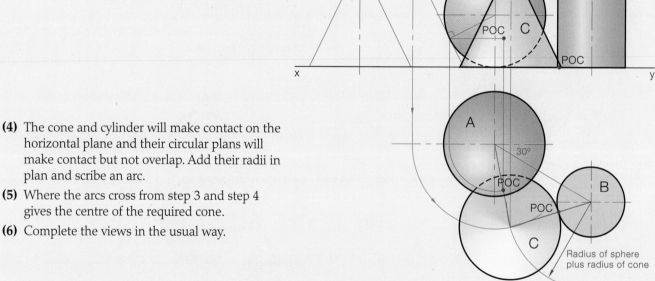

(4) The cone and cylinder will make contact on the horizontal plane and their circular plans will make contact but not overlap. Add their radii in plan and scribe an arc.

(5) Where the arcs cross from step 3 and step 4 gives the centre of the required cone.

(6) Complete the views in the usual way.

▲ Fig. 3.47

Problem 4

The diagram shows the projection of a sphere A which rests on the horizontal plane, Fig. 3.48.

(i)   Draw the sphere in plan and elevation.

(ii) Draw the projections of a sphere of 50 mm diameter which touches the sphere A at a point 60 mm above the horizontal plane and also touches the vertical plane. Show the point of contact in both views.

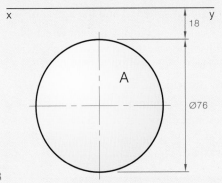

▲ Fig. 3.48

(1) Draw the plan and elevation of sphere A.

(2) Mark the height of the point of contact, 60 mm above the xy line.

(3) Where this height line intersects the circumference gives point P_1. Construct the new sphere to touch P_1 as shown in Fig. 3.49.

(4) Drop this sphere's centre to plan and rotate about the plan until it crosses a line 25 mm (the radius of the new sphere) from the xy line, the vertical plane.

(5) Draw the elevation of this sphere and find the point of contact in the usual way, Fig. 3.49.

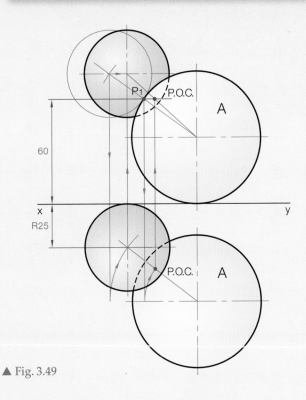

▲ Fig. 3.49

Problem 5

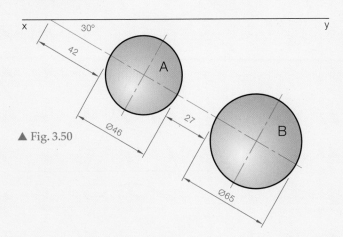

▲ Fig. 3.50

Fig. 3.50 shows the plan of two spheres A and B resting on the horizontal plane.

(i)   Draw the plan and elevation of the two spheres and show the projections of the smallest sphere which rests on the horizontal plane and touches both sphere A and sphere B.

(ii) Show the points of contact in all views.

(1) Draw the plan and elevation of the solids.

(2) The smallest sphere to touch both existing solids will have its centre in line with the centres of sphere A and sphere B in plan. Project an auxiliary elevation with the x_1y_1 line parallel to the line joining the centres of sphere A and B. This auxiliary will show the space between the spheres.

(3) Locate the centre of the new sphere by the use of loci. Draw the locus of points which are equidistant from the circumference of sphere A and the x_1y_1 line.

HIGHER LEVEL

(4) Similarly for sphere B and the x_1y_1 line.

(5) The loci intersect giving a point which is equidistant from the sphere A, the sphere B and the x_1y_1 line.

(6) Draw the sphere and project back through the views.

(7) The points of contact are also found in the auxiliary and projected back through the views, Fig. 3.51.

> See worksheet 3.4

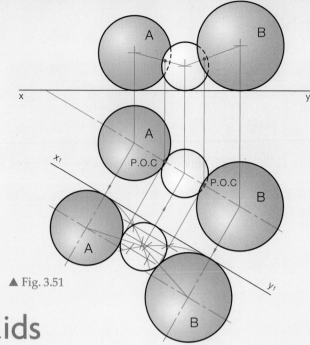

▲ Fig. 3.51

Tangent Planes to Solids

Problem 1

> To draw a plane tangential to a sphere at a given point P on its surface.

▼ Fig. 3.52

(1) In plan join the sphere centre to P.

(2) Project an auxiliary view having x_1y_1 parallel to cP.

(3) Locate point P in the auxiliary. It will be on the circumference.

(4) Draw the edge view of the tangent plane in auxiliary.

(5) Find the traces.

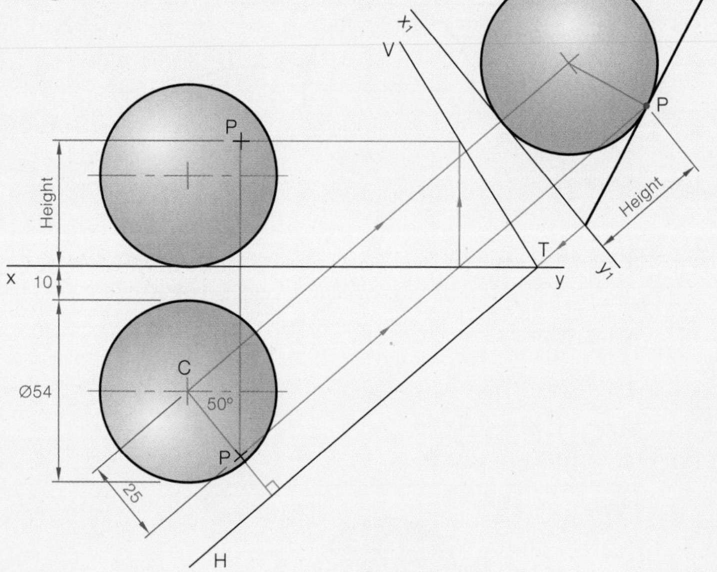

Problem 2

> To draw a plane tangential to a cone at a given point P on its surface.

(1) In plan, draw the generator from the cone apex through point P to the base of the cone. The horizontal trace will be perpendicular to this.

(2) Find P in elevation and the vertical trace in the usual way.

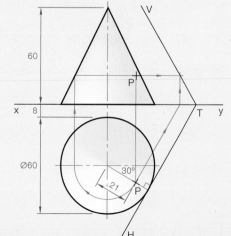

▲ Fig. 3.53

Problem 3

To draw the traces of a plane that is tangential to the cone A and that contains point P.

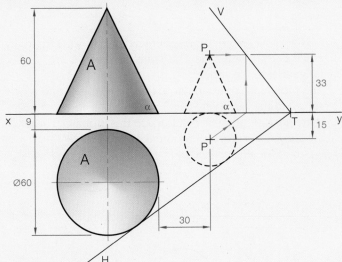

▲ Fig. 3.54

(1) Set up the question.

(2) Draw the plan and elevation of a cone, having the same base angle as cone A and having point P as its apex.

(3) The horizontal trace will be tangential to the two base circles. The vertical trace is found as before.

The tangent plane's horizontal trace will be tangential to the base circles of the cones. It can also be seen from the pictorial that the plane makes contact with the cones along a whole generator, Fig. 3.55.

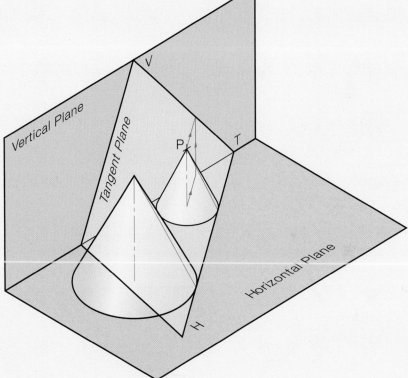

▲ Fig. 3.55

Problem 4

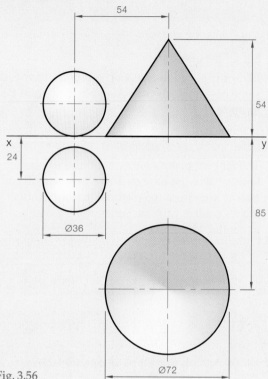

▲ Fig. 3.56

To determine the traces of a plane which shall be tangential to a given cone and a given sphere.

A cone is placed over the sphere having the same base angle as the given cone. This cone's generators are tangential to the sphere.

The problem is now similar to the previous one and is solved in the same way, Fig 3.57. It should be noted that there are four possible solutions to this problem. These are shown in Figures 3.58 and 3.59.

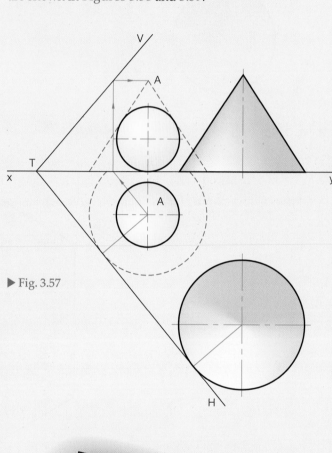

▶ Fig. 3.57

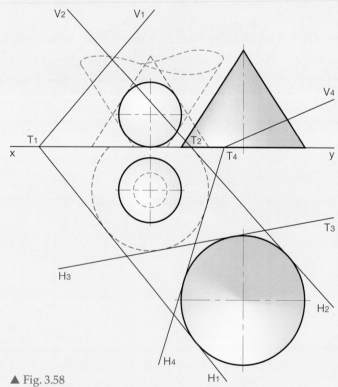

▲ Fig. 3.58

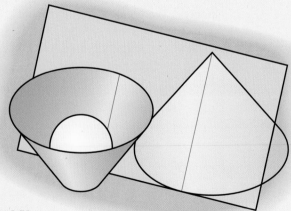

▲ Fig. 3.59

Activities

Q1. Fig. 3.60 shows the elevation of a cone and a sphere. The cone is in contact with the sphere A at point P. Draw the elevation and plan of the solids in contact and determine the exact position of point P.

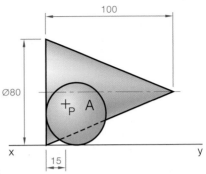

▲ Fig. 3.60

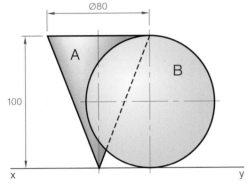

▲ Fig. 3.61

Q2. Fig. 3.61 shows the elevation of a right cone A and a sphere B. Both solids are in contact.

    (i) Draw the plan and elevation of the solids.

    (ii) Draw the projections of the smallest possible sphere that touches the cone A, the sphere B and the horizontal plane.

Q3. Fig. 3.62 shows the elevation of a sphere A in contact with a cone B.

    (i) Draw the plan and elevation of the two solids showing the point of contact clearly.

    (ii) Draw the projections of a second sphere C of diameter 30 mm which touches both solids. Sphere C makes contact with sphere A at a point 44 mm above the horizontal plane.

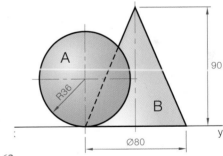

▲ Fig. 3.62

Q4. Fig. 3.63 shows the elevation of a right cone A in contact with a sphere B.

    (i) Draw the elevation and plan of the two solids showing the point of contact in both views.

    (ii) Draw the projections of another sphere C of 30 mm diameter is position S. Sphere C must make contact with the other two solids. Show all points of contact.

    (iii) Draw the traces of a plane that is tangential to cone A and sphere C.

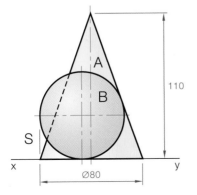

▲ Fig. 3.63

Syllabus Outline

Areas to be studied:
- Projection of right and oblique solids.

Learning Outcomes

Students should be able to:

Higher and Ordinary levels
- Project views of right solids such that any face or edge of the solid may be on one of the principal planes of reference.

Higher Level only
- Project views of oblique solids (axis inclined to one of the principal reference planes only) such that any face or edge of the solid may be on one of the planes of reference or inclined to one of both planes of reference.

Rotation and Inclination of Right Solids

The plan of a cube is shown in Fig. 4.1. Draw a front elevation, end elevation and plan of the cube when the bottom face is inclined at 25° to the horizontal plane and the edge bc rests on the horizontal plane.

(1) Draw the given plan.

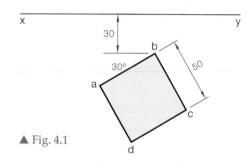

▲ Fig. 4.1

(2) Edge bc will be the axis of rotation. Project an auxiliary elevation viewing along bc.

(3) In the auxiliary the cube is rotated to the required angle to the HP, Fig. 4.2.

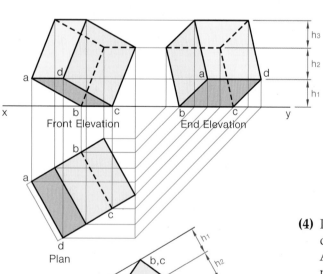

▲ Fig. 4.3

Auxiliary Elevation

(4) Project the rotated cube back to the plan. All points will move perpendicular to the axis line bc in plan.

(5) Project both sets of elevations. The heights for the corners are found in the auxiliary elevation, Fig. 4.3.

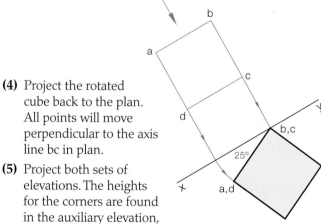

▲ Fig. 4.2

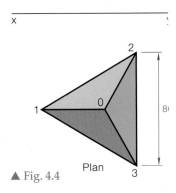

x
2
1 0 8(
Plan 3
▲ Fig. 4.4

(1) The construction is the same as the previous problem. View in the direction of edge 1,3.

(2) The edge 2,0 will be a true length in the auxiliary.

(3) Project the views back from the auxiliary and the heights are taken from the auxiliary, Fig. 4.5.

Fig. 4.4 shows the plan of a tetrahedron. Draw the front elevation, end elevation and plan of the solid when the base is rotated at 30° to the HP about the edge 1,3.

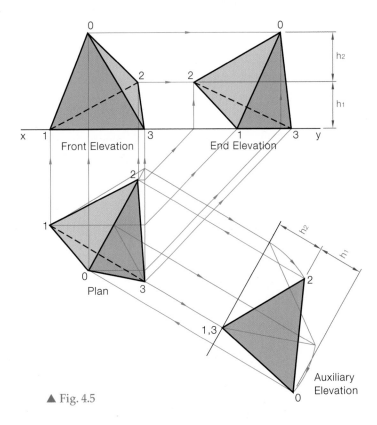

▲ Fig. 4.5

Project views of the square-based pyramid shown in Fig. 4.6 such that surface A is on the horizontal plane.

(1) The solid is drawn in its normal position.

(2) Edge ab is a point view in elevation and will act as the axis of rotation. Rotate the apex about ab in elevation until point o intersects the xy line.

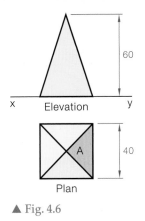

x Elevation y
60
A 40
Plan
▲ Fig. 4.6

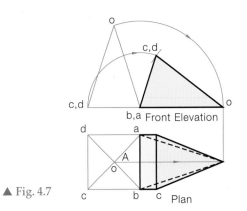

▲ Fig. 4.7

(3) Rotate points c and d about ab in elevation.

(4) The length from o to cd in the original elevation is used in the new elevation to locate c and d in the new elevation, Fig. 4.7.

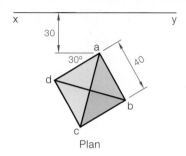

▲ Fig. 4.8

Shown in Fig. 4.8 is the plan of a square-based pyramid of altitude 60 mm. Draw the front elevation and end elevation of the pyramid when its base is inclined at 45° to the horizontal plane and edge ad remains touching the horizontal plane.

(1) Draw the given plan. Edge ad will form the axis of rotation for the solid.

(2) Draw an auxiliary view of the pyramid looking along the line ad. Rotate the pyramid in this view about ad which is a point of view.

(3) Project the rotated pyramid to plan. Remember that the points move perpendicular to the axis of rotation in plan.

(4) The front elevation is projected, with the heights being taken from the auxiliary, Fig. 4.9.

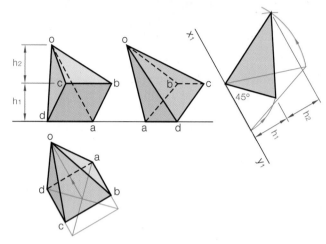

▲ Fig. 4.9

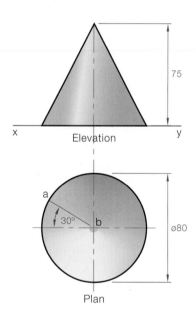

▲ Fig. 4.10

Shown in Fig. 4.10 is a right cone. Draw the front elevation, end elevation and plan of the cone when the generator ab rests on the horizontal plane.

(1) Draw the plan of the cone with the base on the horizontal plane.

(2) Draw an auxiliary elevation of the cone with x_1y_1 parallel to the generator ab.

(3) Rotate the cone in the auxiliary.

(4) The circular base is divided into parts and the points are projected through the views to locate the ellipses in all three views, Fig. 4.11.

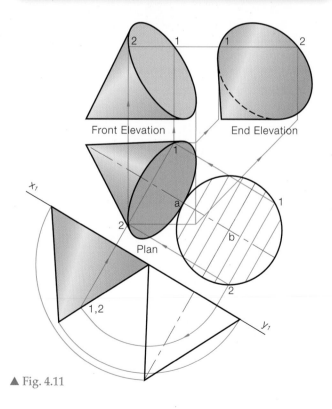

▲ Fig. 4.11

The plan and elevation of a pentagonal-based right pyramid are shown in Fig. 4.12. Draw new views of the object when the surface abc is parallel to the vertical plane.

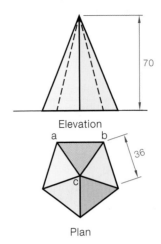

▲ Fig. 4.12

Elevation

Plan

(1) Draw the given plan and project the end view.
(2) In the end view, surface abc appears as an edge view.
(3) Rotate the pyramid until surface abc is vertical.
(4) Project the remaining views from the end view, Fig. 4.13.

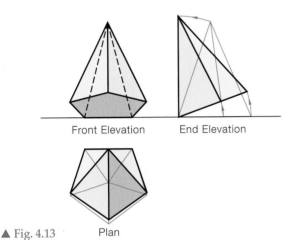

Front Elevation   End Elevation

▲ Fig. 4.13   Plan

Activities

Inclined solids

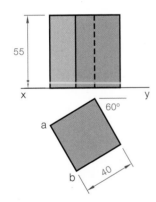

▲ Fig. 4.14

Q1. The plan and elevation of a square-based prism are shown in **Fig. 4.14**. Draw a front elevation, end elevation and plan of the prism when the bottom face is inclined at 20° to the horizontal plane and edge ab rests on the horizontal plan.

Q2. The plan and elevation of a rectangular-based pyramid are shown in **Fig. 4.15**. Draw the front elevation, end elevation and plan of the pyramid when the edge co is vertical and corner c rests on the horizontal plane.

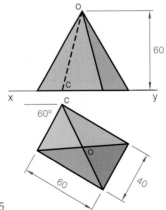

▲ Fig. 4.15

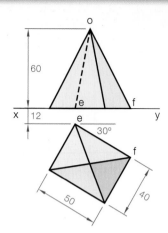

▲ Fig. 4.16

Q3. The pyramid in **Fig. 4.16** is to be rotated about edge ef until the apex o touches the vertical plane. Draw the front elevation, end elevation and plan of the pyramid in its new position.

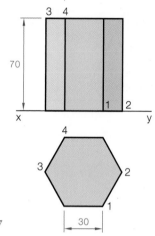

▲ Fig. 4.17

Q4. **Fig. 4.17** shows the plan and elevation of a hexagonal-based prism. The prism is to be rotated about edge 1,2 until edge 3,4 is directly above edge 1,2. Draw the plan, front elevation and end view of the prism in its new position.

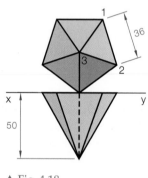

▲ Fig. 4.18

Q5. A pentagonal-based pyramid rests on the vertical plane. The pyramid is rotated about edge 1,2 until surface 1,2,3 rests on the vertical plane. Draw the front elevation, end elevation and plan of the solid in its new position, **Fig. 4.18**.

Q6. **Fig. 4.19** shows the plan and elevation of a cone. The cone is to be tilted on point P so that the base makes an angle of 20° with the horizontal plane. Draw the front elevation, end elevation and plan of the solid when it is tilted.

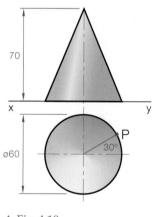

▲ Fig. 4.19

Syllabus Outline

Areas to be studied:
- Isometric drawing of solids.
- *Derivation,* construction and application of the isometric scale.
- The axonometric plane and axes.
- Principles of orthogonal axonometric projection.

Learning Outcomes

Students should be able to:

Higher and Ordinary levels
- Complete isometric drawings of solids containing plane and/or curved surfaces.
- Complete a portion of the axonometric plane given the projection of the axes of the planes of reference.
- Determine the true shape of the planes of reference, showing the axonometric plane.
- Determine the isometric projections of solids, including the sphere, using the isometric scale.
- Determine the axonometric projections of solids, including the sphere, using the axes method.
- Project a two-dimensional view of an object from its axonometric view on to one of the principal planes of reference.
- Demonstrate a knowledge of the principles involved in the isometric scale.

Higher Level only
- *Project orthogonal axonometric views of objects when the axes are inclined in isometric, dimetric or trimetric positions.*

 # Isometric Drawings

In isometric drawings, measurements are transferred onto isometric lines that are parallel to the isometric axes. These are pictorial views and will often show a solid more clearly than an orthographic can. Sloping lines do not maintain their true length in isometric drawings, circular curves become elliptical and angles do not show their true angle. Care must be taken when producing isometrics and they can often be slow to produce.

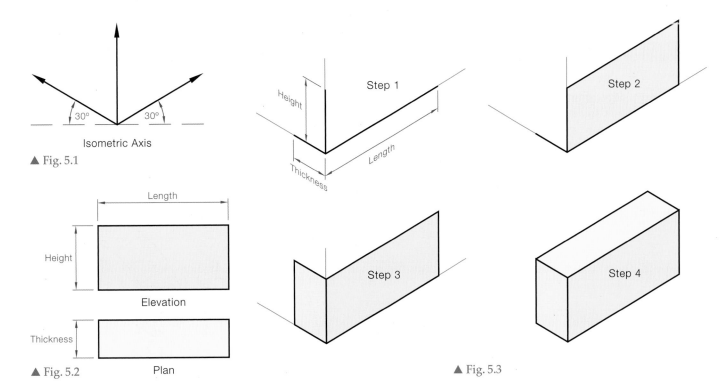

▲ Fig. 5.1 Isometric Axis

▲ Fig. 5.2 Elevation / Plan

▲ Fig. 5.3

Sloping Lines and Surfaces

Sloping lines do not maintain their true length in isometric drawings and angles do not measure as true angles. No angular measurements can therefore be used in these drawings. Angular measurements must be changed into linear measurements along the isometric axes.

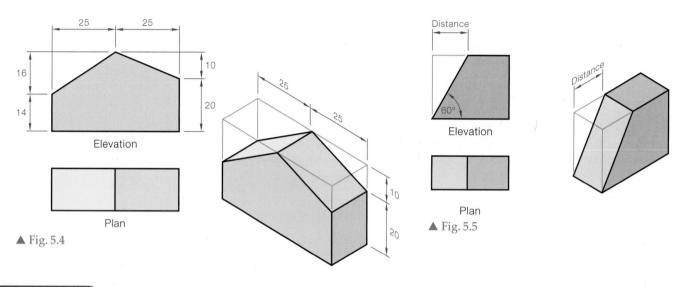

▲ Fig. 5.4

▲ Fig. 5.5

Circles

Circles will appear elliptical in isometric drawings, and depending on the size of the circle and the accuracy needed we have the choice of several methods of construction.

Coordinate method

This is the most accurate method, as the number of points which can be found on the curve is limitless. The curve is divided up in the orthographic view by using a number of ordinates, Fig. 5.6.

Draw the same ordinates in the isometric. Since the ordinates are parallel to one of the isometric axes they will appear as true lengths. Transfer the height of each ordinate from the orthographic to the isometric, Fig. 5.7a. Join the plotted points on the curve, freehand, to produce the front face. The thickness of the object is stepped back from this curve to give the back curve, Fig. 5.7b.

5 4 3 2 1 0

Elevation

W

Plan

▲ Fig. 5.6

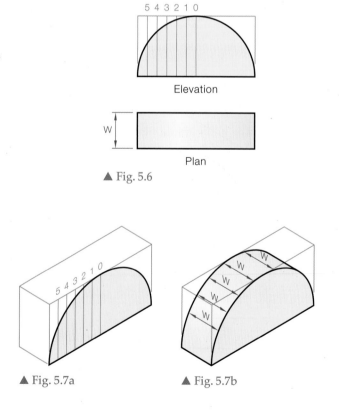

▲ Fig. 5.7a

▲ Fig. 5.7b

The coordinate method is ideal for irregular curves, as can be seen in **Fig.** 5.8.

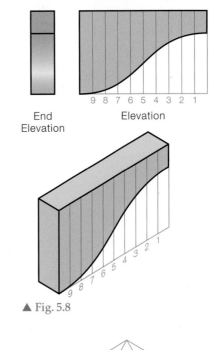

End Elevation   Elevation

▲ Fig. 5.8

Four-centre ellipse

For most isometric drawings which contain circles, an approximate ellipse is perfectly satisfactory, as exact measurements are rarely taken from isometrics. They are used more for explanatory purposes. For this reason an ellipse which can be constructed quickly with the aid of a compass is very useful, **Fig** 5.9.

(1) Draw the isometric box to contain the circle.

(2) Draw lines from the corners perpendicular to the opposite sides. These will be 60° lines.

(3) Where these lines cross gives the centres for the small arcs.

(4) The top and bottom corners are the centres for the large arcs.

When drawing an object having concentric circles (**Fig.** 5.10) it should be noted that each ellipse has its own parallelogram and centres (**Fig.** 5.11).

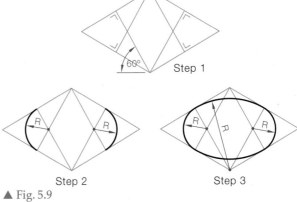

Step 1

Step 2   Step 3

▲ Fig. 5.9

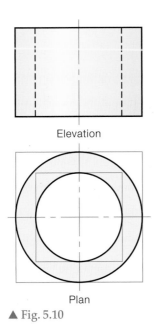

Elevation

Plan

▲ Fig. 5.10

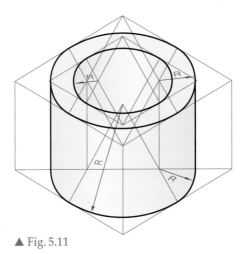

▲ Fig. 5.11

It should be noted again that this construction of ellipses is not accurate, but it is sufficient for most isometrics. A closer approximation to a true ellipse can be found by the following method.

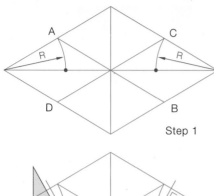

Step 1

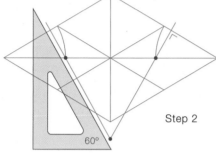

Step 2

60°

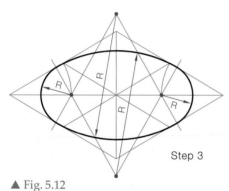

Step 3

▲ Fig. 5.12

Hidden lines and centre lines should only be drawn if they are needed to make the drawing clearer or for dimensioning.

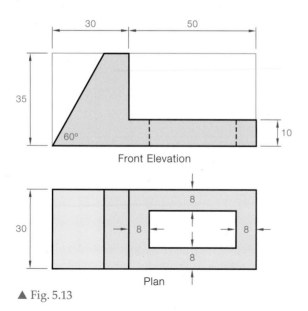

Front Elevation

Plan

▲ Fig. 5.13

Ortho four-centre ellipse

(1) Draw the isometric of the square which will contain the isometric circle. The sides of the square will equal the length of the diameter.

(2) Join the diagonals and the bisectors of the sides AB and CD.

(3) Swing the ends of the bisectors onto the diagonal as shown. This gives the centre of the small arcs.

(4) Draw perpendiculars to the sides, through these centre points locating the centres for the large arcs.

(5) Complete the drawing with the compass.

Crating or Boxing

Objects can be more easily constructed in isometric by the use of crating. This involves constructing a box around the whole object or parts of the object in the orthographic, Fig. 5.13.

These boxes can then be drawn in isometric giving a good starting point for the rest of the drawing details to be filled in, Fig. 5.14.

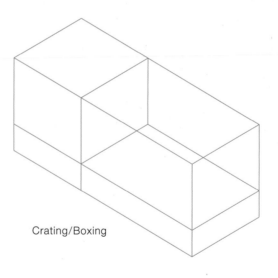

Crating/Boxing

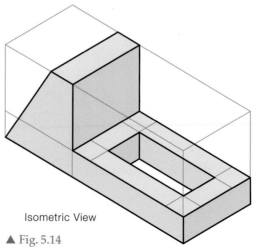

Isometric View

▲ Fig. 5.14

Worked Examples

Given the front elevation, end elevation and plan of a shaped solid. Draw the given views and produce an isometric view of the object.

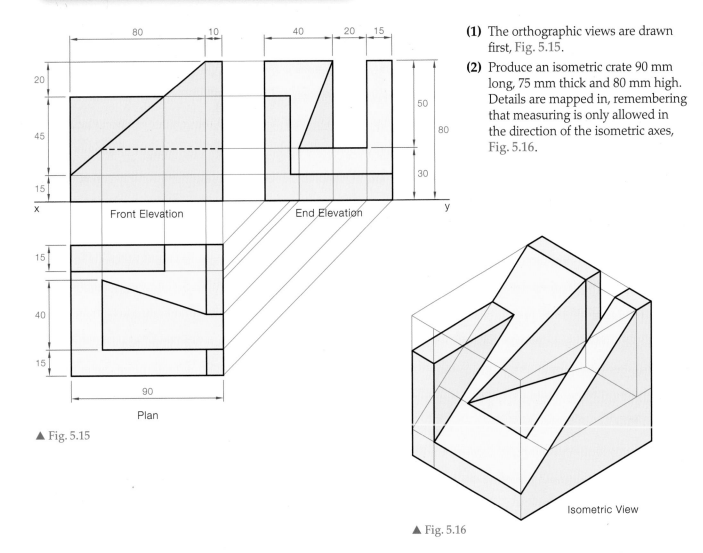

Front Elevation

End Elevation

Plan

▲ Fig. 5.15

Isometric View

▲ Fig. 5.16

(1) The orthographic views are drawn first, Fig. 5.15.

(2) Produce an isometric crate 90 mm long, 75 mm thick and 80 mm high. Details are mapped in, remembering that measuring is only allowed in the direction of the isometric axes, Fig. 5.16.

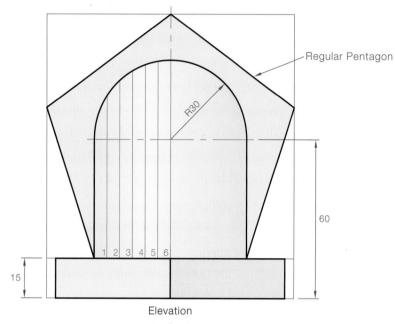

Regular Pentagon

R30

60

Elevation

1 2 3 4 5 6

15

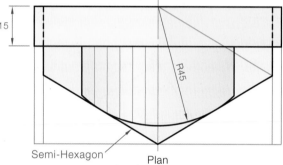

15

R45

Semi-Hexagon

Plan

▲ Fig. 5.17

Fig. 5.17 shows the plan and elevation of a solid. Draw the given views and draw an isometric of the solid.

(1) Draw the elevation of the central portion.

(2) From this, draw the regular pentagon using a protractor. Pentagon sides will be 60 mm long.

(3) The semi-hexagon in plan will be tangential to the radius 45 mm curve in plan. The length of the sides of the hexagon can be found by drawing a 30° line from the circle centre. Alternatively we could work out that the width of the base will be 90 mm, i.e. the diameter of the circle forming the central portion.

(4) The best way to approach the isometric is by crating.

(5) The curved central portion must be constructed using ordinates as shown. The fact that the front is doubly curved means that the four-centre ellipse will not work. For the sake of clarity some of the ordinates have not been shown in the isometric, Fig. 5.18.

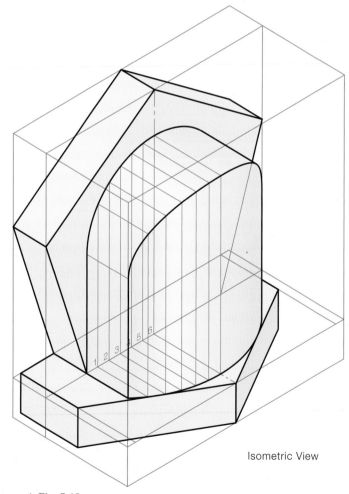

1 2 3 4 5 6

Isometric View

▲ Fig. 5.18

See worksheets 5.1 and 5.2

Activities

Q1, Q2 and Q3.
Draw the given plan and elevation and draw an
isometric view of the solid, **Figures 5.19, 5.20 and 5.21**.

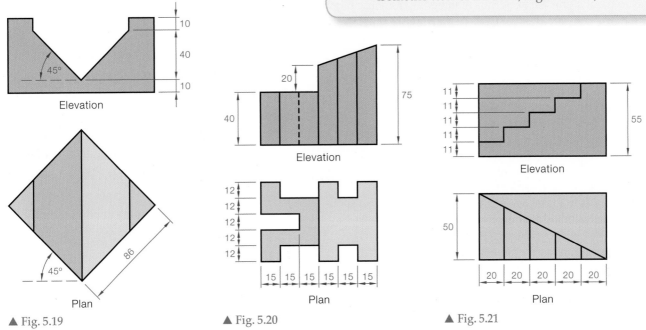

▲ Fig. 5.19   ▲ Fig. 5.20   ▲ Fig. 5.21

Q4 and Q5. Draw the given plan and elevation. Produce an isometric of the
solid. Curves should be found with ordinates, **Figures 5.22 and 5.23**.

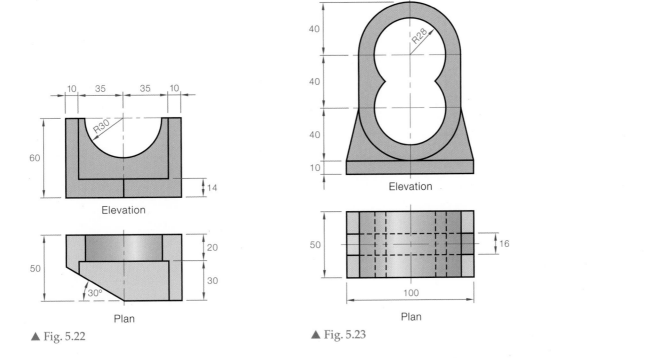

▲ Fig. 5.22   ▲ Fig. 5.23

Isometric Scale

When we make a visual comparison between the orthographic projections of a solid with its corresponding isometric projections, it can be seen that the isometric appears and actually is larger. The reason for this is that the solid drawn in isometric is inclined to the horizontal plane, tilted up on one of its corners. This means that all edges are sloping and therefore do not show their true length.When we draw an isometric we ignore this fact and measure the full measurement along the axes, thus making the isometric larger than the orthographic. In order to give the correct proportions between the two types of drawing we must use an **isometric scale**.

Example of how isometric gives a distorted view

We will take the example of a cube of 30 mm sides. The isometric of the cube shows corners 3 and 8 on the same point, so therefore the diagonal 3,8 will be a horizontal line. It can be proved that in order to get this diagonal horizontal, we must tilt the cube by 35°16′ (35 degrees 16 minutes). We may now draw an end view of the cube, from the isometric, having its base on the inclined plane as shown in Fig. 5.24. All edges of the cube will be inclined to the vertical plane and will not show true lengths in the isometric.

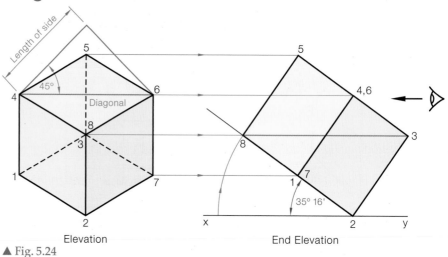

▲ Fig. 5.24

Getting back to the isometric (elevation).The diagonal 4,6 will be seen as a true length in this view. If we have the diagonal of a square we can easily find the length of the side of that square (the sides of a square make an angle of 45° to the diagonal).When we do this we find that the length of the side is much more than 30 mm, as was required. The isometric cube is too big and does not represent a cube of 30 mm side.To rectify this we need a reducing scale.

Isometric scale

The scaling factor needed for isometric is a constant for all isometrics and can be derived from the cube example given previously.The 45° line shows the true length of the cube side and the 30° line shows the isometric representation of that length, Fig. 5.25.

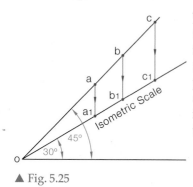

▲ Fig. 5.25

We set up a 45° line (Fig. 5.26) to show true lengths and a 30° line to show their isometric equivalents. Lengths oa, ob and oc are drawn on the 45° line. These are projected vertically to give oa, ob and oc as the isometrical scaled distances. An isometric scale measurement is 0.816 of the true length distance.

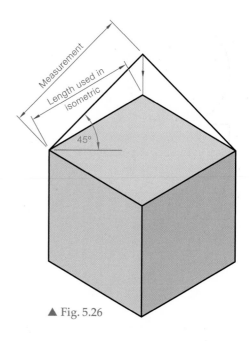

▲ Fig. 5.26

Worked Example Using Isometric Scale

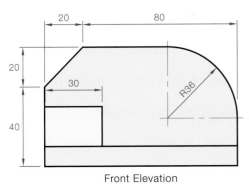

▲ Fig. 5.27

Front Elevation   **End Elevation**

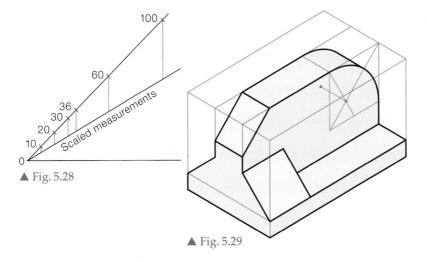

▲ Fig. 5.28

▲ Fig. 5.29

(1) Draw the front and end elevation of the shaped solid using full measurements, Fig. 5.27.

(2) Set up the isometric scale using a 45° line and a 30° line as explained earlier.

(3) Any measurement needed for the isometric is set out from the corner, along the 45° line, e.g. 10, 20, 30, 36, etc., Fig 5.28.

(4) Drop each measurement vertically to give the scaled measurements used in the isometric. Draw the isometric, Fig. 5.29.

(5) If you are constructing a circle or curve using ordinates, the length of each ordinate would have to be scaled also.

The Sphere in Isometric

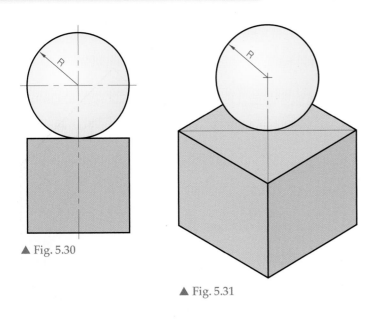

▲ Fig. 5.30

▲ Fig. 5.31

When drawing a sphere in isometric we must first consider what type of isometric we are producing. Are we drawing an isometric using full sizes or with scaled sizes? It should be noted that a sphere looks the same regardless of which way it is viewed or which plane it is projected onto. Having said that, it must also be noted that an unscaled isometric gives a distorted view, an enlarged view of objects. It stands to reason therefore that an unscaled drawing of an object containing a sphere, or part of a sphere, should give an enlarged view of that sphere. When drawing a sphere in isometric we must lengthen the radius unless we are producing a scaled isometric.

Fig. 5.30 shows the elevation of a pedestal with a sphere on top having a diameter equal to the pedestal width. Fig. 5.31 shows the isometric and it can be seen that the sphere appears too small even though the radius is the same as in Fig. 5.30.

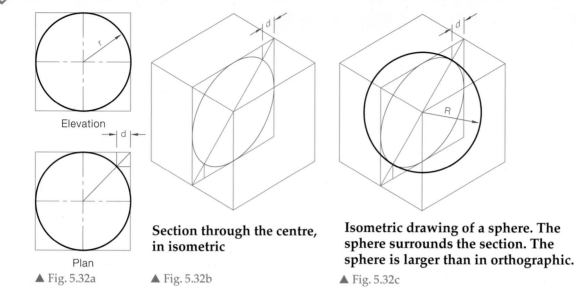
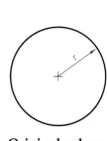

Elevation

Plan

▲ Fig. 5.32a

Section through the centre, in isometric

▲ Fig. 5.32b

Isometric drawing of a sphere. The sphere surrounds the section. The sphere is larger than in orthographic.

▲ Fig. 5.32c

Original sphere as comparison

▲ Fig. 5.32d

Fig. 5.32 shows how to find the radius for an unscaled isometric sphere. The radius of the sphere will equal half the major axis of the ellipse. The sectional ellipse need not be drawn. The length of the major is all that is needed.

Scaled Isometric of a Sphere

When drawing an isometric using the isometric scale, the size of the sphere will not be distorted and its radius remains unchanged, Fig. 5.33.

(1) Draw the elevation.

(2) Set up the isometric scale.

(3) The width of the pedestal changes from w to w_1 for the isometric.

(4) The height changes from h to h_1 for the isometric.

(5) The point of contact between the two solids is found by joining the diagonals.

(6) The centre of the ellipse is stepped up. The distance used is R_1, the scaled radius. The sphere is drawn with radius R.

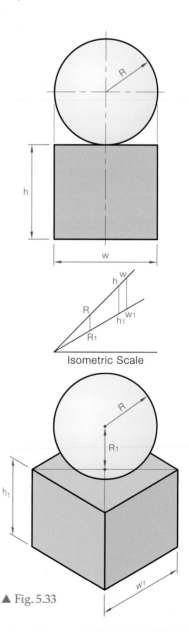

Isometric Scale

▲ Fig. 5.33

Activities

Q1 to Q3. Draw a true isometric of the following objects using an isometric scale.

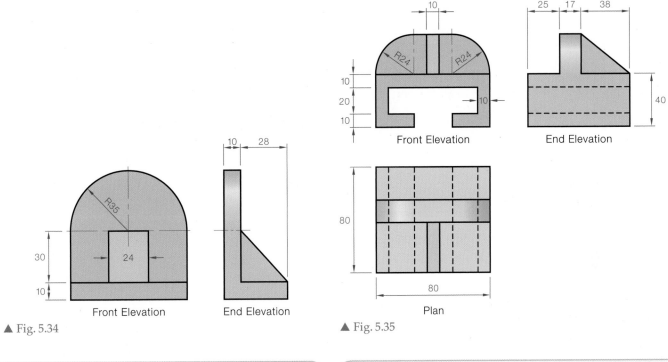

▲ Fig. 5.34

▲ Fig. 5.35

Q1.	Fig. 5.34

Q2.	Fig. 5.35

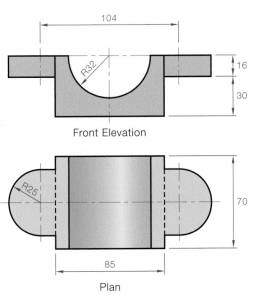

▲ Fig. 5.36

Q3.	Fig. 5.36

Axonometric Plane

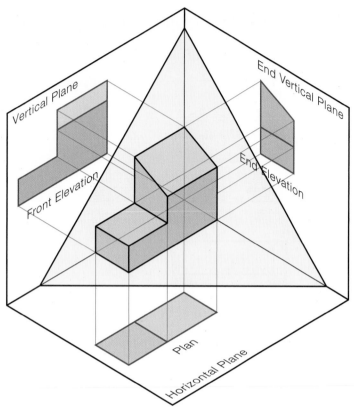

▲ Fig. 5.37

Fig. 5.37 shows a pictorial drawing of the planes of reference and an axonometric plane. When lines are projected from an object perpendicularly onto the axonometric plane we get an isometric of that object. What is happening here is that rather than tilting the object, as in Fig. 5.24 on a plane at 35°16′, we are tilting the plane onto which the object is projected. For isometric, this plane must make equal angles with the horizontal, vertical and end vertical planes. The plane itself will be an equilateral triangle. The axonometric plane is seen as a true shape in the pictorial. The isometric will be a scaled isometric.

True Isometric

Draw a true isometric of the object shown in Fig. 5.38 using the axonometric plane method.

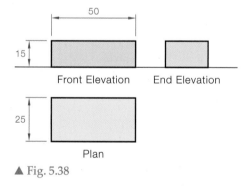

▲ Fig. 5.38

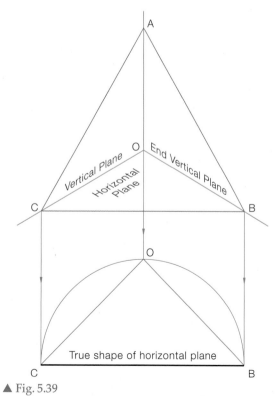

▲ Fig. 5.39

Step 1

Draw the axonometric plane. It will be an equilateral triangle ABC. Draw the lines of intersection between the horizontal, the vertical and the end vertical planes OC, OB and OA. These lines meet in the background.

Step 2

In order to draw the isometric we need a minimum of two orthographic views. We will use the plan and end elevation. The true shape of the triangular portion of the horizontal plane OBC is found as shown in Fig. 5.39. The angle COB must be a right angle so the construction is based on the angle in a semicircle.

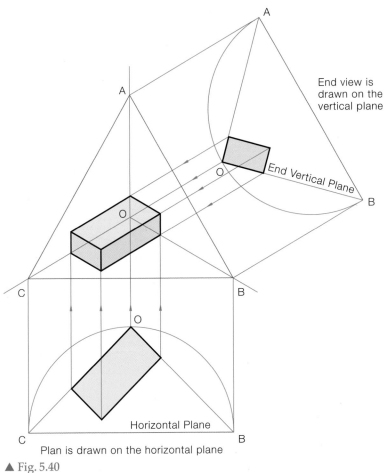

▲ Fig. 5.40

Step 3

A similar construction is used for finding the true shape of the end vertical plane AOB.

Step 4

The plan and end view are drawn as shown in Fig. 5.40.

Step 5

Find the pictorial view by projection from the plan and end view. Note that the pictorial is a true isometric. The drawing is scaled as if we had used an isometric scale.

Draw a true isometric of the object shown in Fig. 5.41 using the axonometric plane method.

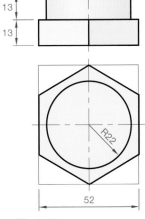

▲ Fig. 5.41

(1) Set up the axonometric plane, an equilateral triangle.

(2) Draw any two orthographic views. In Fig. 5.42 we have used the plan and the front elevation.

(3) Crating may still be used to aid the setting up of these views.

(4) Project the isometric of the base section of the solid, Fig. 5.42.

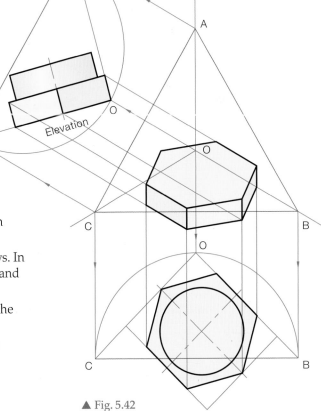

▲ Fig. 5.42

(5) The top of the circular section is constructed using the ortho four-centre ellipse but could easily be constructed using ordinates. The following example will be done using ordinates. The circle is crated in the plan. The crate is constructed in the isometric, Fig. 5.43. The centre lines are found.

(6) The centre points for the four curves are found as shown earlier in the chapter in Fig. 5.12.

(7) The lower curve is found by drawing the bottom of the crate. Draw in the diagonal.

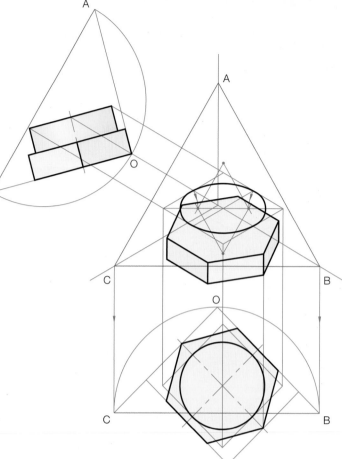

▲ Fig. 5.43

(8) Drop down the centres for the small arcs onto this diagonal, Fig. 5.44.

(9) The centre for the large arc can be found by dropping down the centre from the top ellipse or by drawing 60° lines as we did here.

(10) Complete the isometric. Hidden detail is not shown in isometric unless essential for dimensioning or to clarify some detail.

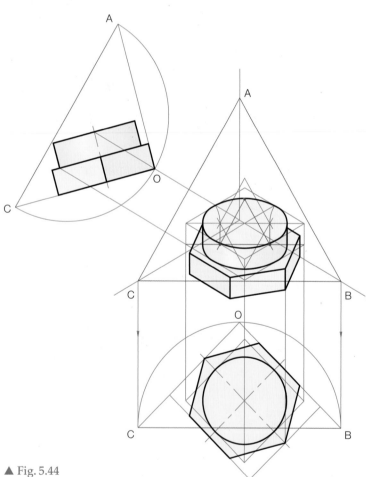

▲ Fig. 5.44

Draw a true isometric of the given solid, Fig. 5.45, using the axonometric plane method.

(1) Set up the axonometric plane and draw the plan, Fig. 5.46.

(2) Draw the elevation.

(3) Divide the quarter-circles in plan, giving points 1–8.

(4) Find points 1–8 in elevation, Fig. 5.47.

(5) Project isometric.

(6) Similar approach for points a–f, Fig. 5.48.

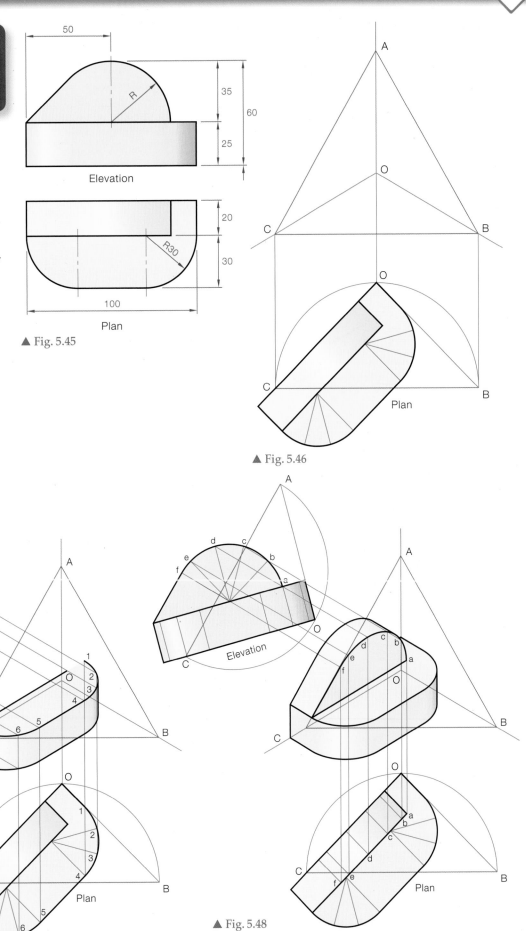

▲ Fig. 5.45

▲ Fig. 5.46

▲ Fig. 5.47

▲ Fig. 5.48

See worksheets 5.3 and 5.4

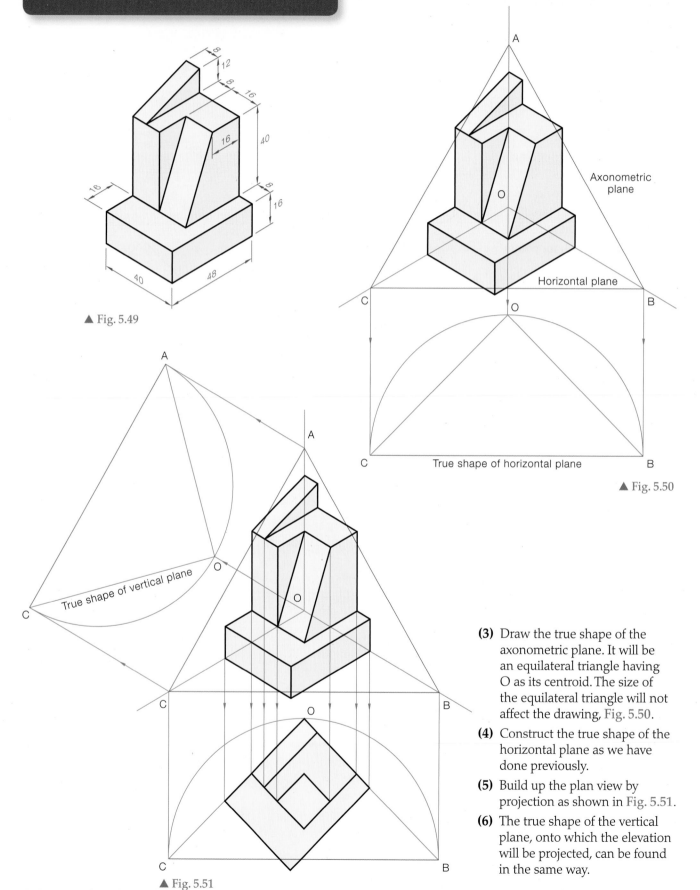

To project a two-dimensional view of an object from its axonometric view.

(1) Draw the object as given in the question, Fig. 5.49.
(2) Draw in the axes OA, OB and OC.

▲ Fig. 5.49

Axonometric plane

Horizontal plane

True shape of horizontal plane

▲ Fig. 5.50

True shape of vertical plane

▲ Fig. 5.51

(3) Draw the true shape of the axonometric plane. It will be an equilateral triangle having O as its centroid. The size of the equilateral triangle will not affect the drawing, Fig. 5.50.

(4) Construct the true shape of the horizontal plane as we have done previously.

(5) Build up the plan view by projection as shown in Fig. 5.51.

(6) The true shape of the vertical plane, onto which the elevation will be projected, can be found in the same way.

(7) Similar construction for the end vertical plane if it is needed.

(8) Front elevation and end view are found as shown in Fig. 5.52.

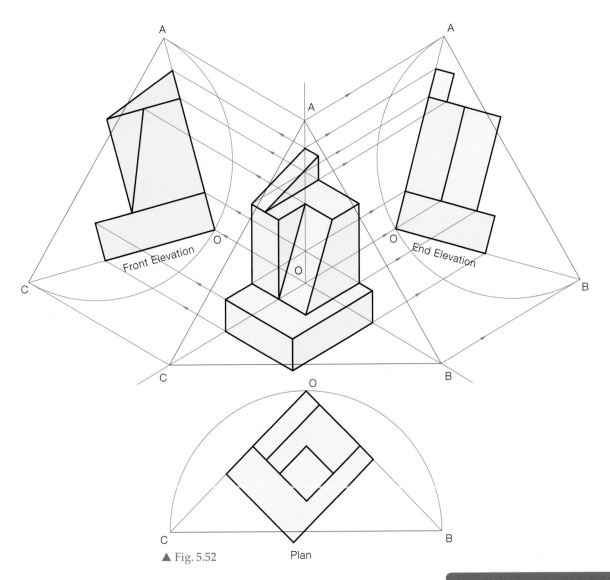

▲ Fig. 5.52

Plan

See worksheet 5.5

Isometric, Dimetric and Trimetric Projection – A Comparison

Isometric

So far we have only looked at isometric projection. In isometric the principal edges (axes) of an object make equal angles with the plane of projection, either by tilting the object (Fig. 5.24) or by using an axonometric plane (Fig. 5.37).

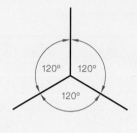
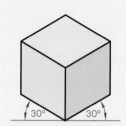

▲ Fig. 5.53

Dimetric (Two measures)

A dimetric projection is an axonometric projection of an object having two of its axes equally inclined to the projection plane. The third axis makes a different angle to the projection plane. Generally the object is so placed that one of its axes will be vertical when projected.

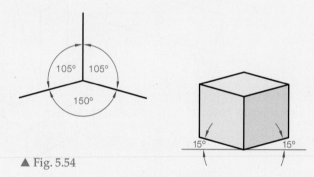

▲ Fig. 5.54

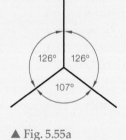

▲ Fig. 5.55a

This choice of angles shows more of the top face of the object.

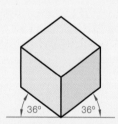

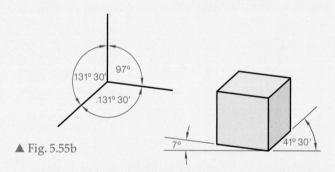

▲ Fig. 5.55b

A different choice of angles shows more of the left face.

Trimetric (Three Measures)

A trimetric projection is an axonometric projection of an object placed in such a position that none of its axes makes an angle with the projection plane equal to that made by any other axis. As with dimetric, the object is usually placed so that one of its edges will appear vertical when projected.

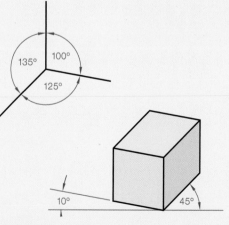

▲ Fig. 5.56

HIGHER LEVEL

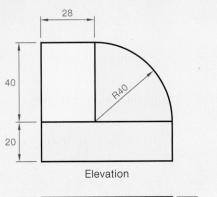

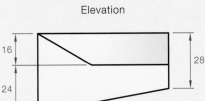

Elevation

Plan

▲ Fig. 5.57

Draw a dimetric projection of the given
solid Fig. 5.57 having axes inclined as shown.
Use the axonometric plane method.

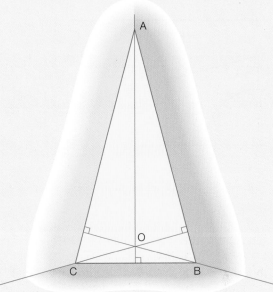

▲ Fig. 5.58

(1) Set up the axes as shown in Fig. 5.58.

(2) The axonometric plane is now drawn.
The plane is drawn such that edge AB
is perpendicular to axis CO, edge BC is
perpendicular to axis AO and edge CA is
perpendicular to axis BO. The size of the
triangle does not matter.

(3) Find the true shape of the triangular
portion of the horizontal plane BOC in
the same way as we did for isometric
projection.

(4) Similarly for the vertical plane, triangle
COA.

(5) Construct the orthographic views on these
true shapes.

(6) The dimetric view is found by projection
from the elevation and plan as we have
done for isometric.

(7) The pictorial will be scaled automatically,
Fig. 5.59.

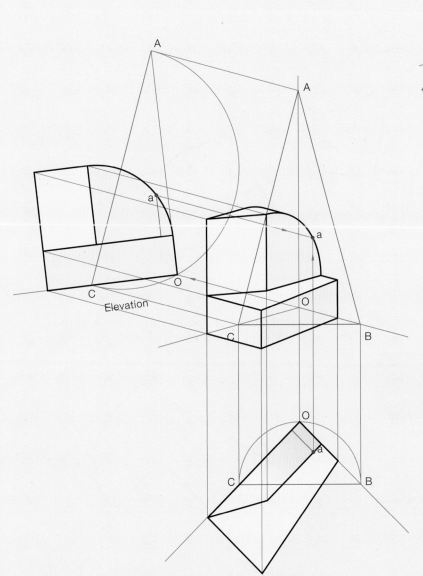

Plan

▲ Fig. 5.59

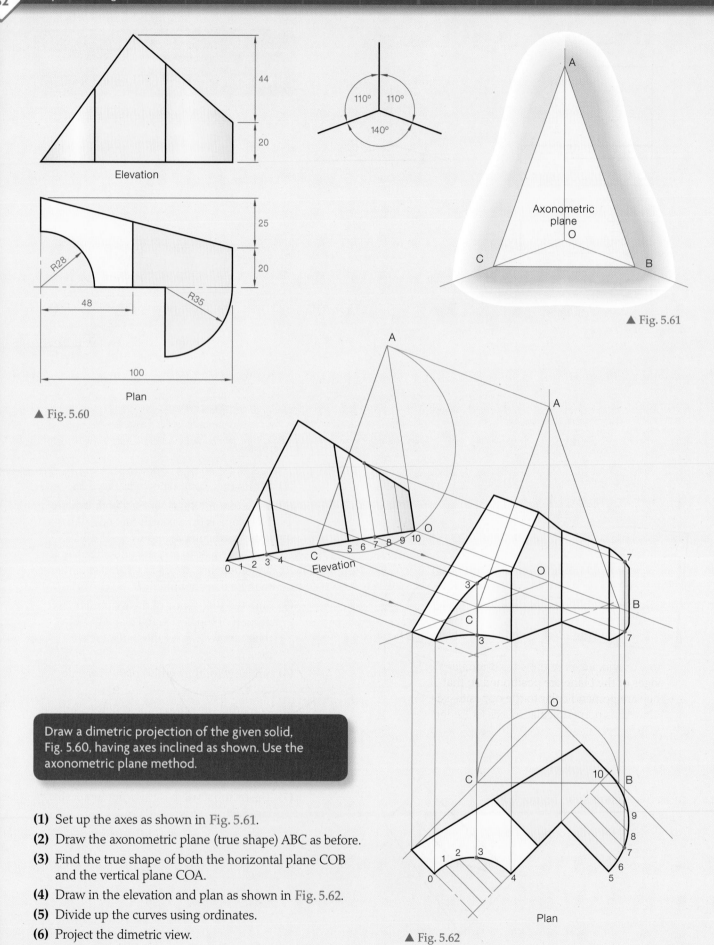

Elevation

R28

48

R35

25

20

44

20

100

Plan

▲ Fig. 5.60

110°   110°

140°

A

Axonometric
plane

O

C   B

▲ Fig. 5.61

A

A

O

0 1 2 3 4   C   5 6 7 8 9 10   O
Elevation   B

3   7

C   7

3

O

C   10   B

9

8

1 2 3   7

0   4   6

5

Plan

▲ Fig. 5.62

Draw a dimetric projection of the given solid,
Fig. 5.60, having axes inclined as shown. Use the
axonometric plane method.

(1) Set up the axes as shown in Fig. 5.61.
(2) Draw the axonometric plane (true shape) ABC as before.
(3) Find the true shape of both the horizontal plane COB
and the vertical plane COA.
(4) Draw in the elevation and plan as shown in Fig. 5.62.
(5) Divide up the curves using ordinates.
(6) Project the dimetric view.

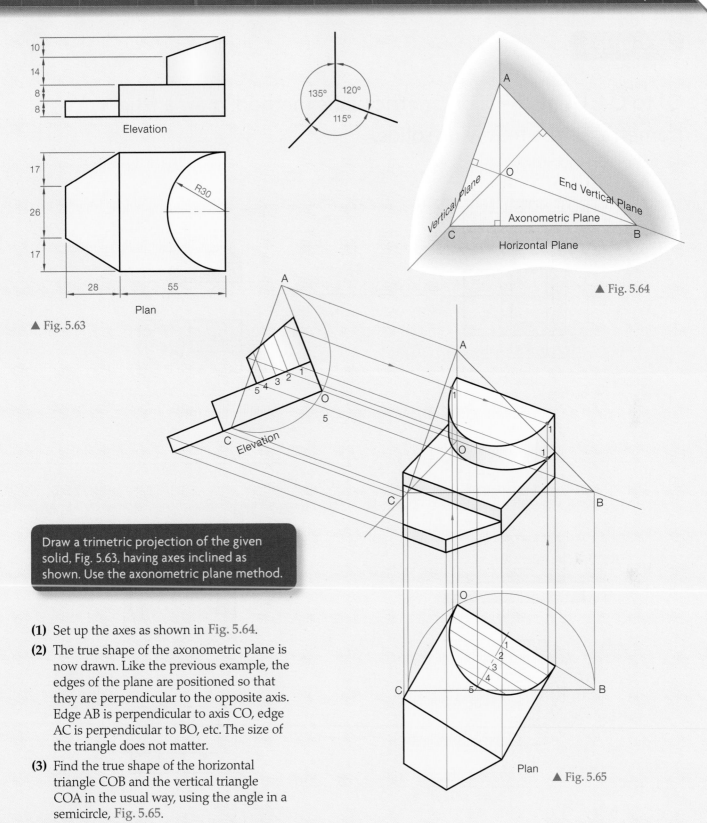

Elevation

Plan

R30

▲ Fig. 5.63

135° 120° 115°

A

O

Vertical Plane

End Vertical Plane

Axonometric Plane

C   B

Horizontal Plane

▲ Fig. 5.64

A

1   2   3   4   5

O

5

C   Elevation

A

1

O

1

1

C   B

O

1
2
3
4
5

C   B

Plan   ▲ Fig. 5.65

Draw a trimetric projection of the given solid, Fig. 5.63, having axes inclined as shown. Use the axonometric plane method.

(1) Set up the axes as shown in Fig. 5.64.

(2) The true shape of the axonometric plane is now drawn. Like the previous example, the edges of the plane are positioned so that they are perpendicular to the opposite axis. Edge AB is perpendicular to axis CO, edge AC is perpendicular to BO, etc. The size of the triangle does not matter.

(3) Find the true shape of the horizontal triangle COB and the vertical triangle COA in the usual way, using the angle in a semicircle, Fig. 5.65.

(4) Construct the orthographic views in these triangles.

(5) The trimetric is found by projection from these views parallel to the axes.

(6) The cylindrical portion is found by using ordinates as shown.

(7) The lengths are scaled automatically using this method.

See worksheet 5.6

Activities

Q1 to Q4. Using the axonometric plane method, draw a true isometric of the following solids.

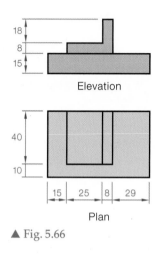

Elevation

Plan

▲ Fig. 5.66

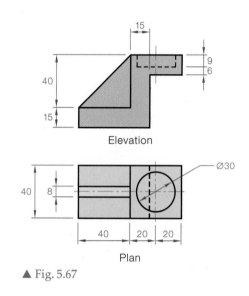

Elevation

Plan

▲ Fig. 5.67

Q1. Fig. 5.66

Q2. Fig. 5.67

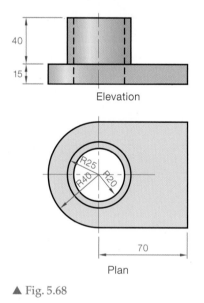

Elevation

Plan

▲ Fig. 5.68

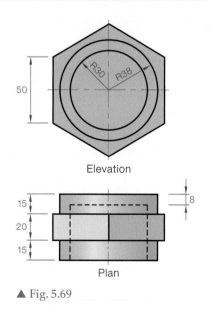

Elevation

Plan

▲ Fig. 5.69

Q3. Fig. 5.68

Q4. Fig. 5.69

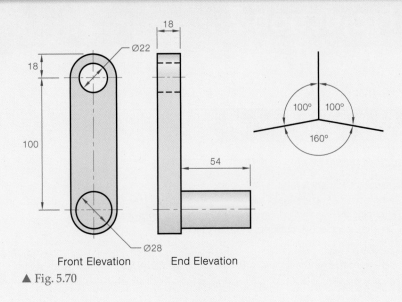

Front Elevation   End Elevation

▲ Fig. 5.70

Q5.   Fig. 5.70 Contruct a dimetric view of the object shown. The axes angles are given.

Syllabus Outline

Learning Outcomes

Areas to be studied:
- Principles of pictorial perspective drawing.
- Parallel and angular perspective.
- Vanishing points for horizontal lines.
- *Derivation of vanishing points for inclined lines.*

Students should be able to:

Higher and Ordinary levels
- Demonstrate a knowledge of vanishing points, picture plane, ground line and horizon lines.
- Determine the vanishing points and height lines for horizontal lines.
- Complete perspective drawings of given objects.

Higher Level only
- *Determine the vanishing points for sets of inclined lines (auxiliary vanishing points).*

 Perspective

Perspective is a pictorial representation of objects which very closely matches the view from the human eye. It is different from all other projection systems because the projection rays radiate from/to a single point. In the other systems of projection the projection rays are parallel. The effect this has on the pictorial is that objects that are in the distance will appear smaller than the same objects closer to the observer. If you walk up close to an object it appears bigger than if you see the same object from a long distance away. We see everything in perspective and are therefore used to making the adjustment for size. Look down a straight street of houses. The house in the distance appears very small compared to the house nearby, yet we know that all the houses are the same size. The sides of the street appear to narrow in the distance yet we know they stay parallel, Fig. 6.1.

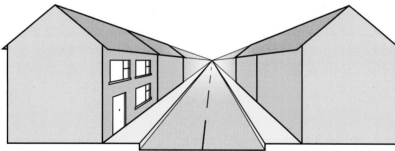

Perspective gives a very realistic view of objects and is very useful for that reason but it should not be used to give sizes as it does not show true lengths.

▲ Fig. 6.1

Terms Associated with Perspective

Picture Plane

As with all projection systems the image is projected onto a plane. This plane is called the picture plane. The picture plane may be passing through the object, may be between the object and the observer or may be behind the object. Fig. 6.2 shows each of these arrangements. It can be seen that the placing of the picture plane does not affect the proportions of the perspective, only the size of the perspective.

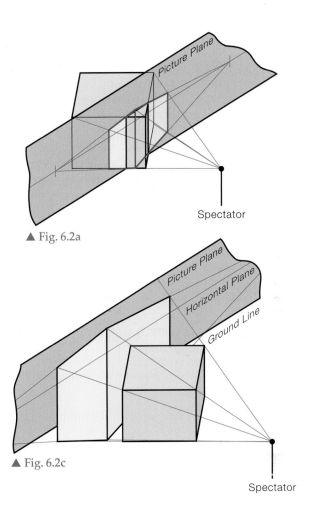

▲ Fig. 6.2a

▲ Fig. 6.2c

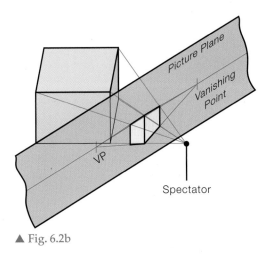

▲ Fig. 6.2b

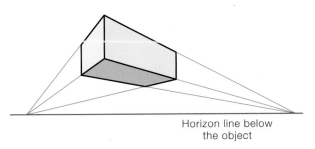

Horizon line below the object

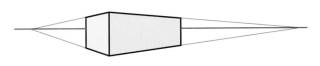

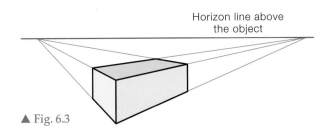

Horizon line above the object

▲ Fig. 6.3

When the picture plane is in front of the object the perspective drawing is smaller than the object. Having the picture plane behind the object means that the perspective projects larger than the object.

Horizon Line

The horizon line is a line on the picture plane at the eye level of the spectator. The position of the horizon line will affect the final perspective view of a given object. When the horizon line is above the object it means that the spectator has a high viewpoint and can see the top surface of the solid. Having the horizon below the object results in a perspective that shows the bottom surface of the object. Fig. 6.3 demonstrates how horizon level changes the perspective.

The upper diagram in Fig. 6.3 shows a perspective with the spectator lower than the object. The horizon line is below the perspective of the object and therefore we see its bottom surface. The lower diagram shows the other extreme – the spectator's viewpoint is high, the horizon is therefore high and so we see the upper surface of the object.

Position of the Station Point

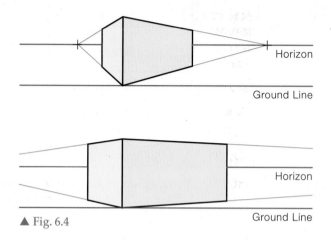

The position of the station point (SP) relative to the object also has a huge effect on the final perspective. When the SP is close to the object we are viewing the object from nearby and when the SP is far away we are viewing the object from a long distance away. Fig. 6.4 shows two perspective views of the same object. The upper diagram is produced by having the spectator near the object and the view we get is quite distorted. The lower diagram is produced by having the spectator further away. The sides of the box are closer to being parallel. It is worth noting that the perspective produced when the spectator (S) is further from the object, the second perspective, is actually larger than the first.

▲ Fig. 6.4

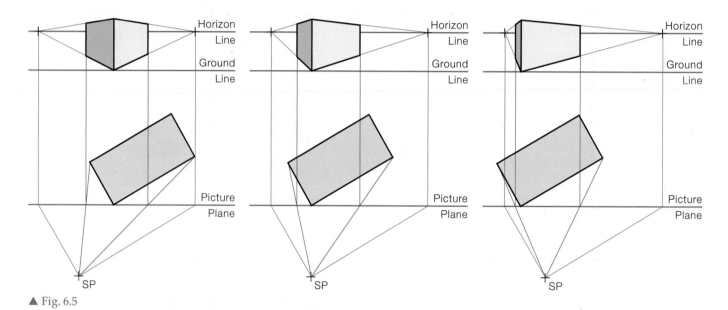

▲ Fig. 6.5

This would appear to break the rules. Objects in the distance should appear smaller than objects nearby. It is, however, the position of the picture plane that determines the size of the perspective, not the position of the spectator. The spectator can be moved from left to right, and again this will affect the final view. In general, the centre line of the cone of visual rays should be directed toward the centre of the object, or the centre of interest of the object, see Fig. 6.5.

Terms Used in Perspective

Just a quick recap on some of the terminology.

Picture Plane: The image is projected onto the picture plane. It is a vertical plane and can be moved. The position of the picture plane, relative to the object being viewed, affects the size of the finished perspective. Having the picture plane behind the object means an enlarged perspective, a view larger than the actual object. Having the picture plane in front of the object means a reduction in the size of the perspective.

Ground Line: The ground line is the line of intersection between the picture plane and the horizontal plane.

Horizon Line: This is a horizontal line on the picture plane that matches the height of the spectator's eyes.

Spectator: The person viewing the object.

Station Point: The position of the spectator relative to the object and the picture plane.

Vanishing Points: All lines vanish off into the distance. Sets of parallel lines vanish off to the same point, a vanishing point. Horizontal lines will have vanishing points on the horizon line.

 # Types of Perspective

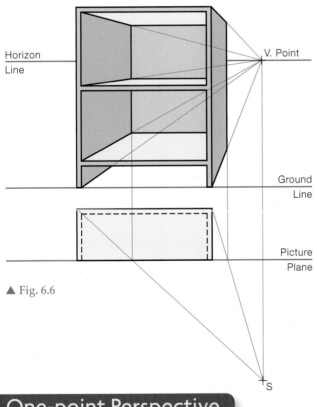

▲ Fig. 6.6

One-point Perspective

Two of the object's principal axes must be parallel to the picture plane, leaving the third to vanish off to a single vanishing point. This is the least complicated of the perspectives and is quick to produce. Useful for presentation work and for representing the interior of a room. It is also useful for solids containing circular curves. Position the object so that the surface(s) containing the circles are parallel to the picture plane and the perspective view of these circles can be drawn with the compass, Figures 6.6 and 6.7.

So far we have been experimenting with the various elements of perspective to see how they affect the final drawing. We have moved the picture plane, horizon line and the spectator, each making its own changes to the perspective produced. The last variable is the object itself and its orientation to the picture plane. Placing the object so that one of its faces is parallel to the picture plane results in a **one-point perspective** or **parallel perspective**. Tilting the object so that two faces are at an angle to the picture plane, while still having vertical edges parallel to the picture plane, produces a **two-point perspective** or **angular perspective**. Finally, if the object is placed so that none of its edges is parallel to the picture plane we get a **three-point perspective**.

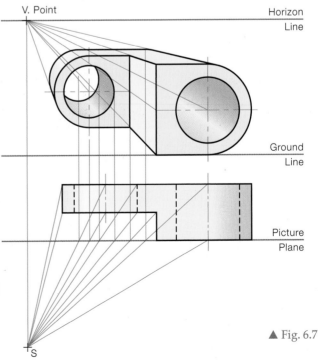

▲ Fig. 6.7

Two-point Perspective

This is the most commonly used perspective. The object is placed so that one set of edges is vertical and therefore parallel to the picture plane and the other two sets are inclined to the picture plane, thus giving two vanishing points. It produces a very realistic view and is used extensively to represent buildings in architecture, Fig. 6.8.

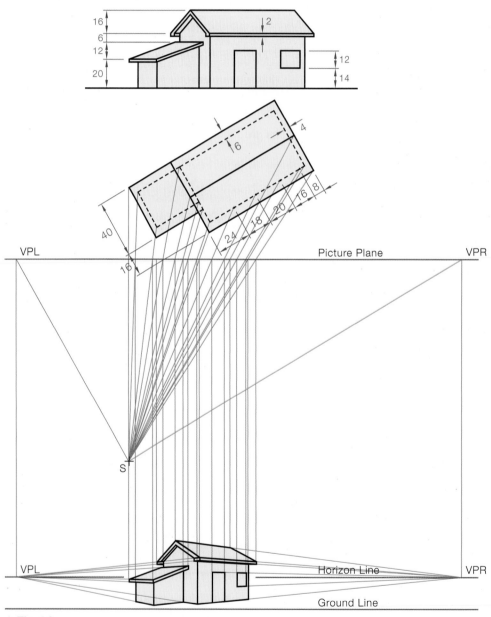

▲ Fig. 6.8

Method of constructing a one-point perspective.

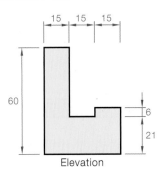

The following series of diagrams illustrate how to set up and construct a one-point perspective of a simple object. Given the plan and elevation of an object, the position of the spectator and the picture plane, Fig. 6.9a:

(1) Set up the problem on the page. Usually we do not need to draw the elevation. Draw the ground line as shown in Fig. 6.9b. The ground line is drawn parallel to the picture plane.

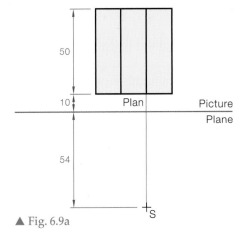

▲ Fig. 6.9a

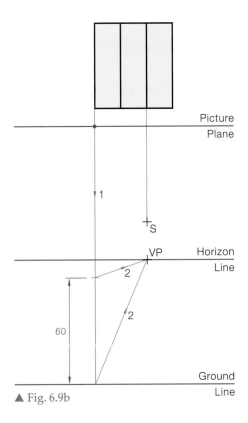

▲ Fig. 6.9b

(2) Draw the horizon line parallel to the ground line. The spacing between the horizon line and the ground line is usually given in the question and shows the viewing height of the spectator.

(3) Since the object is behind the picture plane we extend one edge to hit the picture plane. This point is then projected down to the ground line. The height of the object is measured from the ground up. The top and bottom of the height line are vanished back to the vanishing point, which is found on the horizon line, directly below the spectator.

(4) A visual light ray is brought from the two corners of the plan to the spectator, as shown in Fig. 6.9c. Where these light rays pierce the picture plane they are dropped down to the perspective finding the front left edge and the back corner.

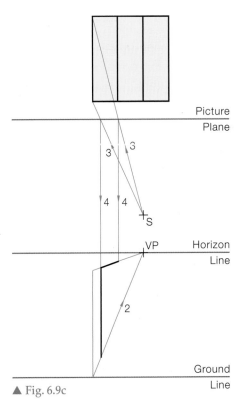

▲ Fig. 6.9c

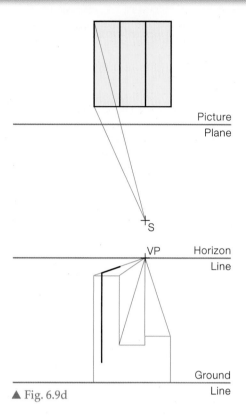

▲ Fig. 6.9d

(5) The elevation of the object is built up using the height line as one of its edges as shown in Fig. 6.9d.

(6) What we have done is lengthened the object until it hits the picture plane. **Objects in the picture plane show their true sizes.** That is why we can draw the elevation full size on the ground line. The corners of this elevation are vanished back to the vanishing point.

(7) Corners of the perspective are located by using rays of light as in Step 4. Rays are brought from the two corners on the right. Where they pass through the picture plane they are projected into the perspective view as shown in Fig. 6.9e.

Note: In the top half of the drawing we are looking at the plan of the object, the plan of the picture plane (we are seeing it edge on) and we are seeing the plan of the spectator. In the lower half of the drawing we are seeing through the spectator's eyes and looking at the picture plane. The ground line is the line of intersection between the picture plane and the horizontal plane. The horizon line is at the spectator's eye level. The perspective itself is the projection of an image of the object onto the picture plane, using rays of light.

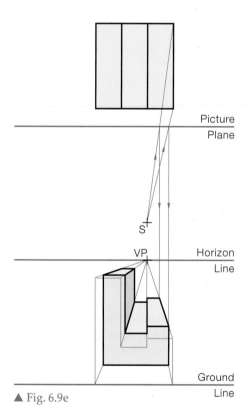

▲ Fig. 6.9e

Method of constructing a two-point perspective.

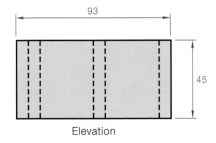

Elevation

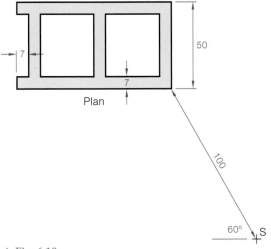

Plan

▲ Fig. 6.10a

The following series of diagrams illustrate the process of producing a two-point perspective of an object. Given the plan and elevation of an object (Fig. 6.10a). Also given the direction of the spectator and its distance from the corner. The spectator is 70 mm above the ground. We have not been given the picture plane's position so our first step is to locate it in plan. **The picture plane is always perpendicular to the central line of sight.** To get a balanced perspective we will have the spectator view towards the centre of the object.

(1) The extreme corners of the plan are joined back to the spectator. The angle formed is bisected giving the centre of vision as shown in Fig. 6.10b. The picture plane is now drawn.

(2) The location of the vanishing points on the picture plane is the next step. The vanishing points are found by drawing lines from the spectator parallel to the principal axes of the object and finding their piercing points in the picture plane.

(3) The ground line and horizon line are now drawn parallel to the picture plane. The spacing between them is usually given in the question.

(4) The two vanishing points located on the picture plane are now projected onto the horizon line.

(5) To start the perspective we need a height line. One edge ab is extended to hit the picture plane at c. This point c is projected down to the ground line. The height of the object is measured on this line.

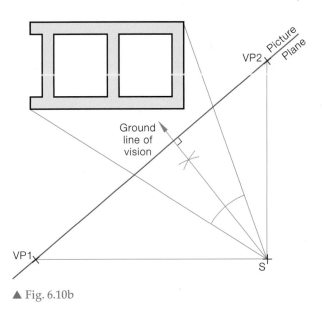

▲ Fig. 6.10b

(6) The top and bottom of the height line are vanished back to VP1. VP1 is used because edge ab and all edges parallel to it vanish to VP1, Fig 6.10c.

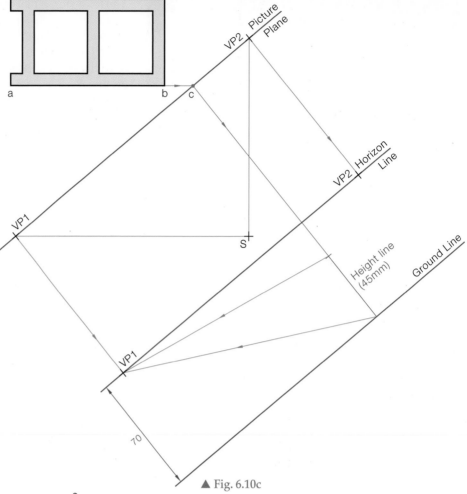

▲ Fig. 6.10c

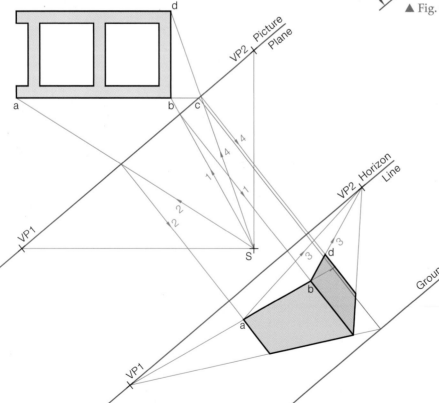

▲ Fig. 6.10d

(7) Light rays are brought from points a and b back to the spectator where they pierce the picture plane. They are brought down to the perspective, finding a and b in the perspective view.

(8) Points a and b in the perspective are vanished off to VP2, Fig. 6.10d.

(9) Point d is found in the same way as points a and b.

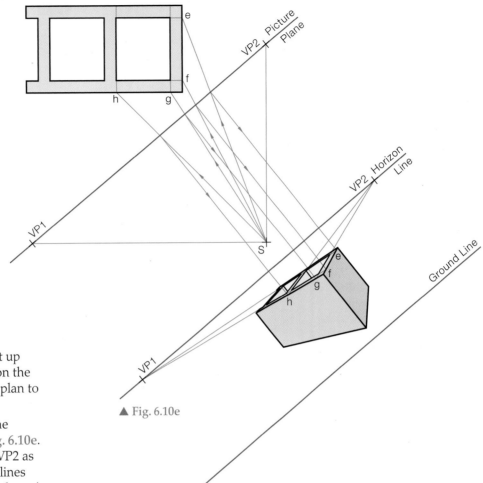

▲ Fig. 6.10e

(10) The top of the block is built up in the same way. The lines on the top surface are extended in plan to points e, f, g and h.

(11) Find these four points in the perspective as shown in Fig. 6.10e. Vanish lines off to VP1 and VP2 as appropriate. Repeat for the lines further in the distance (not shown).

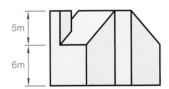

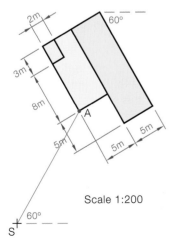

Scale 1:200

▲ Fig. 6.11a

Given the plan and elevation of a building. Draw a perspective view of the building when the position of the spectator is 19 m from the corner A, the picture plane touches the corner A and the horizon line is 5 m above the ground line.

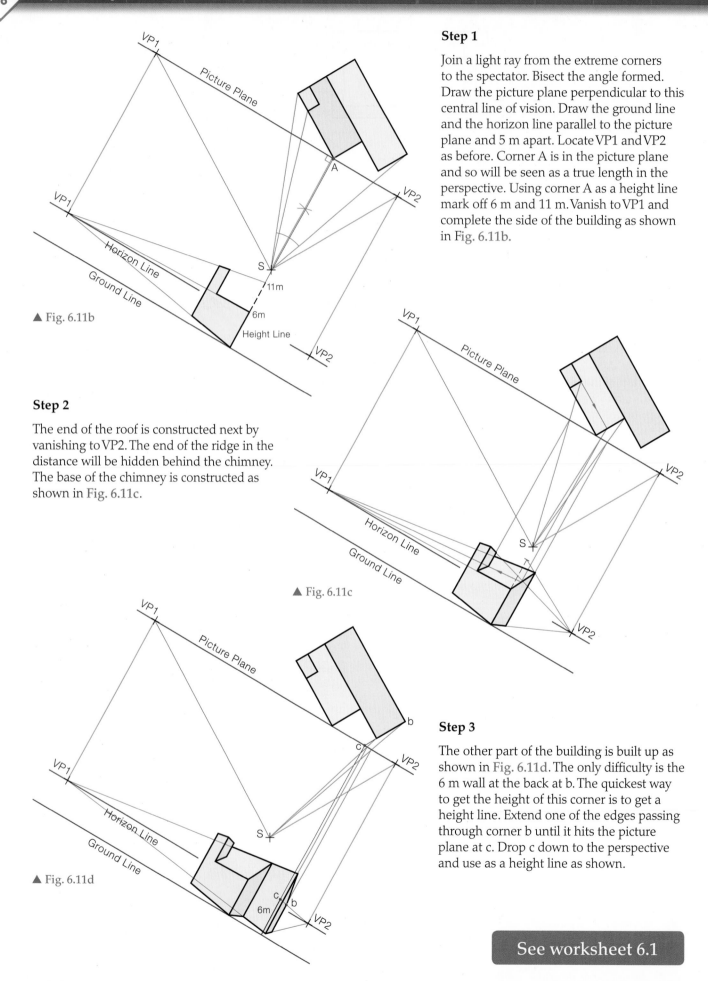

Step 1

Join a light ray from the extreme corners to the spectator. Bisect the angle formed. Draw the picture plane perpendicular to this central line of vision. Draw the ground line and the horizon line parallel to the picture plane and 5 m apart. Locate VP1 and VP2 as before. Corner A is in the picture plane and so will be seen as a true length in the perspective. Using corner A as a height line mark off 6 m and 11 m. Vanish to VP1 and complete the side of the building as shown in Fig. 6.11b.

▲ Fig. 6.11b

Step 2

The end of the roof is constructed next by vanishing to VP2. The end of the ridge in the distance will be hidden behind the chimney. The base of the chimney is constructed as shown in Fig. 6.11c.

▲ Fig. 6.11c

Step 3

The other part of the building is built up as shown in Fig. 6.11d. The only difficulty is the 6 m wall at the back at b. The quickest way to get the height of this corner is to get a height line. Extend one of the edges passing through corner b until it hits the picture plane at c. Drop c down to the perspective and use as a height line as shown.

▲ Fig. 6.11d

See worksheet 6.1

Circles and Curves in Perspective

We have already established that if a circle is parallel to the picture plane the perspective view of it will be circular. If the circle is inclined to the picture plane we generally get an ellipse. Fig. 6.12 shows how the circle is divided up into ordinates and from these the circle is built up point by point. The height line is found first by extending the front face of the cylinder to intersect the picture plane. Half the elevation is constructed on this height line in order to find heights for the perspective. The elevation is divided up into divisions using ordinates. The same ordinate spacing is used in the plan and the perspective is built up as shown using these ordinates.

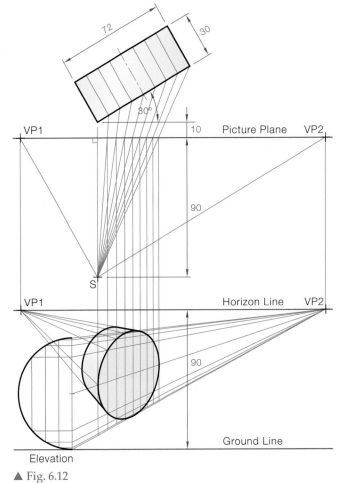

▲ Fig. 6.12

See worksheet 6.2

Activities

Q1 to Q3.

Draw a one-point perspective of the solids shown.

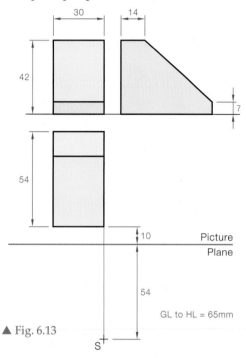

▲ Fig. 6.13

GL to HL = 65mm

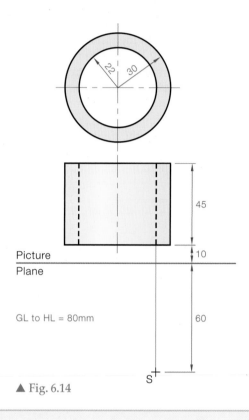

▲ Fig. 6.14

GL to HL = 80mm

Q1.   Fig. 6.13

Q2.   Fig. 6.14

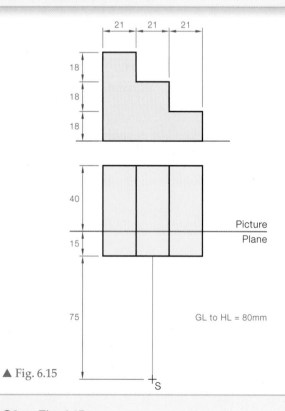

▲ Fig. 6.15

GL to HL = 80mm

Q3.   Fig. 6.15

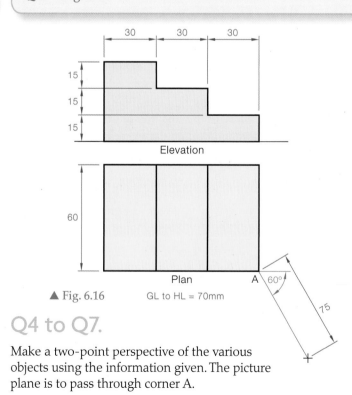

▲ Fig. 6.16   GL to HL = 70mm

Q4 to Q7.

Make a two-point perspective of the various objects using the information given. The picture plane is to pass through corner A.

Q4.   Fig. 6.16

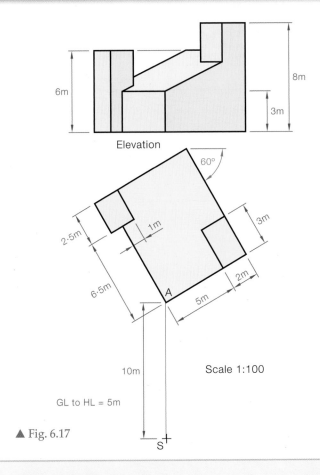

Elevation

6m

8m

3m

60°

2·5m

1m

3m

6·5m

2m

A

5m

10m

Scale 1:100

GL to HL = 5m

▲ Fig. 6.17

S

Q5. Fig. 6.17

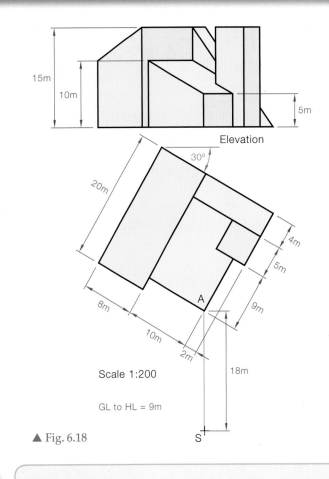

15m

10m

Elevation

5m

30°

20m

4m

5m

8m

A

9m

10m

2m

18m

Scale 1:200

GL to HL = 9m

▲ Fig. 6.18

S

Q6. Fig. 6.18

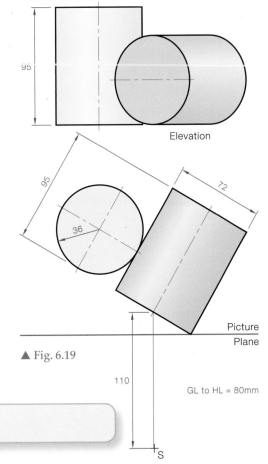

95

Elevation

95

72

36

Picture
Plane

▲ Fig. 6.19

110

GL to HL = 80mm

S

Q7. Fig. 6.19

Vanishing points of inclined lines

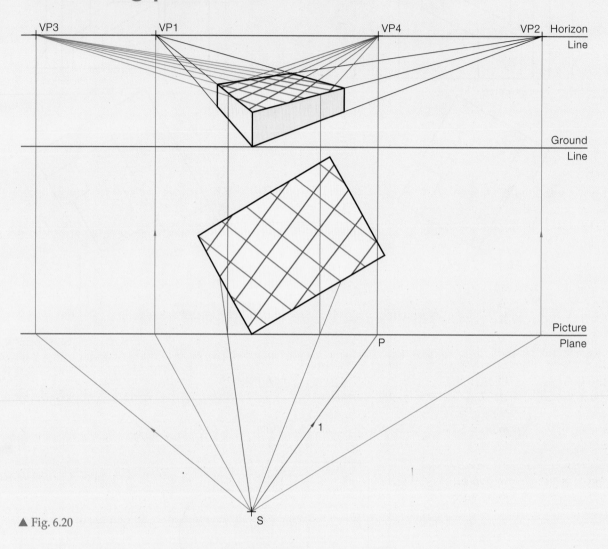

▲ Fig. 6.20

For all the perspectives we have dealt with so far we have used vanishing points of horizontal lines. The vanishing points have been found on the horizon line. Vanishing points for horizontal lines will always be found on the horizon line. Furthermore, parallel lines vanish to the same vanishing point, see Fig. 6.20.

The parallel blue lines on the prism's top surface are horizontal and therefore will vanish to a vanishing point (VP) on the horizon, VP4. This vanishing point is found, as for all lines, by finding the piercing point in the picture plane of a line drawn from the spectator, parallel to the given line. A line is drawn from S parallel to the blue set of lines and is continued to the picture plane at P. Point P is projected to the horizon line giving VP4. A similar approach can be used for the green set of lines. Sets of parallel inclined lines vanish to vanishing points either above or below the horizon line and these vanishing points are called auxiliary vanishing points.

> **Lines which are sloping upwards as they go away from the spectator will have an auxiliary vanishing point above the horizon. Lines which are sloping downwards as they go away from the spectator will have an auxiliary vanishing point below the horizon.**

Finding Auxiliary Vanishing Points

(1) Identify the set of sloped lines for which we will need the auxiliary vanishing point. If they are sloping upwards as they go away from the spectator then the vanishing point will be above the horizon. If the lines are sloping downwards as they go away from the spectator then the vanishing point will be below the horizon.

(2) Draw a line from S parallel to this set of lines as they appear in plan. Extend this line until it hits the picture plane.

> **Note: In this example it will be the same line as that used to find VP2. The auxiliary vanishing point will be in line with VP2.**

(3) In this step we find how high the auxiliary VP is above the horizon. Step the length of one of the sloped lines (as it appears in plan) out from the spectator, length ab. Step the difference in height between the start and finish of this sloped line, height bc, out perpendicular to the 'length' at b.

(4) This triangle abc is now continued on and enlarged, giving the height, at the picture plane, that the auxiliary VP is above the horizon, see Fig. 6.21.

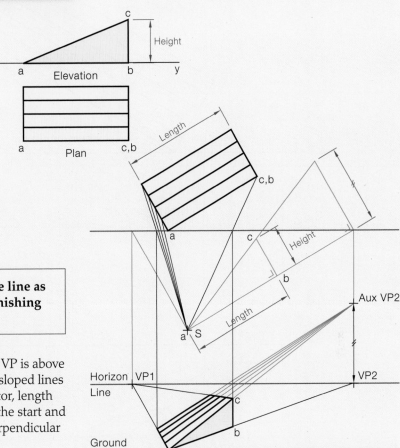

▲ Fig. 6.21

HIGHER LEVEL

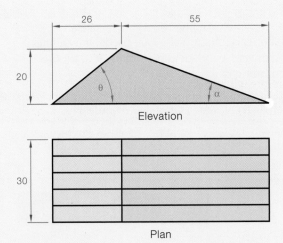

▲ Fig. 6.22

Finding Auxiliary Vanishing Points (Alternative Method)

This method of finding auxiliary vanishing points is almost identical to the first method but uses true angles instead of distances.

Given the solid shown in Fig. 6.22, draw a two-point perspective of this solid using auxiliary vanishing points where appropriate.

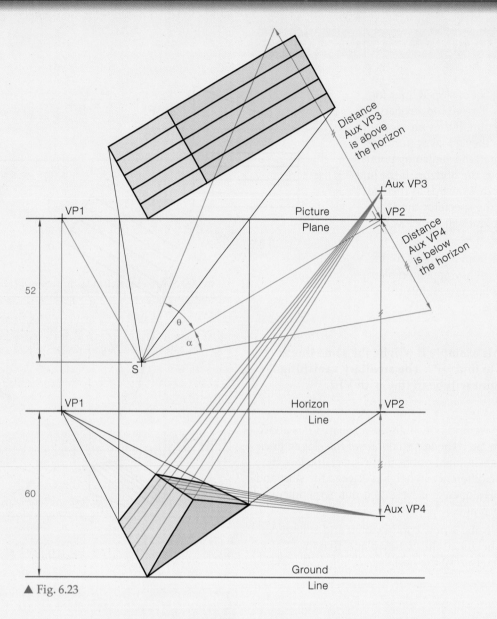

▲ Fig. 6.23

(1) It is worth noting that all perspectives can be drawn by using height lines and avoiding the use of auxiliary vanishing points, but the perspective can be completed quicker and more accurately if they are used. Draw a line from the spectator parallel to the set of lines for which we are finding the auxiliary VP and continue it to hit the picture plane. In this example both sets of inclined parallel lines are running parallel to S, VP2.

(2) From this line create an angle at S equal to the true slope of the lines in elevation. For clarity, since we have two sets of lines, one angle (angle θ) was measured upwards and the other (angle α) was measured downwards, Fig. 6.23.

(3) A perpendicular to S, VP2 at the picture plane is produced to intersect each angle. This gives, for angle θ, the distance the auxiliary VP is above the horizon, and, for angle α, the distance the auxiliary VP is below the horizon.

(4) The perspective is completed in the normal way. No height line is needed.

See worksheet 6.3

Worked Example

It should be noted that extra care should be taken when using angles so that it is the true angle that is used, not the apparent angle. The following example will attempt to demonstrate the difference.

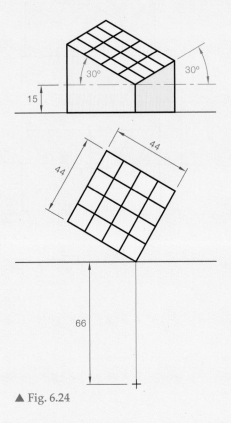

▲ Fig. 6.24

Given the solid shown in Fig. 6.24. Draw a two-point perspective of this solid when the position of the spectator is as shown and the horizon line is 24 mm above the ground line. Use auxiliary vanishing points where appropriate.

(1) In elevation, edge ab and all lines parallel to it appear to make an angle of 30° to the horizontal plane but their true angle is much less, as shown in Fig. 6.25. Line ab has a true angle of θ to the horizontal plane and line ac has a true angle of α to the horizontal plane.

(2) The perspective is completed using these angles as shown in Fig. 6.26.

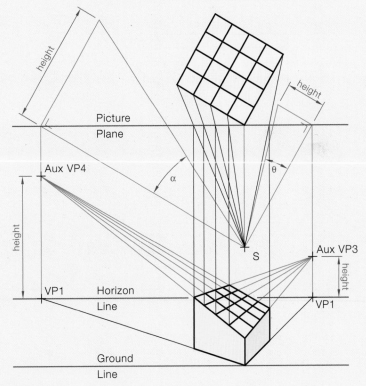

▲ Fig. 6.26

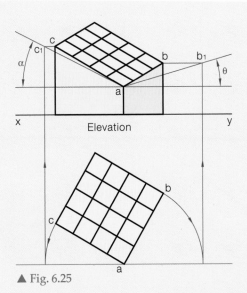

▲ Fig. 6.25

See worksheet 6.4

HIGHER LEVEL

HIGHER LEVEL

Given the structure shown in Fig. 6.27 which has a plan based on semi-hexagonal prisms. Draw a perspective view of the structure. The picture plane passes through corner A. The spectator is 10 m from corner A and the horizon line is 10 m above the ground line. Use auxiliary vanishing points where appropriate.

On examining this question it can be seen that edges AE and CE and all edges parallel to them have a true angle of 30° to the horizontal plane. It should be noted, however, that neither edge AB nor edge CD has a true angle of 30° to the HP even though they appear to be inclined at 30° in the elevation.

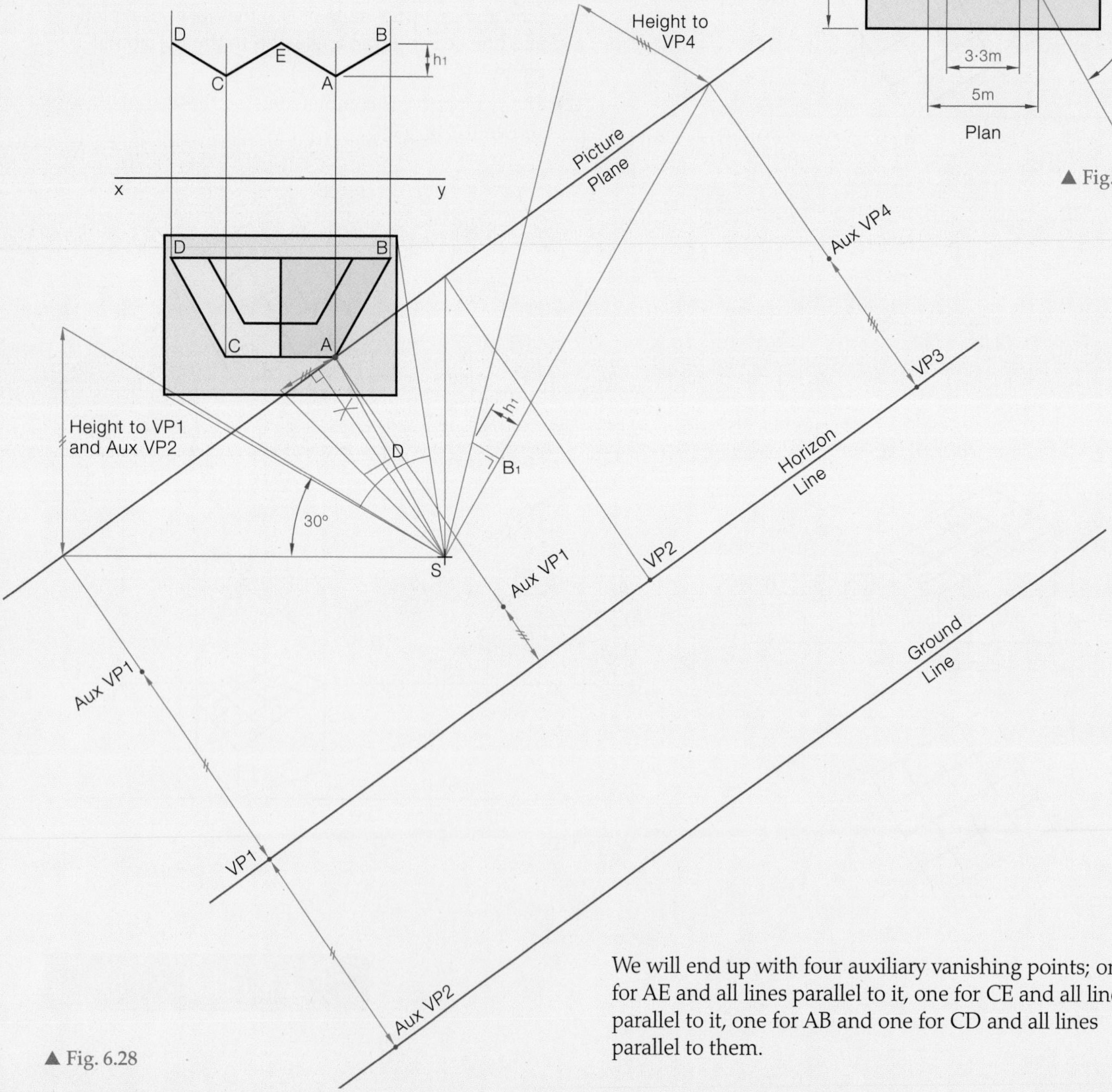

▲ Fig. 6.27

We will end up with four auxiliary vanishing points; one for AE and all lines parallel to it, one for CE and all lines parallel to it, one for AB and one for CD and all lines parallel to them.

▲ Fig. 6.28

(1) The first step is to locate the picture plane. Join the outer corners of the plan back to the spectator. Bisect the angle formed to give the centre of vision. The picture plane is drawn perpendicular to this.

(2) Draw the ground line and horizon line and locate VP1 and VP2, the vanishing points for the horizontal base lines. These vanishing points will be on the horizon.

(3) Vanishing points for edges AE and CE will be on the VP1 line. The auxiliary vanishing point for AE will be above the horizon and the auxiliary vanishing point for CE will be below the horizon. The construction is as shown in Fig. 6.28. We can use the 30° as it is a true angle.

(4) Auxiliary vanishing point for edge AB is found as shown. A line is drawn from S parallel to AB in plan, to hit the picture plane. The length of AB in plan is stepped away from S on this line giving B1. A perpendicular to SB1 is drawn at B_1. The difference in height between A and B is found in elevation (h_1) and stepped out on this perpendicular. Complete the triangle and enlarge to the picture plane. We thus find the height of Aux VP4 above the horizon.

(5) Aux VP3 is found in a similar way.

(6) The perspective is completed in Fig. 6.29.

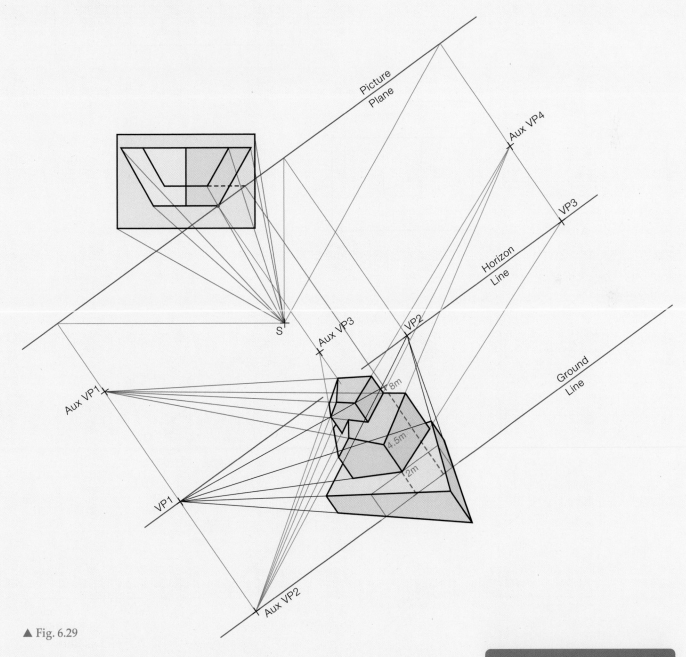

▲ Fig. 6.29

See worksheet 6.5

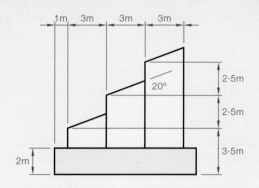

Draw a perspective view of the structure shown in Fig. 6.30. The picture plane passes through corner A. The spectator is 10 m from corner A and the horizon line is 10 m above the ground line. Use auxiliary vanishing points where appropriate.

As before we will start by locating the picture plane, ground line and horizon line. We will also find all necessary vanishing points. It should be noted that the elevation is not needed; we only draw a small portion of it as in the previous example.

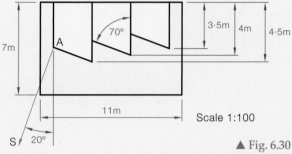

Scale 1:100

▲ Fig. 6.30

HIGHER LEVEL

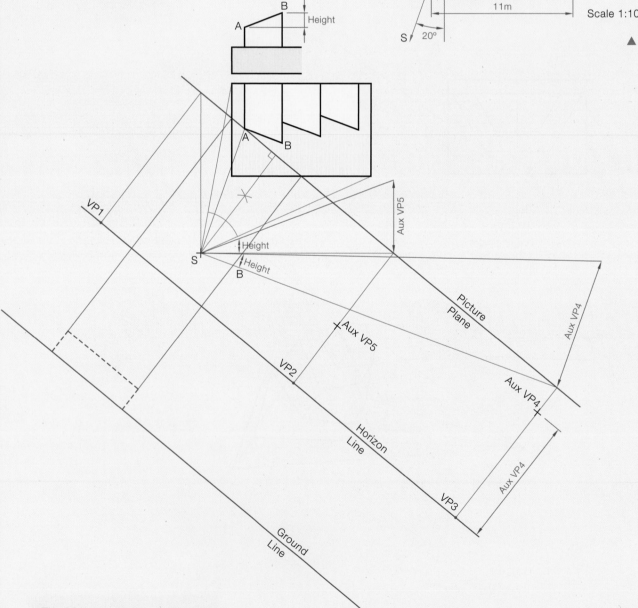

▲ Fig. 6.31

(1) Rays are projected from the two outer corners back to S. The angle formed is bisected, giving the centre of vision. The picture plane is drawn perpendicular to this, Fig. 6.31.

(2) Horizon line and ground line are 10 m apart and parallel to the picture plane.

(3) VP1 and VP2 are vanishing points for the rectangular base. These vanishing points will be on the horizon line because they are vanishing points for horizontal lines.

(4) The line AB in plan actually represents two lines. One of these is running along the top surface of the base, is horizontal, and therefore has a vanishing point on the horizon, VP3. The other is sloping upwards as it goes away from the spectator and will therefore have an auxiliary vanishing point above the horizon.

(5) Draw a line from S parallel to AB in plan. Extend to hit the picture plane. Step the distance AB, from the plan, out from the spectator along this line, giving point B.

(6) Step the difference in height between A and B (obtained from the elevation) out perpendicularly. Create a triangle and enlarge to the picture plane. This gives the height Aux VP4 will be above the horizon. Auxiliary VP5 is found in a similar way.

(7) The perspective is finished as before. See Fig. 6.32.

> **Note: Height lines always vanish to vanishing points on the horizon line.**

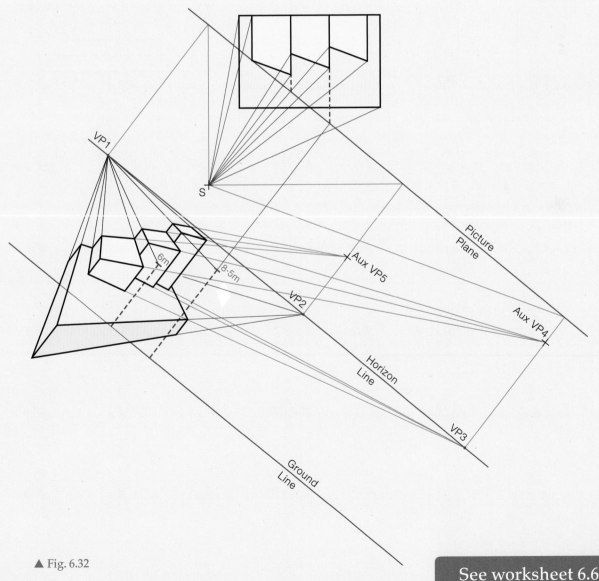

▲ Fig. 6.32

See worksheet 6.6

HIGHER LEVEL

Activities

For each of these questions draw a perspective view using auxiliary vanishing points where appropriate. Picture plane to pass through point A.

HIGHER LEVEL

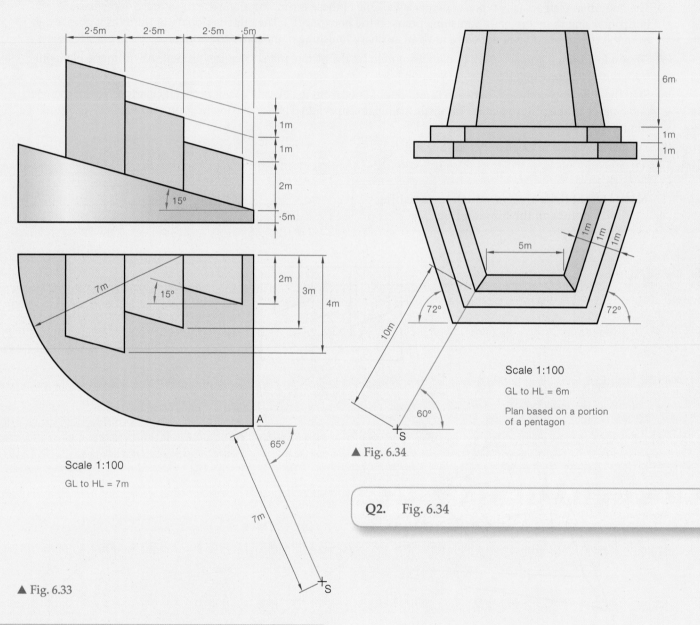

Scale 1:100

GL to HL = 7m

▲ Fig. 6.33

Scale 1:100

GL to HL = 6m

Plan based on a portion of a pentagon

▲ Fig. 6.34

Q1.   Fig. 6.33

Q2.   Fig. 6.34

AREA 2

CONIC

SECTIONS

Syllabus Outline

Areas to be studied:

- Terminology for conics.
- The ellipse, parabola and hyperbola as sections of a right cone.
- Understanding of focal points, focal sphere, directrix and eccentricity in the context of conic sections.
- *Derivation of focal points, directrix and eccentricity using the focal sphere and solid cone.*
- *Construction of conic curves as geometric loci.*
- Geometric properties common to the conic curves.
- Tangents to conics.
- Construction of hyperbolae from focal points and transverse axis.

Learning Outcomes

Students should be able to:

Higher and Ordinary levels

- Understand the terms used in the study of conics, e.g. chord, focal chord, directrix, vertex, ordinate, tangent, normal, major and minor axes/auxiliary circles, eccentricity, transverse axis.
- Construct ellipse, parabola, hyperbola as true sections of solid cone.
- Construct the conic sections, the ellipse, parabola and hyperbola as plane loci from given data relating to eccentricity, foci, vertices, directrices and given points on the curve.
- Construct ellipse, parabola and hyperbola in a rectangle given principal vertice(s).
- Construct tangents to the conic sections from points on the curve.

Higher Level only

- *Understand the terms used in the study of conics, double ordinate, latus rectum, focal sphere etc.*
- *Construct ellipse, parabola, hyperbola as true sections of solid cone and derive directrices, foci, vertices and eccentricity of these curves.*
- *Construct tangents to the conic sections from points outside the curve.*
- *Construct a double hyperbola given the foci and a point on the curve, or given the length of the transverse axis and the foci.*
- *Determine the centre of curvature and evolute for conic sections.*

Parabola as a Section of a Cone

A parabola is produced by slicing a cone with a plane that is parallel to a side of the cone in elevation.

Construction

(1) Draw the plan and elevation of a cone.

(2) Divide the plan into a number of generators which are projected onto the elevation.

(3) Draw in the cutting plane parallel to the side of the cone.

(4) As the generators are cut in elevation they are projected down to the corresponding elements in plan, producing a curve as shown in Fig. 7.1.

(5) The parabola is produced by finding the true shape of this section. Projection lines are produced perpendicular to the section plane and widths are taken from the plan.

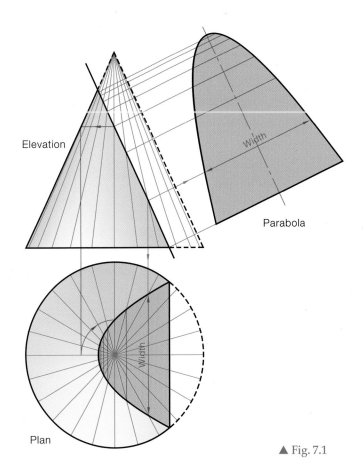

▲ Fig. 7.1

Focal Sphere for a Parabola

A parabola is produced by slicing a cone with a plane that is parallel to a side of the cone in elevation.

If a sphere is inserted into the tip of the cone so that it touches the side of the cone and also the cutting plane we have the focal sphere. This sphere touches the cutting plane at one point only, the focus, hence the name. The sphere also touches the cone all the way round to form a circle. If this circle is extended to form a plane, where the two planes intersect will give the directrix, Fig. 7.3.

The focal sphere can be constructed for the other two conics in a similar fashion as we will see later in this chapter.

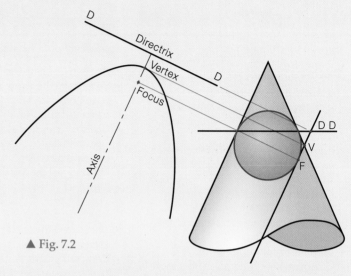

▲ Fig. 7.2

Note: As well as being seen as a conic section, a parabola can also be seen as a locus or path of a point, such that it is at all stages equidistant from a given line (directrix) and a given point (focus).

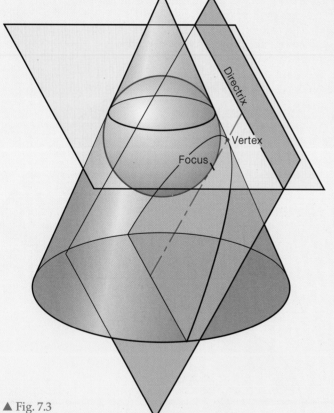

▲ Fig. 7.3

Terminology

Chord – A straight line touching the curve in two places.

Focal Chord – As above, but also passing through the focus.

Latus Rectum – Special focal chord perpendicular to the axis.

Ordinate – A line perpendicular to the axis, starting on the axis and ending on the curve.

Directrix – Line of intersection between the section plane and the plane formed by the intersecting points of the focal sphere and the cone.

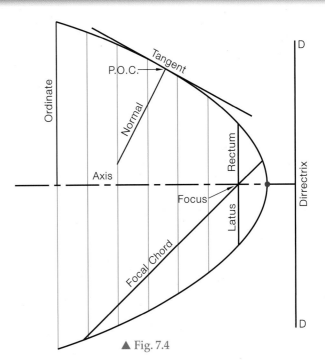

▲ Fig. 7.4

Three Methods of Constructing a Parabola

Rectangle Method

(1) Divide one of the sides in half to find the vertex, e.g. side AD.

(2) Draw the axis through V and perpendicular to the side AD. The rectangle is now halved.

(3) Divide edge AB into any number of **equal** divisions and join each up to V as shown.

(4) Point A to the vertex is now divided into the same number of equal divisions.

(5) Lines are drawn from these points parallel to the axis. Where the two sets of lines intersect, plot the parabola as shown in Fig. 7.5.

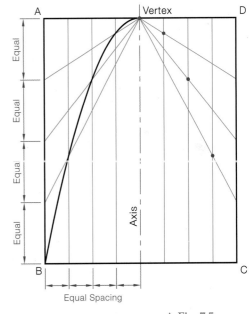

▲ Fig. 7.5

Compass Method

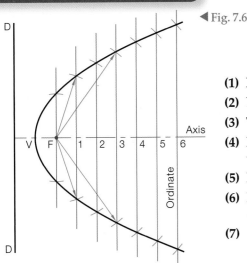

◀ Fig. 7.6

(1) Find the vertex halfway between focus and directrix.

(2) Draw a series of ordinates, F to 6.

(3) Take a radius from the directrix DD to the first ordinate at F.

(4) Move the compass point to the **focus** and scribe arcs above and below the axis on this ordinate at F.

(5) Next take a radius from the directrix to ordinate 1.

(6) Move the compass point to the focus and scribe arcs to cut ordinate 1 above and below the axis.

(7) Continue as necessary remembering to always draw the arcs having F as centre.

Eccentricity Method

The eccentricity for a parabola is always equal to 1 or 1/1. Eccentricity is a ratio between the two distances: (i) from the focus to a point P on the curve, (ii) from the same point on the curve to the directrix.

Eccentricity	= Distance from focus to a point
	Point to directrix
=	F to P
	P to DD

Since the eccentricity of a parabola is unity, any point on the parabola must be equidistant from the directrix and focus.

The eccentricity line for a parabola will always be at 45° to the axis.

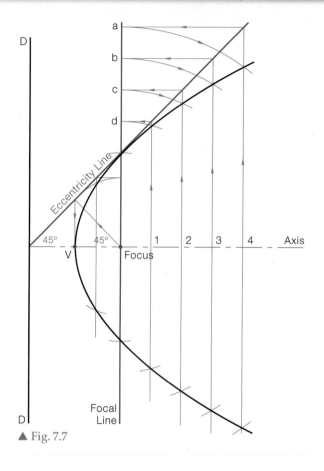

▲ Fig. 7.7

Construction

Given directrix, axis and focus.

(1) Set up the eccentricity line. This will be a 45° line for a parabola.

(2) The vertex is found by projecting up from the focus at 45° to the axis to hit the eccentricity line and down perpendicular to the axis, giving V.

(3) Draw a perpendicular to the axis through the focus giving the focal line.

(4) Where the eccentricity line and focal line intersect is a point on the curve which can be swung below the axis.

(5) Draw lines 1, 2, 3, 4... up to the eccentricity line, perpendicular to the axis, and then project across to the focal line, parallel to the axis. This finds points a, b, c, d...

(6) With the focus as centre, scribe an arc from a to hit line 1 above and below the axis.

(7) With the focus as centre, scribe an arc from b to hit line 2 above and below the axis.

Continue in this manner to plot more points on the curve.

See worksheet 7.1

Tangents to a Parabola from a Point on the Curve

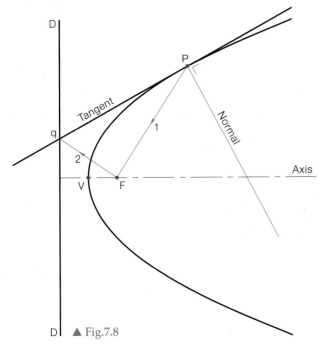

D | ▲ Fig.7.8

Method 1

Fig. 7.8

(1) Join point P on the curve to the focus F.

(2) At F create a 90° angle and extend to hit the directrix DD at q.

(3) Point q is a point on the tangent.

(4) Join P to q to give the tangent. A perpendicular to the tangent at P, the point of contact, will give the normal at P.

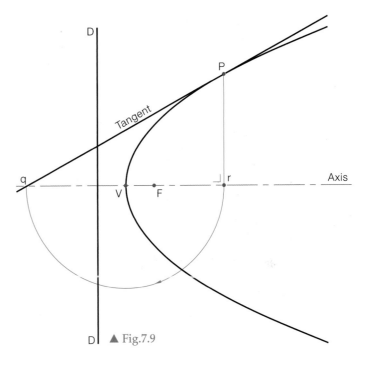

D | ▲ Fig.7.9

Method 2

Fig. 7.9

(1) Draw a perpendicular line to the axis from point P to give point r.

(2) With the vertex as centre rotate point r to give q.

(3) Join P to q to form the tangent.

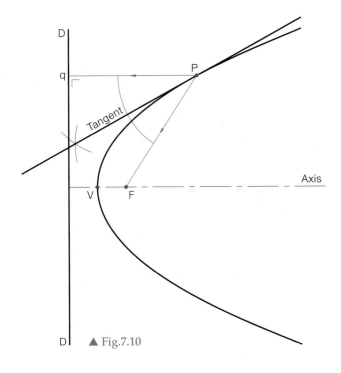

D | ▲ Fig.7.10

Method 3

Fig. 7.10

(1) Join P on the curve to the focus F.

(2) Draw a line from P parallel to the axis to hit the directrix at q.

Note: This line Pq can be considered to be a line joining to a focal point at infinity and hence will tie in with one of the methods of constructing tangents for the hyperbola and ellipse.

(3) The bisector of the angle formed, qPF, will give the tangent.

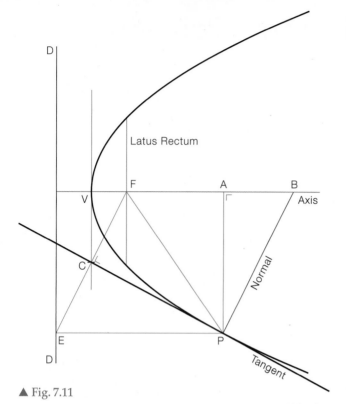

▲ Fig. 7.11

Points of interest about the parabola. Fig. 7.11.

The latus rectum equals 4FV.

Length from A to B equals half the latus rectum.

Length CV equals half of PA.

Length FB equals EP.

Length FC equals CE.

Given a parabola to locate the focus and the directrix. Fig. 7.12.

(1) Draw any ordinate and extend so that AB equals twice AV.

(2) Join B to the vertex V locating point C on the curve.

(3) C will always be a point on the end of the latus rectum. Drop C perpendicular to the axis to locate F the focus.

(4) For a parabola the eccentricity is always one, so VF equals V,DD.

Draw the directrix.

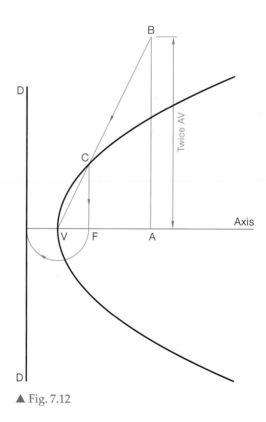

▲ Fig. 7.12

Tangents to a Parabola from a Point P Outside the Curve

> To draw a tangent from a point P outside the directrix.

Method 1

Fig. 7.13

(1) With P as centre swing an arc from the focus F onto the directrix giving points r and q.

(2) Project these points parallel to the axis to give the points of contact.
Draw the tangents.

Note: The lines from r and q drawn parallel to the axis can be considered to be lines drawn from a focal point at infinity and hence this method will tie in with similar methods for the ellipse and hyperbola.

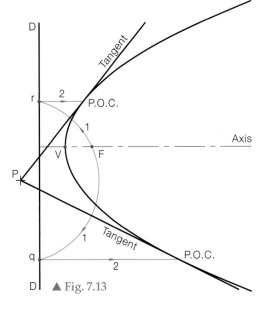
▲ Fig. 7.13

Method 2

Fig. 7.14

Join P to the focus. Bisect this line and draw a circle with PF as diameter. Draw a tangent to the parabola at the vertex V. This tangent will intersect the circle at two places, giving points q and r, which will be points on the required tangents. Draw the tangents.

Note: The tangent drawn at V can be considered to be a circle through V with a radius of infinity. This will tie this construction in with similar methods used for the ellipse and hyperbola.

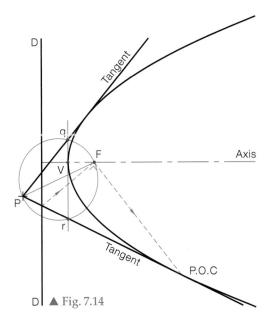
▲ Fig. 7.14

See worksheet 7.2

Activities

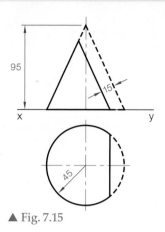

▲ Fig. 7.15

Q1. Draw the elevation and complete the plan of the cone and find the true shape of the section (parabola), **Fig. 7.15**.

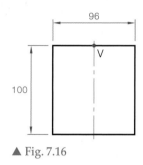

▲ Fig. 7.16

Q2. Construct a parabola in the given rectangle having its vertex in the position shown, **Fig. 7.16**.

Q3. Construct a parabola in the given rectangle having its vertex in the position shown, **Fig. 7.17**.

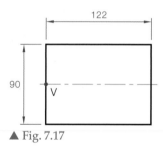

▲ Fig. 7.17

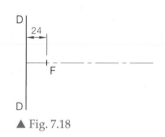

▲ Fig. 7.18

Q4. Given the directrix and the focus construct the parabola using the compass method, **Fig. 7.18**.

Q5. Given the directrix and the vertex construct the parabola using the eccentricity method, **Fig. 7.19**.

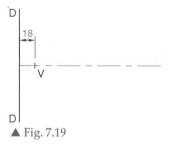

▲ Fig. 7.19

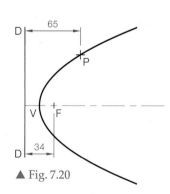

▲ Fig. 7.20

Q6. Construct the given parabola. Draw a tangent to the curve at the given point P, **Fig. 7.20**.

Q7. Given the directrix, axis and a tangent to a parabola. Point P is the point of contact. Draw the parabola, **Fig. 7.21**.

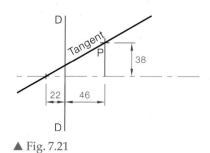

▲ Fig. 7.21

Q8. Given the directrix, axis, tangent and point of contact P of a parabola. Find the focus and draw the parabola, Fig. 7.22.

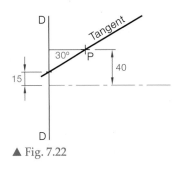
▲ Fig. 7.22

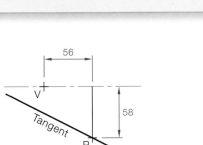

▲ Fig. 7.23

Q9. Given the axis, vertex and point of contact for a tangent. Construct the tangent, find the focus and directrix and draw a portion of the parabola, Fig. 7.23. Hint: See points of interest about the parabola, Fig. 7.11.

Q10. Given the cone in Fig. 7.24 which is sectioned as shown. Construct the focal sphere and hence find the focus, vertex and directrix of the parabola. Draw a portion of the curve.

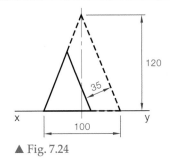
▲ Fig. 7.24

Q11. AB and AC are two tangents to a parabola. They meet at an angle of 70°. The focus of the parabola is 45 mm from AB and 35 mm from AC. Draw a portion of the curve.

Q12. Draw a triangle ABF. AB = 140 mm, AF = 95 mm and BF = 70 mm. If AB is a tangent to a parabola having A on the directrix, and F is the focus, determine the axis, directrix and draw the curve.

Ellipse as a Section of a Cone

An ellipse is produced by a cutting plane which passes through both sides of a cone or will cut both sides of the cone when extended.

Construction

(1) Draw the plane and elevation of a cone.

(2) Divide the plan into sections using generators and project these onto the elevation.

(3) In elevation, draw in the cutting plane so that it cuts both sides of the cone or will cut both sides of the cone if the plane and cone are extended.

(4) The points where the generators are cut in elevation are projected down to the plan producing a curve as shown.

(5) The true shape of this curve is an ellipse and is produced by projecting perpendicularly from the cutting plane.

The widths are taken from the plan.

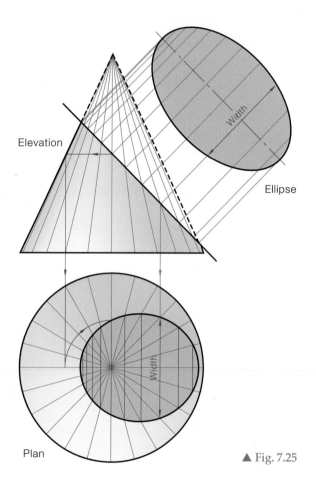

▲ Fig. 7.25

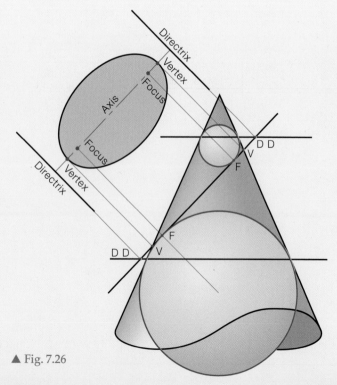

▲ Fig. 7.26

Focal Spheres for an Ellipse

Similar to the construction for a parabola, a sphere is inserted into the space between the cutting plane and the cone's vertex. The sphere is to touch the side of the cone and will touch the cutting plane at one point, the focus. The directrix is found by creating a plane at the level where the sphere makes contact with the cone, and extending it to intersect with the cutting plane. The line of intersection thus formed is the directrix, Fig. 7.26.

A second focal sphere is found underneath the cutting plane giving the second focus and the second directrix, Fig. 7.27.

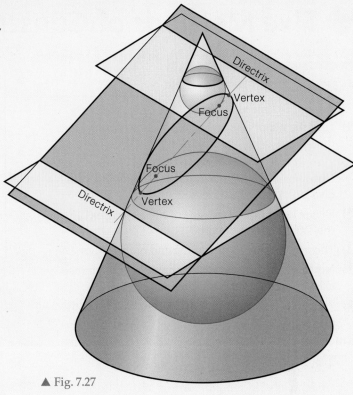

▲ Fig. 7.27

Terminology

Major Axis – The longest axis going through the centre of the ellipse.

Minor Axis – The shortest line going through the centre of the ellipse. The major and minor axes cross at 90° and bisect each other.

Major Auxiliary Circle – The circle passing through both vertices and having its centre on the axis at C.

Minor Auxiliary Circle – The circle passing through both ends of the minor axis and having its centre on the axis at C.

Focal Points – The focal points are two points on the major axis. They are symmetrical about C. They are located a distance of ½ major axis from the ends of the minor axis. Ellipses with focal points near the centre C will be very circular. Ellipses having focal points near the ends of the major axis will be flat ellipses.

Point P – For any point P on the curve the distances F_1P and F_2P added together will equal the length of the major axis. $F_1P + F_2P = V_1V_2$ (Major Axis).

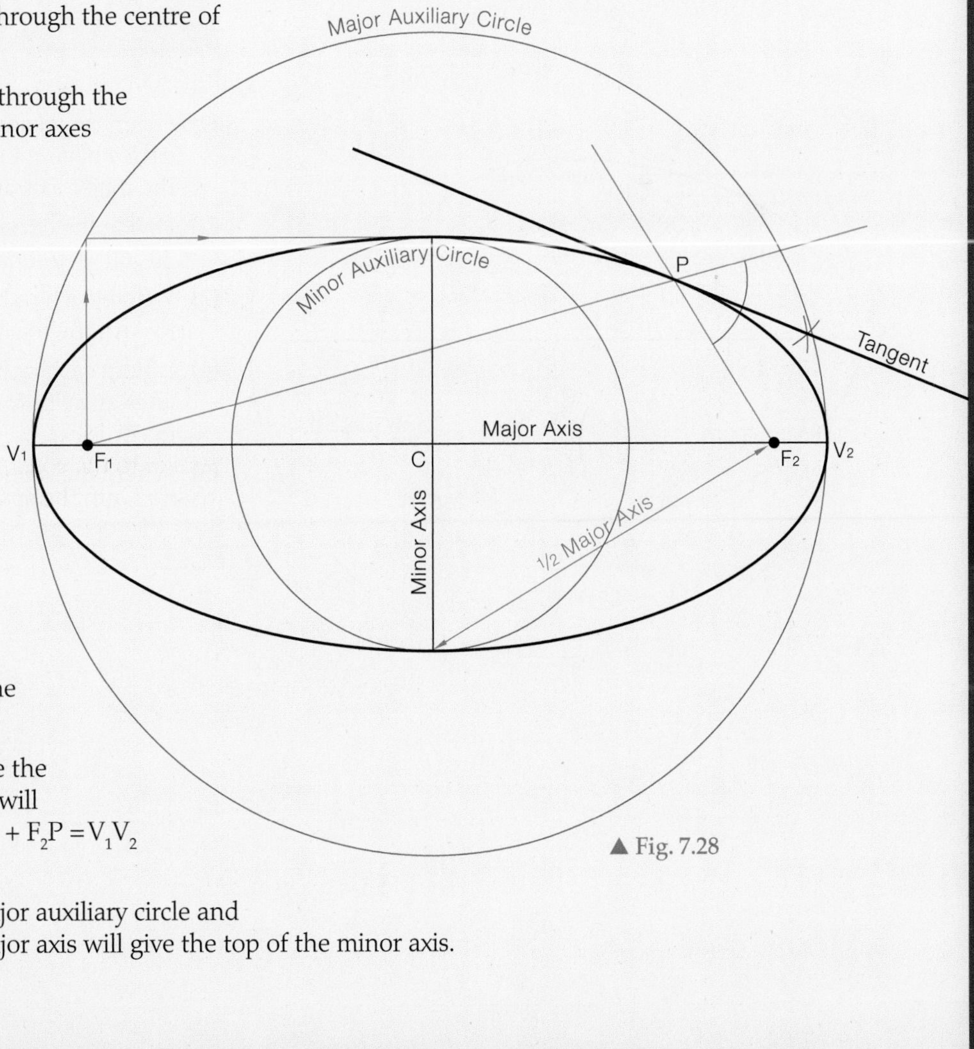

▲ Fig. 7.28

A vertical from the focus to hit the major auxiliary circle and then brought across parallel to the major axis will give the top of the minor axis.

Five Methods of Constructing an Ellipse

Rectangle Method

(1) Find the major axis and minor axis by halving the sides.

(2) The ellipse is constructed one quarter at a time. Divide half the major axis into a number of equal divisions, e.g. OD divided into five equal parts.

(3) Divide half of the short side of the rectangle (CD) into the same number of parts.

(4) These points are joined to the end of the minor axis.

(5) Now radiate lines from the other end of the minor axis through the points found on OD.

(6) The intersection of these two sets of lines plots the ellipse as shown.

Note: This construction will also work to construct an ellipse in a parallelogram.

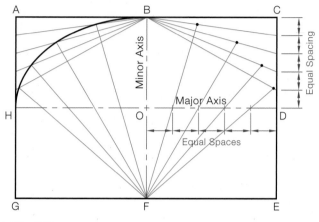

▲ Fig. 7.29

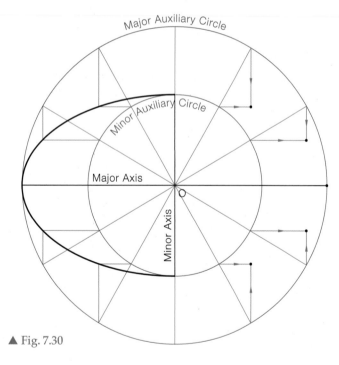

▲ Fig. 7.30

Circle Method

(1) Given the major and minor axes, construct the two circles having O as centre and radii equal to half of the major axis and half the minor axis.

(2) Divide the circles up from the centre, usually with the 30°/60° set-square.

(3) Where each radial line hits the major circle, draw lines toward the major axis and parallel to the minor axis.

(4) Where each radial line crosses the minor circle, draw lines away from the minor axis and parallel to the major axis.

(5) Where these lines intersect plots points on the curve.

Eccentricity Method

The eccentricity for an ellipse is always less than 1, e.g. ¾, ⅔, 0.7, 0.61, etc., but is a constant for that particular ellipse.

As in the parabola, it is an expression of the relationship between the two distances:

(i) From the focal point to a point P on the curve.

(ii) From the same point on the curve to the directrix.

Eccentricity	=	Distance from focus to a point
		Point to directrix
	=	$\dfrac{\text{F to P}}{\text{P to DD}}$

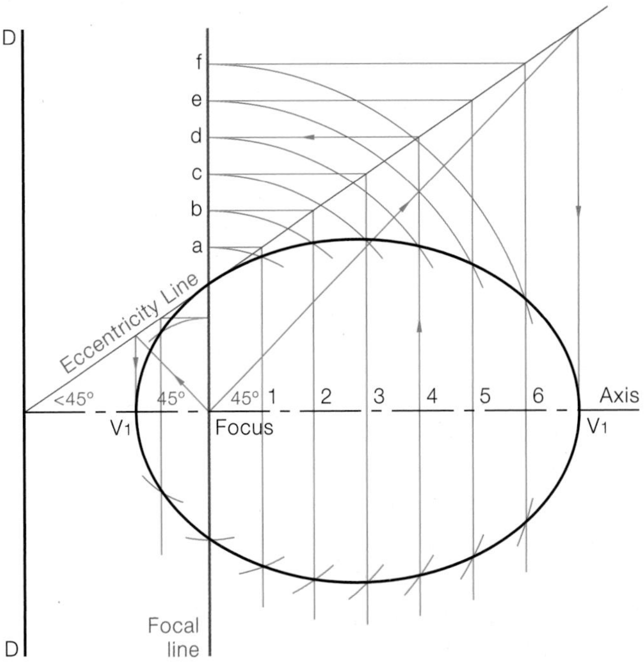

▲ Fig. 7.31

The eccentricity line for an ellipse will always be at an angle of less than 45° to the axis.

Construction

Given the directrix, axis, focal point and eccentricity of ⅔.

(1) Set up the eccentricity line by measuring out on the axis a set distance from the directrix, e.g. 30 mm. Construct a perpendicular to the axis at this point. Measure up from the axis on this line a distance equal to ⅔ of the previous distance; 20 mm in this example.

(2) This gives a point on the eccentricity line which can now be drawn.

(3) Now follow the normal procedure as explained for the parabola in Fig. 7.7.

(4) The ellipse has two vertices and these are found by constructing 45° lines to the axis from the focus to hit the eccentricity line. These points are projected to give V_1 and V_2.

(5) Points on the curve are found by drawing ordinates. Where these intersect the eccentricity line projects across, parallel to the axis, to the focal line.

(6) With the focus as centre, rotate the points found on the focal line back to each ordinate, above and below the axis.

(7) The points found in this way can be joined giving an ellipse.

Trammel Method

This is a very useful method of constructing an ellipse as it is both quick and accurate.

(1) Cut a piece of paper to use as a trammel. It should be slightly longer than half the major axis.

(2) Mark the length of half the minor axis on the trammel AB.

(3) Using A as an end point, now mark half the major axis on the paper, AC.

(4) The trammel can now be placed on the major and minor axis so that point B rests on the major axis and point C on the minor axis.

(5) Plot the location of point A which is a point on the curve.

(6) Rotate the trammel, keeping the points B and C on their appropriate axes. Continue to plot points at A.

(7) Join these plotted points to form an ellipse.

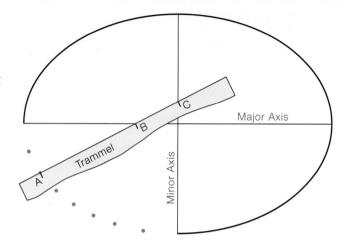

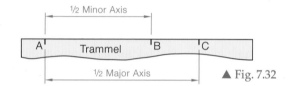

▲ Fig. 7.32

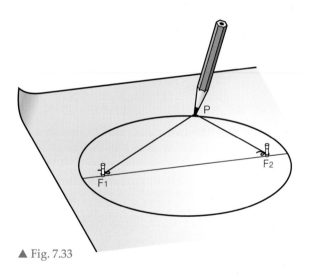

▲ Fig. 7.33

Pin and String Method

This is a good method for drawing large-scale ellipses. The method of construction is based on the fact that the distance from F_1P added to F_2P will remain constant and equals the length of the major axis.

$$F_1P + F_2P = \text{Major Axis}$$

(1) The pins are fixed at the focal points.

(2) String is tied to the pins so that the amount of string left between the pins equals the length of the major axis of the required ellipse.

(3) By keeping the string stretched with a pencil and moving it around, an ellipse will be plotted.

Tangent to an Ellipse from a Point on the Curve

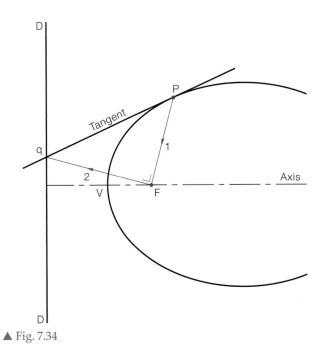

▲ Fig. 7.34

Method 1

Fig. 7.34

This method works for all conics and was shown in Fig. 7.8 for the parabola.

(1) Draw a line joining point P back to the focus.

(2) At the focus, draw a new line perpendicular to PF and extend to hit the directrix DD at q.

(3) Point q is a second point on the tangent.

(4) Join P to q, forming the tangent.

Method 2

Fig. 7.35

(1) Join F_1 to P and extent to q.

(2) Join F_2 to P and extent to r.

(3) The line that bisects the angle F_2Pq will be the required tangent.

(4) Alternatively F_1Pr could be bisected.

(5) The normal could be found by bisecting the angle F_1PF_2. See the similarity to that used for the parabola in Method 3, Fig. 7.10.

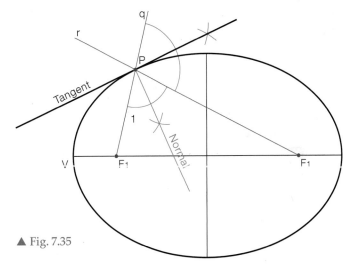

▲ Fig. 7.35

Tangent to an Ellipse from a Point P Outside the Curve

To draw a tangent to an ellipse from a point P outside the directrix. Fig 7.36.

Method 1

Fig. 7.36

With P as centre and PF_1 as radius, swing an arc to hit the directrix at R and q. Join from R and q back to F_2 giving the points of contact. Draw the tangents.

Note the similarity with construction for a parabola, **Fig. 7.13.**

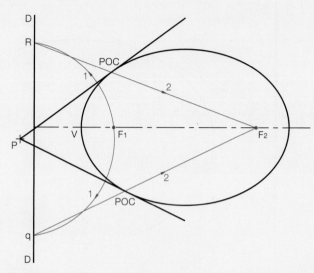

▲ Fig. 7.36

Method 2

Fig. 7.37

Join P to F_1 and place a circle on this line having PF_1 as its diameter. Draw the major auxiliary circle for the ellipse, i.e. the circle which has V_1V_2 as a diameter. These two circles intersect at points r and q, which will be points on the tangents. Draw the tangents.

Note the similarity to construction for a parabola, **Fig. 7.14.**

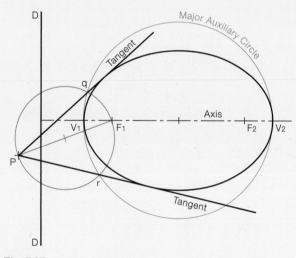

▲ Fig. 7.37

Method 3

Fig. 7.38

With point P as centre and PF_1 as radius, draw an arc. Now take the length of the major axis as radius V_1V_2. Using F_2 as the centre point swing an arc to cut your first arc in two places, q and r. Points q and r are joined back to F_2. Where these lines cross the ellipse give the points of contact for the tangents. Draw the tangents.

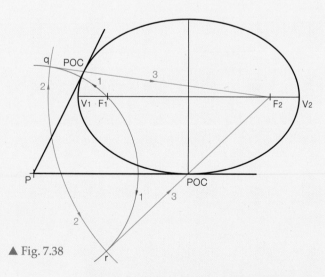

▲ Fig. 7.38

See worksheets 7.3 and 7.4

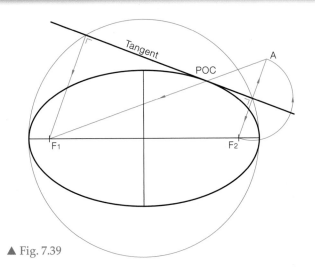

▲ Fig. 7.39

Given a tangent to an ellipse to find the point of contact (POC). Fig 7.39

Fig. 7.39

(1) Draw the major auxiliary circle.

(2) Where the tangent and auxiliary circle intersect draw perpendiculars to the tangent. These perpendiculars will pass through the focal points F_1 and F_2.

(3) On either of these perpendiculars you double its length as shown, finding point A.

(4) Join A back to the focus to find the POC.

Activities

Q1. Draw the given plan and elevation of the cone and find the true shape of the section (ellipse), Fig. 7.40.

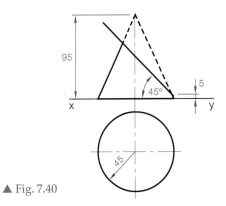

▲ Fig. 7.40

Q2. Construct an ellipse in a rectangle of side 140 mm by 80 mm using the rectangle method.

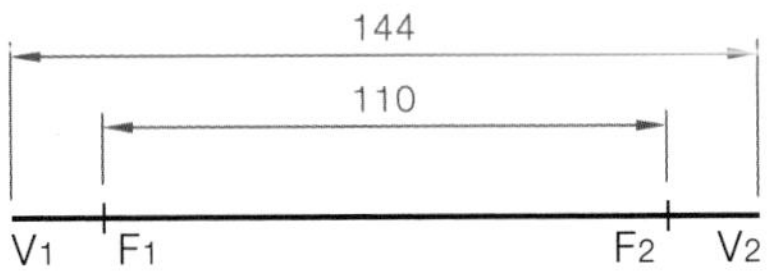

Q3. Given the major axis and the foci, construct the ellipse, Fig. 7.41.

▲ Fig. 7.41

Q4. Given the minor axis and the foci, construct the ellipse, Fig. 7.42.

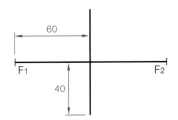

▲ Fig. 7.42

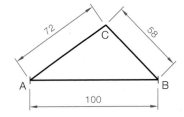

▲ Fig. 7.43

Q5. Given the triangle ABC where A and B are focal points of an ellipse and C is a point on the curve. Draw the ellipse, Fig. 7.43.

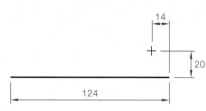

▲ Fig. 7.44

Q6. Given the major axis and a point P on the curve. Draw the ellipse, **Fig. 7.44.**

Q7. Given the minor axis of an ellipse and a point P on the curve. Construct the ellipse, **Fig. 7.45.**

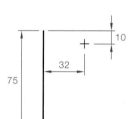

▲ Fig. 7.45

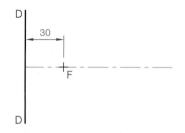

▲ Fig. 7.46

Q8. Given the directrix, axis, focus of an ellipse and an eccentricity of 0.8. Draw a portion of the curve, **Fig.7.46.**

Q9. Given the focus and vertex of an ellipse having an eccentricity of 0.8. Draw a portion of the curve, **Fig.7.47.**

▲ Fig. 7.47

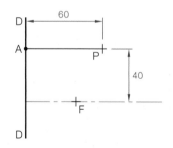

Fig. 7.48 ▶

Q10. Given the directrix, axis, eccentricity of 0.75 and a point P on the curve. Determine the position of the focus and draw a portion of the curve. Construct a tangent to the curve from point A, **Fig. 7.48.**

Q11. Given the major axis of 110 mm, focus and a point P on an ellipse. Draw the curve, **Fig. 7.49.**

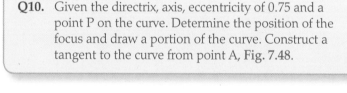

▲ Fig. 7.49

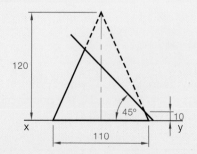

▲ Fig. 7.50

Q12. Given the cone in Fig. 7.50 which is sectioned as shown. Construct the focal spheres and hence find the focus, vertex and directrix of the ellipse. Draw the ellipse.

Q13. Given the triangle APF. AP is a tangent to an ellipse with P as the point of contact. F is a focal point and the major axis is 120 mm long, **Fig. 7.51**. Draw the ellipse.

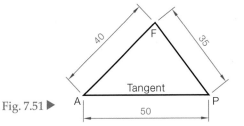

Fig. 7.51 ▶

Q14. Given the major axis V_1V_2 of an ellipse and a tangent to it. Draw a portion of the curve to include the point of contact, **Fig. 7.52**.

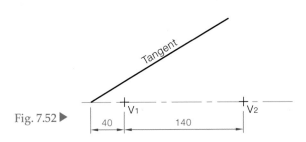

Fig. 7.52 ▶

Hyperbola as a Section of a Cone

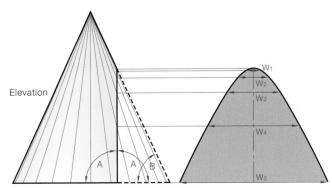

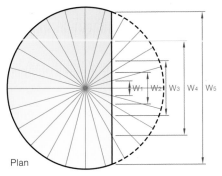

▲ Fig. 7.53

If a cone is cut by a cutting plane such that either angle at the base (angle A) is equal to 90°, or is between 90° and the angle of the side of the cone (angle B), then a hyperbola is produced. The cutting plane only cuts one side of the cone no matter how far the cone and plane are extended.

Construction

Fig. 7.53

The construction is the same as that for the parabola and ellipse.

(1) Draw the plan, elevation, elements and cutting plane.

(2) The auxiliary view is projected perpendicularly from the cutting plane in elevation.

(3) Points where the cutting plane crosses elements are projected out.

(4) Widths are taken from the plan as shown.

Focal Sphere

The hyperbola has one focal sphere. The position and size of the sphere is such that it is tangential to both the sides of the cone and the cutting plane, i.e. it fits neatly into the top of the cone and also touches the cutting plane at one spot, the focus. The directrix is found by finding the intersection between the plane through the sphere containing all the points of contact between the sphere and the cone and the cutting plane.

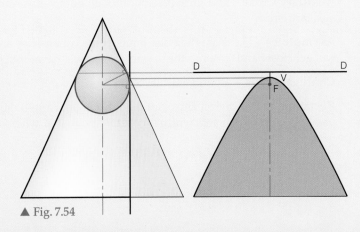

▲ Fig. 7.54

HIGHER LEVEL

Terminology

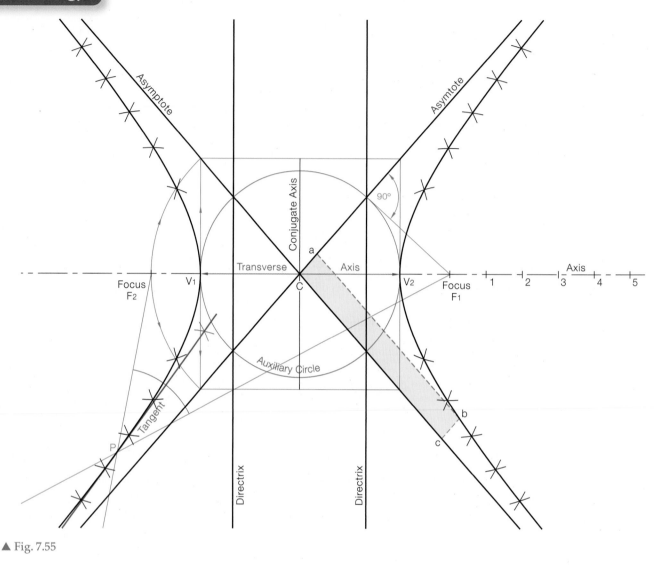

▲ Fig. 7.55

Distance from Focus$_2$ to P – Distance from Focus$_1$ to P = Transverse Axis

$F_2P - F_1P$ = Transverse Axis

$F_2P - F_1P = V_1V_2$

Transverse Axis – The part of the axis between the vertices V$_1$ to V$_2$ Transverse Axis.

Auxiliary Circle – The circle passing through both vertices and having its centre on the axis at C is called the auxiliary circle.

Asymptotes – These are the outer limits of the cones. They are straight lines which cross at C. The hyperbola curve will get closer and closer to the asymptote but will never touch it.

Conjugate Axis – A perpendicular to the axis through the centre C is called the conjugate axis.

Rectangle abcC – Select any point b on the curve. From b draw ba and bc parallel to the asymptotes. The resulting parallelogram has an area which is constant no matter where on the curve point b is selected.

Three Methods of Constructing a Hyperbola

Method 1: Rectangle Method

Fig. 7.56

(1) The two rectangles must be of equal size and share an axis as shown.

(2) V_1 and V_2, the vertices of the hyperbolas, are located.

(3) The edge CB is divided into a number of equal parts, five in this example.

(4) These points are joined to V_2.

(5) The edge AB is now divided into the same number of parts as edge CB.

(6) These points are joined to V_1.

(7) Where the two sets of construction lines cross, plot points on the curve as shown.

(8) The rest of the curve is found in a similar way.

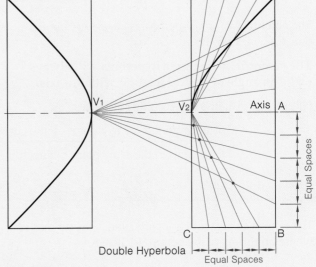

▲ Fig. 7.56

Method 2: Compass Method

Fig. 7.57

(1) Draw an axis and mark the two vertices V_1 and V_2.

(2) Locate the focal points F_1 and F_2. The distance from F_1 to V_1 must be the same as from F_2 to V_2.

(3) Choose points a, b, c, d etc. on the axis beyond F_2.

(4) With radius V_1a and centre F_1 draw an arc.

(5) With F_2 as centre draw another arc.

(6) With radius V_2a and centre F_2 draw arcs above and below the axis to cut the previous arc giving two points on one branch of the curve.

(7) Using the same radius repeat this process using F_1 as centre giving two points on the second branch of the curve.

(8) Repeat this process using points b, c, d etc. plotting the path of the curve.

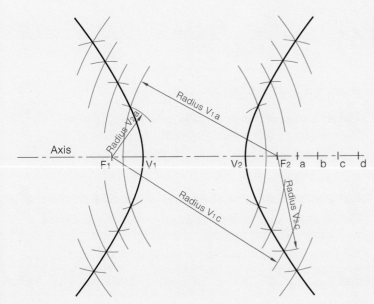

▲ Fig. 7.57

See worksheet 7.5

HIGHER LEVEL

Method 3: Eccentricity Method

Fig. 7.58

The eccentricity for a hyperbola is always greater than one, e.g. 7/4, 12/5, 1.6 etc.

The eccentricity line for a hyperbola will always make an angle of greater than 45° with the axis.

Eccentricity is a ratio between two distances

$$= \frac{\text{Distance from focus to a point on the curve}}{\text{Distance from the same point to directrix}}$$

$$= \frac{\text{F to P}}{\text{P to DD}}$$

The ratio is a constant for a particular curve, no matter where on the curve the point P is chosen.

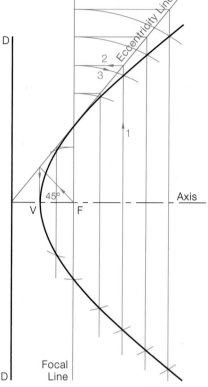

▲ Fig. 7.58

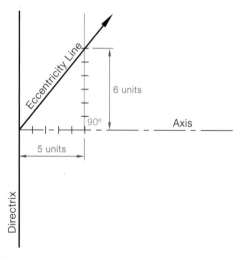

▲ Fig. 7.59

Construction

Given directrix focus and eccentricity of 1.2.

The advantage of the eccentricity method is that once the eccentricity line is set up correctly the process of construction is the same for all three conics.

(1) Draw the directrix, axis and focus.

(2) Eccentricity of 1.2 can be written as a fraction 6/5.

(3) Measure out from the directrix five units, e.g. 5 (5 mm units) = 25 mm, and mark a point on the axis.

(4) Draw a perpendicular to the axis at this point and measure up from the axis six units, e.g. 6 (5 mm units) = 30 mm.

(5) The eccentricity line can now be drawn.

Note: The bottom portion of the eccentricity fraction is measured out along the axis and the top is measured up on a perpendicular.

(6) A line drawn up from the focus, at 45° to the axis, to hit the eccentricity line and dropped to the axis finds the vertex.

(7) Construction for the curve is the same as for the ellipse and parabola.

Tangent to a Hyperbola from a Point on the Curve

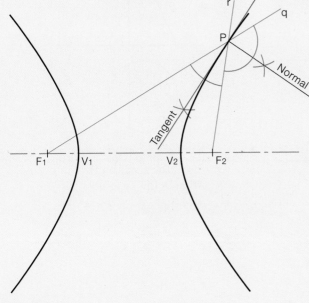

▲ Fig. 7.60

Method 1

Fig. 7.60

(1) Join F_1 to P and extend to q.

(2) Join F_2 to P and extend to r.

(3) The line that bisects angle F_1PF_2 or angle qPr will be the tangent.

(4) The normal is perpendicular to the tangent and can be found by bisecting the angle F_2Pq.

Note: The similarity to the method used for the parabola, Fig. 7.10, and the ellipse, Fig. 7.35.

Method 2

Fig. 7.61

This method works for all three conics and has already been shown in Fig. 7.8 for the parabola and Fig. 7.34 for the ellipse.

(1) Join P back to the focus.

(2) At the focus draw a perpendicular to PF to hit the directrix at q.

(3) Point q is a point on the tangent. Join P to q, forming the tangent.

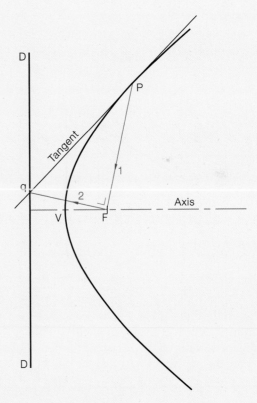

▲ Fig. 7.61

See worksheet 7.6

HIGHER LEVEL

Activities

Q1. Given the plan and elevation of a cone which has been sectioned as shown. Draw the views and determine the true shape of the section, **Fig. 7.62**.

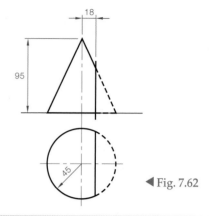

◀ Fig. 7.62

Q2. Given the directrix, axis, focus and eccentricity of 6/5. Draw a portion of the hyperbola, **Fig. 7.63**.

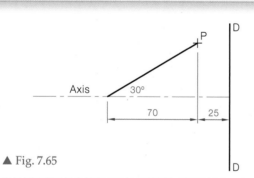

▲ Fig. 7.63

Q3. Given the axis, focus, point P on the curve and eccentricity of 1.25. Draw a portion of the hyperbola **Fig. 7.64**.

▲ Fig. 7.64

Q4. Given the normal, axis, point of contact and directrix. Find the focus and construct a portion of the curve, **Fig. 7.65**.

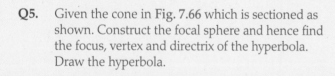

▲ Fig. 7.65

Q5. Given the cone in **Fig. 7.66** which is sectioned as shown. Construct the focal sphere and hence find the focus, vertex and directrix of the hyperbola. Draw the hyperbola.

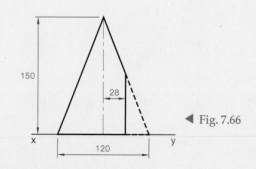

◀ Fig. 7.66

Q6. Construct a double hyperbola in the rectangles shown, **Fig. 7.67**.

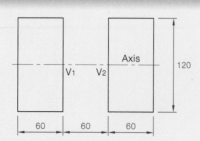

▲ Fig. 7.67

Q7. Given the foci and vertices of a double hyperbola. Construct a portion of each curve. Construct a tangent to the curve from a point 50 mm from F_1, Fig. 7.68.

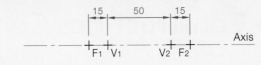

▲ Fig. 7.68

Q8. Given the transverse axis of 80 mm and the distance between F and V of 20 mm. Construct a double hyperbola, directrices, asymptotes, auxiliary circle and conjugate diameter.

Q9. Given the line FPA as shown in Fig. 7.69. If F is the focus, P is a point on the curve and A is a point on the directrix. Construct the hyperbola if the eccentricity is 6/5.

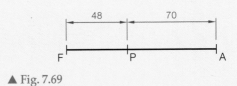

▲ Fig. 7.69

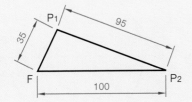

▲ Fig. 7.70

Q10. Given the triangle FP_1P_2. F is one of the focal points on a double hyperbola, P_1 is a point on one branch of the curve and P_2 is a point on the other branch. The transverse axis is 60 mm long. Find the other focal point and draw both curves, Fig. 7.70.

Q11. Given the two focal points of a double hyperbola and a point P on one branch of the curve. Draw the double curve, Fig. 7.71.

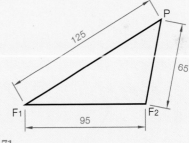

▲ Fig. 7.71

Constructions Common to all Conics

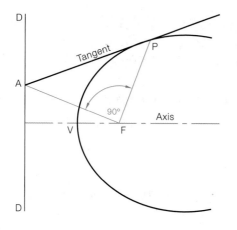

▲ Fig. 7.72

Fig. 7.72

For all conic sections this construction can be used to draw the tangent at a given point P on the curve.

(1) Join P to the focus.

(2) At the focus draw a line FA at 90° to FP. Extend this line to intersect the directrix at A.

(3) Point A is a point on the tangent. Draw the tangent.

Fig. 7.73

Tangents drawn at both ends of a focal chord will always meet on the directrix. This construction is a follow-on from Fig. 7.73. P_1FA forms a 90° angle, as does P_2FA. These two angles added together make 180°, a straight line, a focal chord.

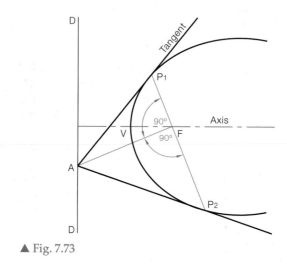

▲ Fig. 7.73

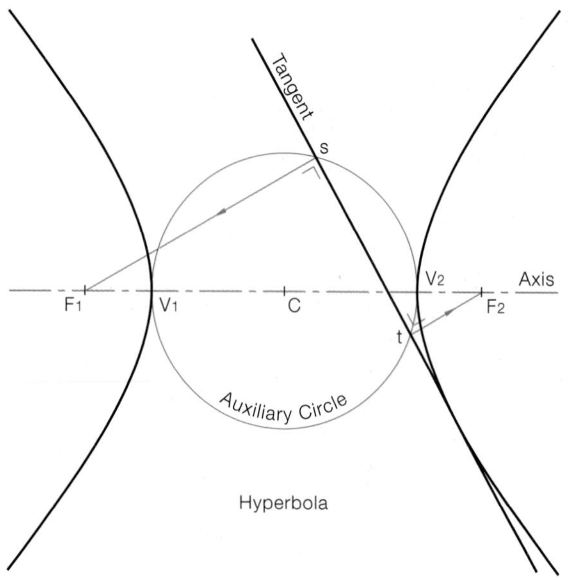

Fig. 7.74

A tangent is drawn to a double hyperbola and will cut through the auxiliary circle in two places, s and t. Perpendicular lines are drawn to the tangent to form these two points. These perpendiculars will always pass through F_1 and F_2, the focal points of the curves.

▲ Fig. 7.74

A tangent drawn to an ellipse will cross the major auxiliary circle in two places, s and t. Perpendiculars drawn to the tangent from these two points will always pass through the focal points F_1 and F_2. Fig. 7.75.

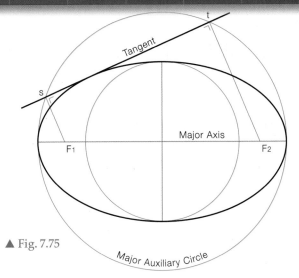

▲ Fig. 7.75

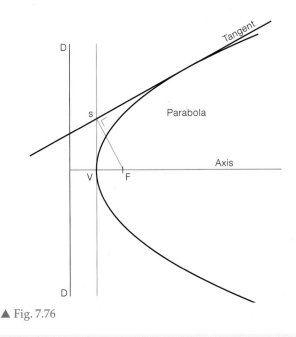

▲ Fig. 7.76

A tangent drawn to the parabola will cross the tangent at the vertex at one point, point s. If a perpendicular is drawn to the tangent at s it will pass through the focus. For a parabola, the tangent at the vertex should be considered as a circle of radius infinity, a small section of which will look like a straight line.

Centre of Curvature and Evolute

The centre of curvature is a specific point inside the curve relating to a specific point P on the curve. If the point of the compass is placed on the centre of curvature C and a radius taken of CP, the curvature of the resulting arc would match the curvature of the conic at point P. Each point on the conic will have its own centre of curvature. If all the centres of curvature are plotted and joined, the resulting path is the evolute of that conic. An evolute is the locus of the centres of curvature.

> To draw the centre of curvature for a point P on a parabola. Fig. 7.77.

(1) Construct a tangent at point P.

(2) Draw the normal to the tangent.

(3) Join P to the focus and extend.

(4) Where the normal crosses the axis at point A construct a perpendicular to intersect the PF line extended. These lines intersect at B.

(5) At B draw a perpendicular to PB to intersect the normal at C. Point C is the centre of curvature for point P.

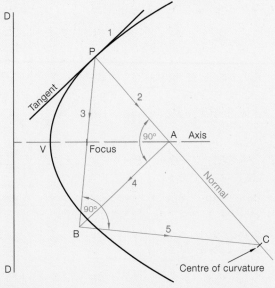

▲ Fig. 7.77

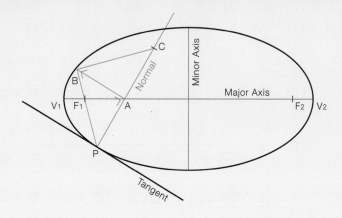

▲ Fig. 7.78

To draw the centre of curvature for a point P on an ellipse. Fig. 7.78.

(1) The construction for an ellipse is the same as that for a parabola. Construct a tangent at P.

(2) Draw the normal to the tangent.

(3) Join P to F_1 and extend.

(4) Where the normal crosses the major axis at A construct a perpendicular to intersect PF_1 at B. At B construct a perpendicular to intersect the normal at C. C is the centre of curvature for P.

Note: The construction for the centre of curvature for a point P on a hyperbola is the same as above.

To find the centre of curvature at the vertex of a parabola. Fig. 7.79.

The method discussed previously will not work at the vertex. A separate construction must be used. For a parabola, the distance from V to F will equal the distance from F to C, the centre of curvature.

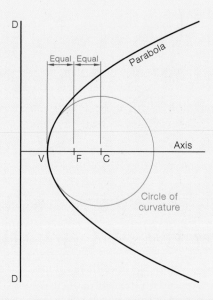

▲ Fig. 7.79

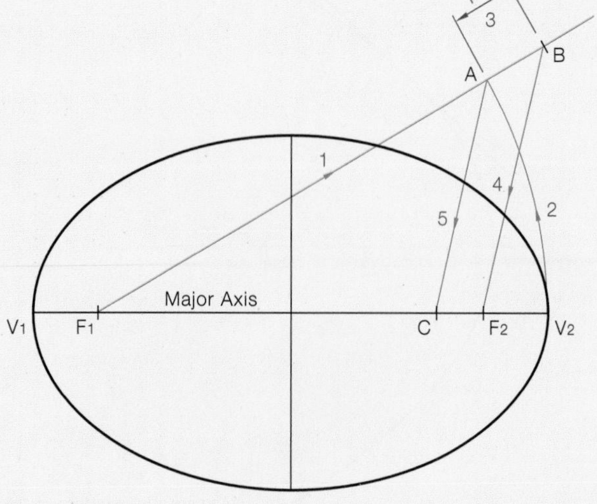

▲ Fig. 7.80

To find the centre of curvature at the vertex of an ellipse. Fig. 7.80.

(1) Draw any sloping line from F_1.

(2) With F_1 as centre and radius F_1V_2, draw an arc to hit this line at point A.

(3) Add the distance between the focus and vertex, FV, beyond point A. This locates point B.

(4) Join B to F_2.

(5) Draw a line parallel to BF_2 starting at point A. This locates point C on the axis, the centre of curvature at the vertex.

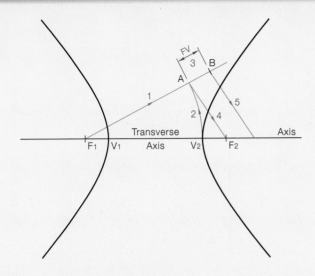

▲ Fig. 7.81

To find the centre of curvature at the vertex of a hyperbola. Fig. 7.81.

(1) Draw any sloping line from F_1.

(2) With F_1 as centre and radius F_1V_2, draw an arc to hit this line at point A.

(3) Step the distance FV past point A to find B.

(4) Join A back to F_2.

(5) From B draw a line parallel to AF_2 finding C the centre of curvature at the vertex.

To draw the evolute to a parabola, an ellipse or a hyperbola. Figures 7.82, 7.83 and 7.84.

Locate a number of centres of curvature to plot the locus of the evolute. The evolute will always be symmetrical about the axis.

Note: To locate the centre of curvature at the vertex of a hyperbola when the second focus is unavailable you can use the construction shown. The ratio CF:FV will be equal to the eccentricity of the curve.

Eccentricity = Focus to point:Point to directrix, or FV:VDD.

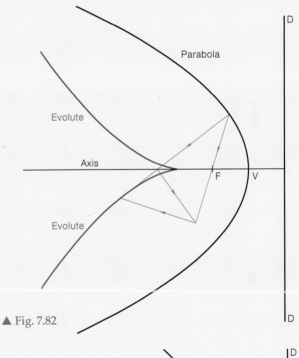

▲ Fig. 7.82

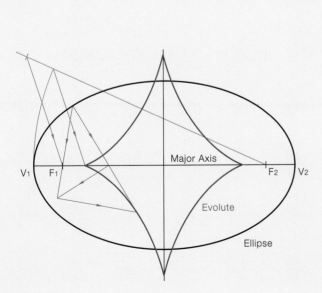

▲ Fig. 7.83

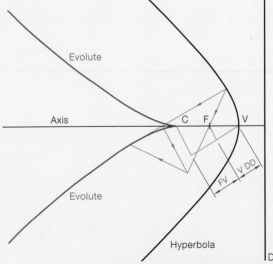

▲ Fig. 7.84

See worksheet 7.7

HIGHER LEVEL

Activities

Q1. Given the vertex, axis and directrix construct the parabola. Construct a tangent from point P. Find the centre of curvature for the point of contact, Fig. 7.85.

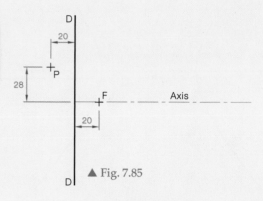

▲ Fig. 7.85

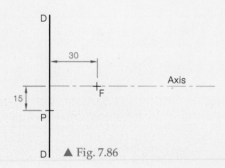

▲ Fig. 7.86

Q2. Given the directrix and focus of an ellipse having an eccentricity of 0.75. Construct a portion of the curve. Draw a tangent to the ellipse from the point P on the directrix. Find the centre of curvature for the point of contact, Fig. 7.86

Q3. Given the vertex and focus of a hyperbola having an eccentricity of 6/5. Draw the curve. Draw a tangent to the curve from a point P which is 40 mm from the focus. Find the centre of curvature for point P, Fig. 7.87.

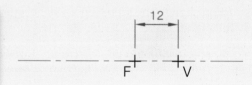

▲ Fig. 7.87

AREA 3

DESCRIPTIVE GEOMETRY OF LINES AND PLANES

8   The Oblique Plane

Syllabus Outline

Areas to be studied:

- Definition of planes, simply inclined and oblique.
- Determination of oblique and *tangent* planes.
- True shape and inclinations of planes to principal planes of reference.
- Intersection of oblique planes, lines and *dihedral angle.*
- Sectioning of right solids by oblique planes.
- *Treatment of planes as laminar surfaces given rectangular coordinates.*
- *Properties and projections of skew lines.*
- *Spatial relationships between lines and planes.*

Learning Outcomes

Students should be able to:

Higher and Ordinary levels

- Distinguish between simply inclined and obliquely inclined plane surfaces.
- Determine the angle of inclination between given planes and the principal planes of reference.
- Determine the true length and inclination of given lines.
- Establish the true shape of an obliquely inclined plane.
- Determine the line of intersection between two planes.
- Determine the projections and true shape of sections of solids resulting from simply inclined and oblique cutting planes.

Higher Level only

- *Construct obliquely inclined planes given the angles of inclination to the principal planes of reference and to include a given line or point.*
- *Establish the dihedral angle between two intersecting planes.*
- *Display knowledge of the relationships between planes and lines.*
- *Understand the concept of a laminar surface defined by spatial coordinates.*
- *Solve a variety of problems involving the intersection, inclination and positioning of laminar plane surfaces.*
- *Define the concept of skew lines and their use in solving practical problems.*
- *Establish various spatial relationships between skew lines and other lines and planes, including distance, inclination and direction.*

A plane is usually represented by its lines of intersection with the principle planes of reference. These lines are called the **traces** of the plane. The line of intersection between the plane and the vertical plane is called the **vertical trace** and the line of intersection between the plane and horizontal plane is called the **horizontal trace**.

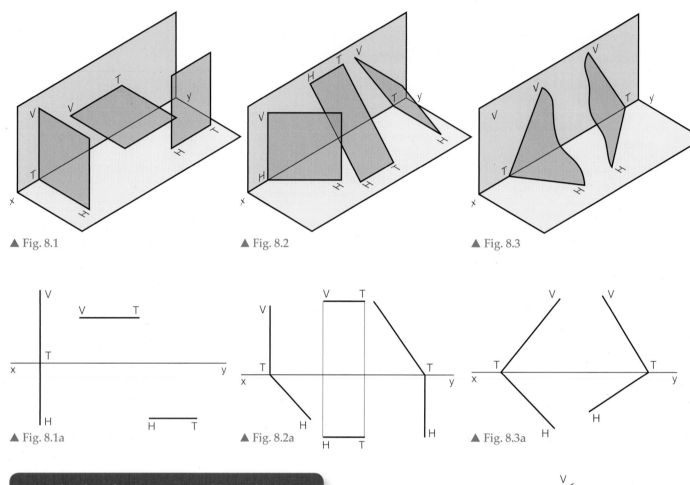

▲ Fig. 8.1

▲ Fig. 8.2

▲ Fig. 8.3

▲ Fig. 8.1a

▲ Fig. 8.2a

▲ Fig. 8.3a

Given the plan of a point P on an oblique plane VTH. Find the elevation of this point. Fig. 8.4.

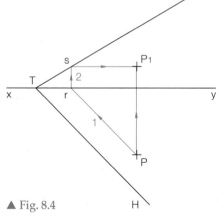

▲ Fig. 8.4

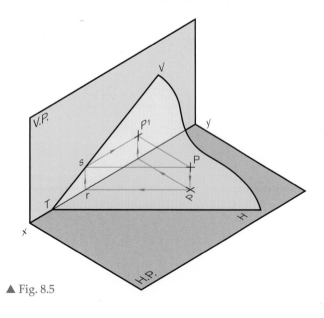

▲ Fig. 8.5

(1) Draw a line parallel to the horizontal trace from point P to hit the xy line at r.

(2) Erect a perpendicular at r to hit the vertical trace at s.

(3) From s, project horizontally (parallel to the xy line).

(4) Project vertically from P in plan to intersect this horizontal thus locating P₁ in elevation, Fig. 8.5.

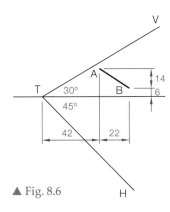

▲ Fig. 8.6

Given the elevation of a line AB on an oblique plane VTH. Find its plan. Fig. 8.6.

(1) From A, project parallel to the VT line to meet the xy line at r.

(2) Project vertically down from r to s on the HT line.

(3) Project s parallel to the xy line.

(4) Drop a perpendicular from A in elevation to find A_1.

(5) Point B is done in a similar manner, Fig. 8.7.

Lines drawn parallel to the vertical trace in elevation will be parallel to the xy line in plan. Lines drawn parallel to the horizontal trace in plan will be parallel to the xy line in elevation.

Given the plan of a lamina ABC on an oblique plane VTH. In plan AB = 32 mm, BC = 55 mm and AC = 44 mm. Find the elevation. Fig. 8.8

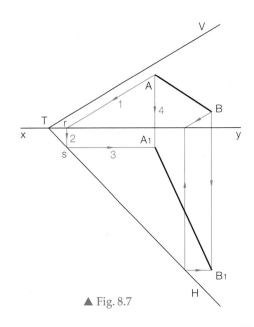

▲ Fig. 8.7

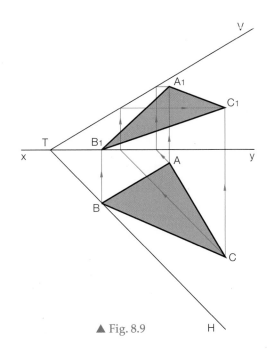

▲ Fig. 8.9

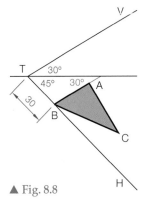

▲ Fig. 8.8

(1) Each point is brought up as in previous examples and found in elevation.

(2) Index each point and join finding $A_1B_1C_1$ in elevation, Fig. 8.9.

Given the plan of a figure resting on the oblique=
plane VTH. Find its elevation. Fig. 8.10.

The construction is the same as in previous examples.

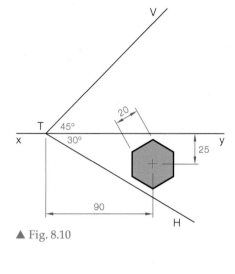

▲ Fig. 8.10

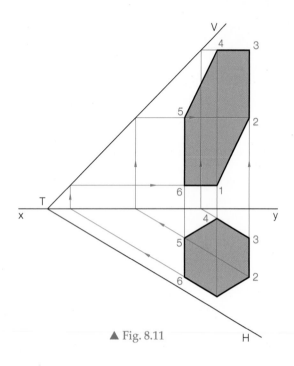

▲ Fig. 8.11

Given the elevation of a figure resting on the oblique
plane VTH. Find its plan. Fig. 8.12.

Since this figure is not made up of straight lines we must
choose points on the curve. In Fig. 8.13 we have chosen
eight points. Once the points are found in plan they are
joined freehand with a fair curve, Fig. 8.13.

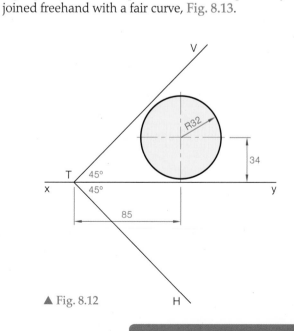

▲ Fig. 8.12

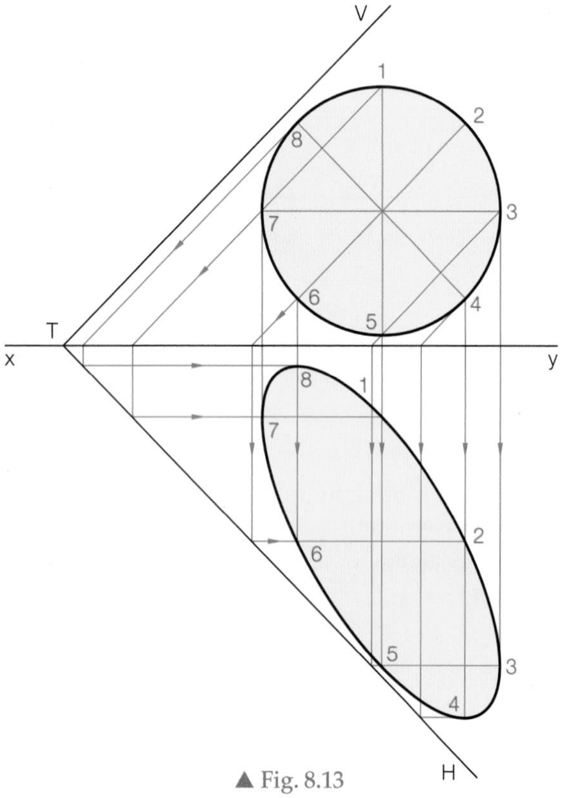

▲ Fig. 8.13

See worksheet 8.1

True Inclination of an Oblique Plane to the VP and the HP

To find the true inclination of an oblique plane to the HP. Fig. 8.14.

To find the true angle, insert a half cone underneath the plane and tangential to it. The base angle of this cone will be the true angle of the plane to the horizontal plane.

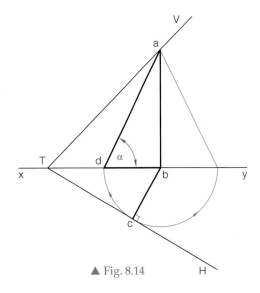

▲ Fig. 8.14

(1) Draw a vertical line ab in elevation.

(2) From b on the xy line, draw a perpendicular to the HT finding c.

(3) Line bc equals the radius of the cone. Draw the half cone in plan.

(4) Draw the elevation of the cone. The base angle of the cone is the true angle of the plane to the horizontal plane, Fig. 8.15.

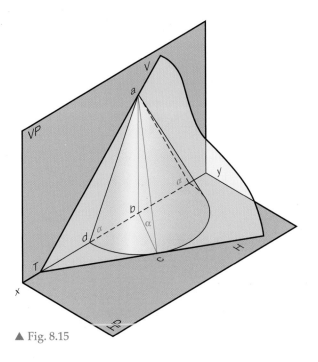

▲ Fig. 8.15

Alternative Method

The true angle an oblique plane makes with the horizontal plane can be found by using an auxiliary elevation. Fig. 8.16.

Note: The point P on the oblique plane is usually chosen at position A as it reduces the amount of projection involved.

(1) Choose any point P on the plane in plan and project it to elevation.

(2) Take an auxiliary elevation viewing along the horizontal trace.

(3) x_1y_1 is drawn perpendicular to the line of sight.

(4) The horizontal trace projects as a point view.

(5) Point P is projected to the auxiliary elevation and its height h is taken from the elevation.

(6) The oblique plane is seen as an edge view showing its true angle to the horizontal plane.

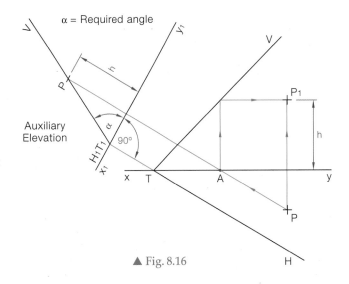

▲ Fig. 8.16

To find the true inclination of an oblique plane to the vertical plane. Fig. 8.17.

The construction is similar to Figures 8.14 and 8.15.

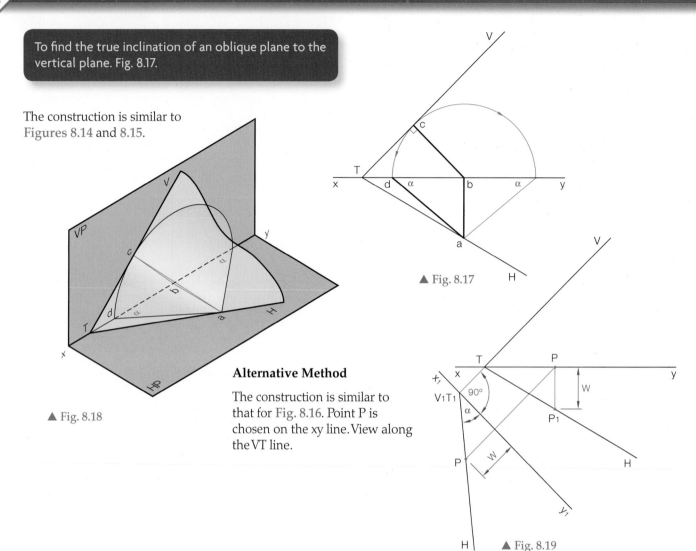

▲ Fig. 8.17

▲ Fig. 8.18

Alternative Method

The construction is similar to that for Fig. 8.16. Point P is chosen on the xy line. View along the VT line.

▲ Fig. 8.19

 # Solids Cut by Oblique Planes

Given the plan and elevation of a square-based prism and the traces of a plane VTH. Show the projections of the prism when it is cut by the oblique plane VTH. Fig. 8.20.

The prism when cut will still look the same in the plan. The cut surface in plan can be projected to elevation as explained earlier, Fig. 8.21.

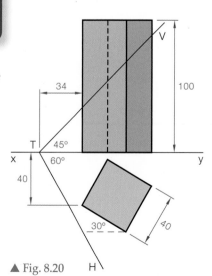

▲ Fig. 8.20

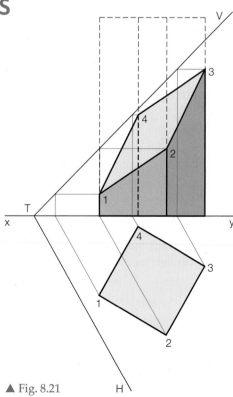

▲ Fig. 8.21

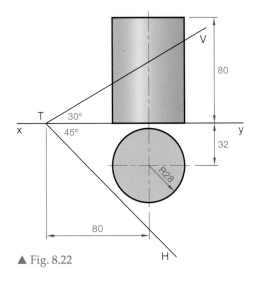

▲ Fig. 8.22

Given the plan and elevation of a cylinder and the traces of a plane VTH. Show the projections of the cylinder when it is cut by the oblique plane VTH. Fig. 8.22.

As in the last example, the plan of the solid is unchanged after it has been cut by the plane. Divide the plan up into a number of divisions. Index the points and project each point to elevation as usual, Fig. 8.23.

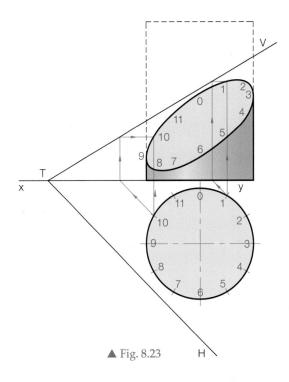

▲ Fig. 8.23

Given the plan and elevation of a square-based pyramid and the traces of a plane VTH. Draw the projections of the solid after it has been cut by the oblique plane. Fig. 8.24.

The plan does not show the cut surface in this case. This type of problem is solved by getting an edge view of the oblique plane and hence determining the cut points on the solid.

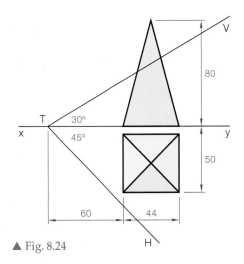

▲ Fig. 8.24

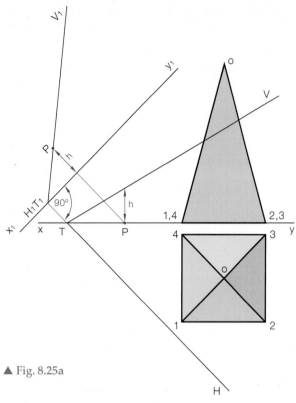

▲ Fig. 8.25a

(1) An edge view of the oblique plane is found by viewing along the horizontal trace. Extend the horizontal trace. Draw the x_1y_1 perpendicular to HT, Fig. 8.25a.

(2) Choose any point P on the xy line and project to the elevation giving height h.

(3) Project P to the auxiliary elevation and use the height h. Draw the edge view of the plane.

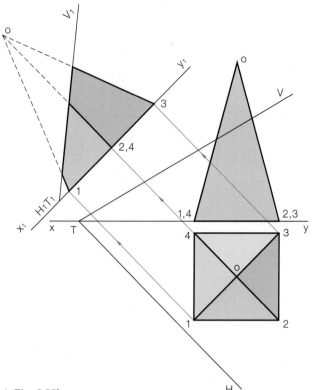

▲ Fig. 8.25b

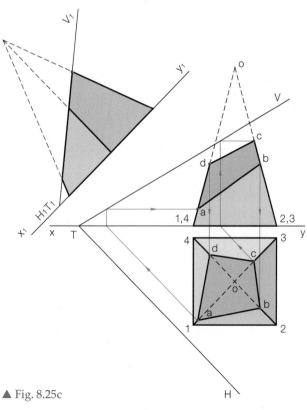

▲ Fig. 8.25c

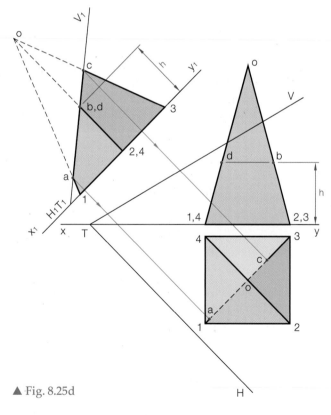

▲ Fig. 8.25d

(4) Project the auxiliary elevation of the pyramid, Fig. 8.25b.

(5) The auxiliary elevation shows the cut points a, b, c and d. Points a and c are projected to plan, the heights of b and d are used to find them in elevation, Fig. 8.25c.

(6) Complete the plan and elevation by projection, Fig. 8.25d.

See worksheet 8.2

Shown in Fig. 8.26 is a regular hexagonal-based pyramid which is to be cut by the plane VTH. Draw the plan and elevation of the cut solid.

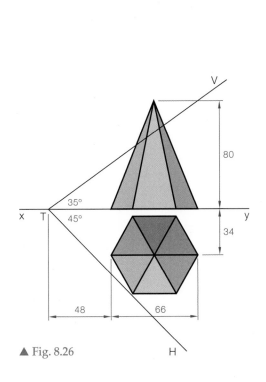

▲ Fig. 8.26

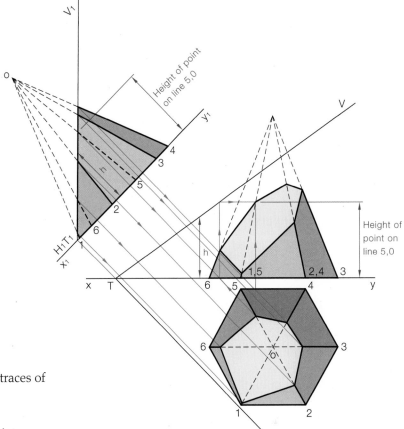

▲ Fig. 8.27

(1) Draw the given plan and elevation and the traces of the plane VTH.

(2) Index the corners.

(3) Project the auxiliary elevation to find the points on the cut surface.

(4) Project to plan and up to the elevation, Fig. 8.27.

Some points, when projected down from the auxiliary elevation to the plan, do not show a clear intersection, e.g. the point on line 5,0. In cases like this the height of the point can be taken from the auxiliary and used in the elevation to find the point which may then be projected to plan.

To Find the True Shape of an Object on an Oblique Plane

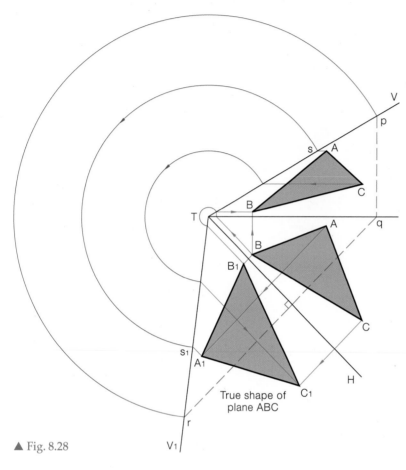

▲ Fig. 8.28

Method 1: Rebatment of the Plane

Fig. 8.28

What is happening here is that the plane is rotated onto the horizontal plane and is hinged about the horizontal trace HT.

(1) From any point p on the vertical trace drop a vertical to the xy line giving q.

(2) Draw a perpendicular to the horizontal trace from q and extend.

(3) With centre T and radius Tp rotate to cut this perpendicular giving r.

(4) Join r to T giving V_1HT, the rebatted plane.

To find the triangle on the rebatted plane:

(1) From point A in elevation project horizontally to the VT giving s.

(2) With T as centre rotate point s to V_1T giving s_1.

(3) Project s_1 parallel to the HT.

(4) From A in plan project across perpendicular to the HT to locate A_1.

(5) Repeat for the other points.

Method 2: Rebatment of the Plane

Fig. 8.29

This is very similar to Method 1.

(1) Rebat the plane as before.

(2) Project A in plan parallel to the HT to give point s on the xy line.

(3) Project s perpendicular to the HT to give s_1 on the V_1T line.

(4) Project s_1 parallel to the HT.

(5) Project from A in the plan, perpendicular to the HT to locate A_1.

(6) Repeat for other points.

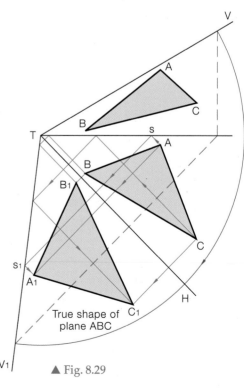

▲ Fig. 8.29

Method 3: Auxiliary Elevation and Rebatment

Fig. 8.30

An edge view of the oblique plane is found and the plane can then be easily rebatted onto the horizontal plane.

(1) View along the HT to see the plane as an edge view. Extend the horizontal trace.

(2) Draw x_1y_1 perpendicular to the HT line extended.

(3) Choose any point p on the xy line and project to the auxiliary.

(4) Find the height of point p from the elevation, height h, and measure on the auxiliary.

(5) Draw the plane in the auxiliary V_1TH.

(6) Project the triangular surface ABC to the auxiliary.

(7) Rotate the points A_1B_1C in the auxiliary, about point T, onto the x_1y_1 line.

(8) Project back to plan.

(9) Project from the plan perpendicular to the HT to locate the points A_2B_2 and C_2.

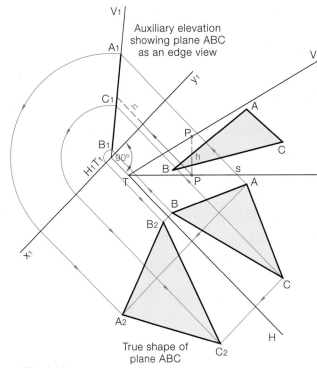

Auxiliary elevation showing plane ABC as an edge view

True shape of plane ABC

▲ Fig. 8.30

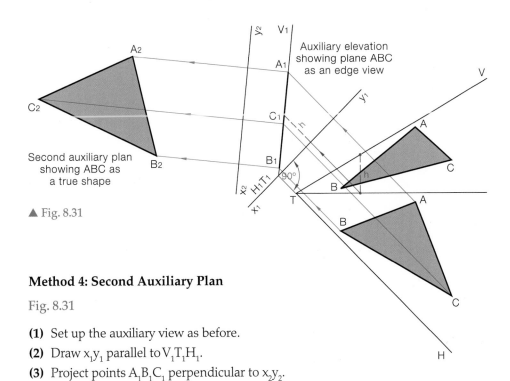

Auxiliary elevation showing plane ABC as an edge view

Second auxiliary plan showing ABC as a true shape

▲ Fig. 8.31

Method 4: Second Auxiliary Plan

Fig. 8.31

(1) Set up the auxiliary view as before.

(2) Draw x_1y_1 parallel to $V_1T_1H_1$.

(3) Project points $A_1B_1C_1$ perpendicular to x_2y_2.

(4) The distance from x_1y_1 to A is taken and used to locate A_2.

(5) Similar for B_2 and C_2.

Worked Examples

Fig. 8.32 shows the elevation and plan of a regular hexagonal prism. The solid is cut by the oblique plane VTH.

(i) Draw the plan and elevation of the solid when it is cut by the oblique plane VTH.

(ii) Draw the true shape of the cut surface of the prism.

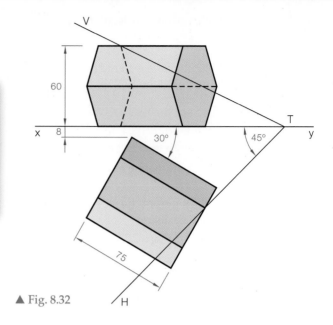

▲ Fig. 8.32

(1) Draw the given views.

(2) Project an auxiliary elevation viewing in the direction of the horizontal trace. This will show the oblique plane as an edge view. The cut points 1, 2, 3 and 4 are found.

(3) These points are projected to plan, giving two point 1s and two point 2s.

(4) The elevation is found by projection.

See worksheets 8.3 and 8.4

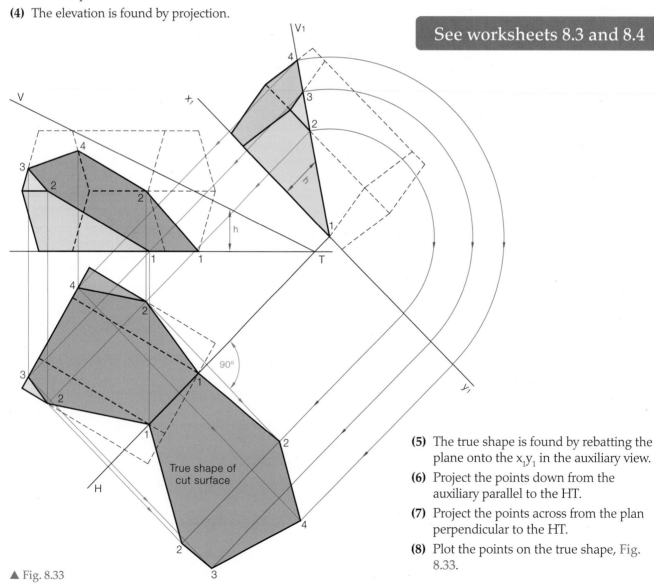

▲ Fig. 8.33

(5) The true shape is found by rebatting the plane onto the x_1y_1 in the auxiliary view.

(6) Project the points down from the auxiliary parallel to the HT.

(7) Project the points across from the plan perpendicular to the HT.

(8) Plot the points on the true shape, Fig. 8.33.

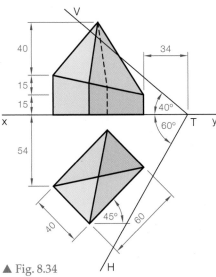

▲ Fig. 8.34

The plan and elevation of a solid which is cut by an oblique plane VTH is shown in Fig. 8.34.

(i) Draw the plan and elevation of the solid when it is cut by the oblique plane VTH.

(ii) Draw the true shape of the cut surface of the solid.

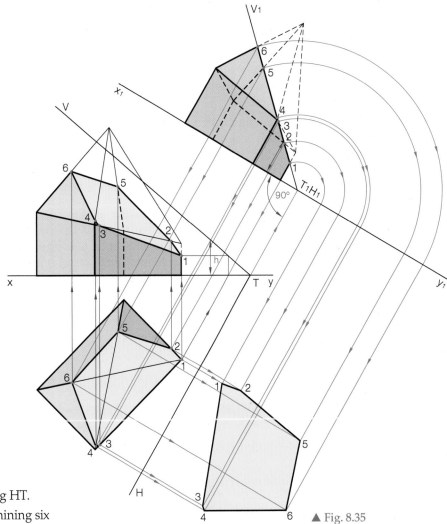

▲ Fig. 8.35

(1) Draw the given views.

(2) Project an auxiliary elevation viewing along HT.

(3) Draw the solid in the auxiliary thus determining six points on the cut surface.

(4) Project the points down from the auxiliary. Point 1 is on a vertical and will be in the corner in plan.

(5) Project all points to elevation. Point 1 being on a vertical, may not be projected directly, but must be brought parallel to the HT to the xy line, vertically to the VT and then horizontally.

(6) The true shape is found by rebatting the oblique plane in the auxiliary, Fig. 8.35.

See worksheet 8.5

Finding the traces of a plane

Given the plan and elevation of a lamina ABC. Find the traces of the plane that contains this lamina. Fig 8.36.

(1) Draw the plan and elevation as given.

(2) In elevation extend an edge, e.g. CA, until it hits the xy line and the horizontal plane at point p.

(3) Extend line CA in plan also.

(4) Drop point p to hit CA in plan, at point q. Point q is on the horizontal trace.

(5) Repeat this process for another edge, e.g. CB. This will find point s which is also on the horizontal trace.

(6) Join s and q and extend to the xy line. This is the horizontal trace.

(7) To find the vertical trace. Project one of the points in plan, e.g. C, parallel to the HT to the xy line. Project vertically and then across from the elevation. The intersection point of these two lines is a point on the vertical trace. Draw the trace, Fig. 8.37.

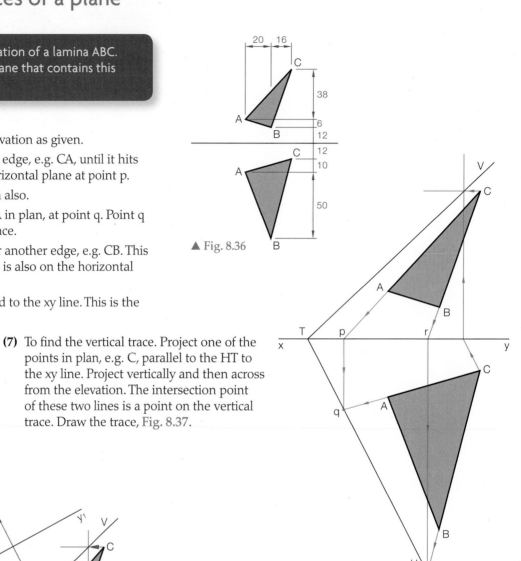

▲ Fig. 8.36

▲ Fig. 8.37

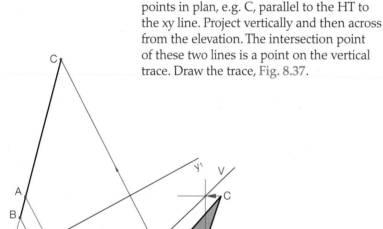

▲ Fig. 8.38

Alternative Method

Fig. 8.38

(1) Draw the plan and elevation.

(2) In elevation draw a level line across the surface. Line AO for example.

(3) Find this line in plan. Point O is projected to plan and is found on edge CB. Join point O to corner A.

(4) View in the direction of OA and project an auxiliary elevation. The lamina projects as an edge view because we are viewing along a true length on its surface.

(5) Extend the edge view in auxiliary to the x_1y_1 line thus giving a point view of the HT. Project the horizontal trace back to plan.

(6) Find the vertical trace as above.

Intersecting oblique planes

The diagram, Fig. 8.39, shows a pictorial view of the planes of reference and two intersecting oblique planes.

When two planes intersect, the line of intersection will always be a straight line.

It should be noted from the diagram that the intersection of the two horizontal traces HT and H_1T_1 at p gives one end of the line of intersection. Similarly the intersection of the two vertical traces at q gives the other end of the line of intersection.

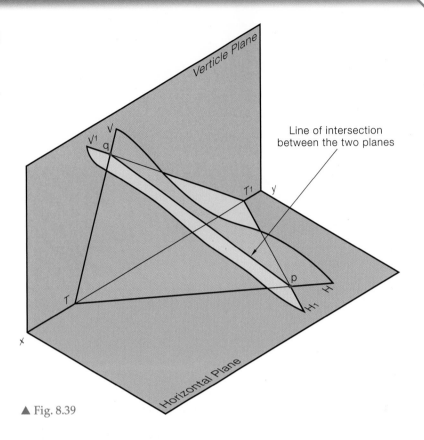

▲ Fig. 8.39

> Given two oblique planes VTH and $V_1T_1H_1$ to find the line of intersection between them. Fig. 8.40.

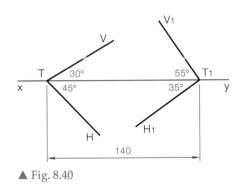

▲ Fig. 8.40

(1) Extend the vertical traces until they intersect at q.

(2) Extend the horizontal traces until they intersect at p. Point q is the elevation of one end of the line of intersection and point p is the plan of the other end.

(3) Project p to elevation (xy line) and join to q.

(4) Project q to plan (xy line) and join to p, Fig. 8.41.

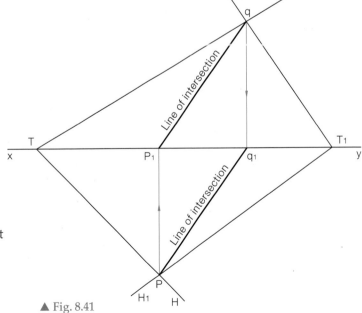

▲ Fig. 8.41

To find the true length of the line of
intersection between two oblique planes.

(1) Find the line of intersection as above.

(2) Consider pq as the hypotenuse of a right-
angled triangle that stands vertically
underneath the line of intersection.
Rotate this triangle until it lies
horizontally, thus showing the true length
of the line pq, **Fig. 8.42**.

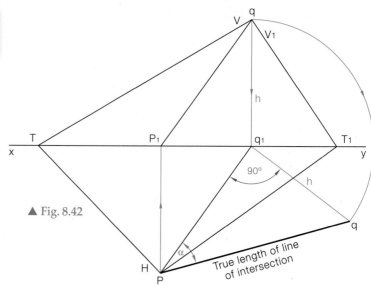

▲ Fig. 8.42

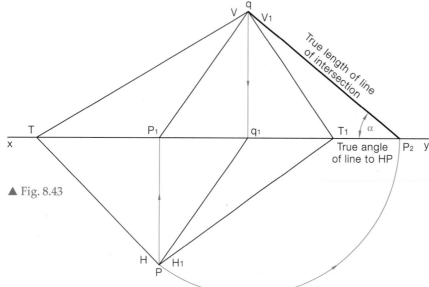

▲ Fig. 8.43

Alternative method of finding
the true length of the line of
intersection. Fig. 8.43.

(1) With the compass on q_1 rotate
point p to p_2 on the xy line.

(2) Join p_2 to q giving the true length of
the line of intersection.

Note: In both methods the true angle,
that the line makes with the horizontal
plane is also found.

Activities

Figures on oblique planes

Q1. Given the traces of an oblique plane VTH and the plan
of a regular pentagon, which rests on the plane. Draw
the given plan and project the elevation, **Fig. 8.44**.

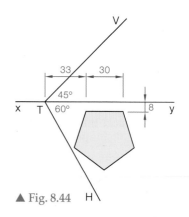

▲ Fig. 8.44

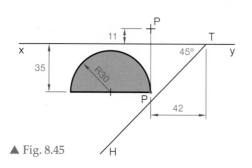

▲ Fig. 8.45

Q2. Given the plan of a figure resting on an oblique
plane of which you are given the horizontal trace.
Also given is the elevation of the corner P. Find the
vertical trace and complete the views, **Fig. 8.45**.

Cut solids

Q3. Given the plan of a tetrahedron resting on the horizontal plane and the traces of a plane VTH. Draw the projections of the solid when it is cut by the plane, **Fig. 8.46**.

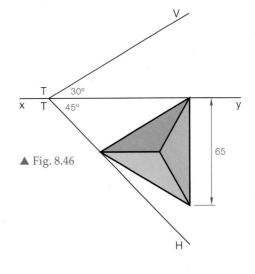

▲ Fig. 8.46

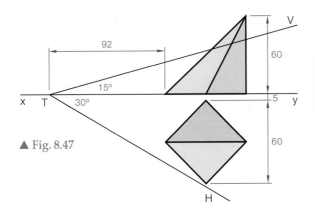

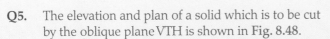

▲ Fig. 8.47

Q4. Given a square-based pyramid which is to be cut by the oblique plane VTH. Draw the plan and elevation of the cut solid, **Fig. 8.47**.

Q5. The elevation and plan of a solid which is to be cut by the oblique plane VTH is shown in **Fig. 8.48**.

    (i) Draw the elevation and plan of the solid when it is cut by the oblique plane VTH.

    (ii) Draw the true shape of the cut surface.

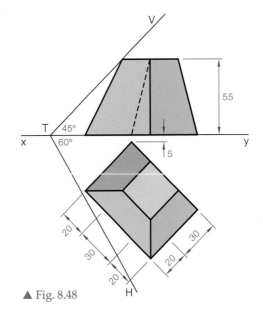

▲ Fig. 8.48

Q6. Fig. 8.49 shows the elevation and plan of a solid that is cut by the oblique plane VTH.

    (i) Draw the plan and elevation of the solid when it is cut by the oblique plane VTH.

    (ii) Draw the true shape of the cut surface.

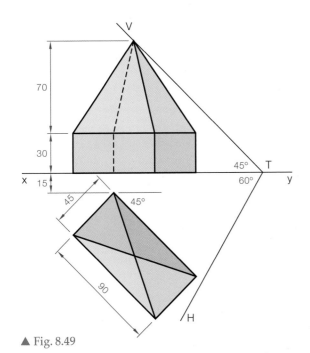

▲ Fig. 8.49

Q7. Fig. 8.50 shows the rebatment of an oblique plane which contains a plane figure. Find the VT and the plan and elevation of the figure.

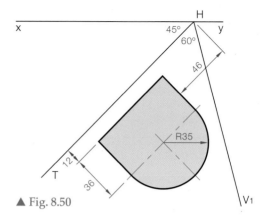

▲ Fig. 8.50

Given two planes VTH and $V_1T_1H_1$. Find the line of intersection between the planes. Determine the dihedral angle between the two planes. Fig. 8.51.

(1) Find the line of intersection in plan and elevation.

(2) Find the true length of the line of intersection.

(3) At any point c on the true length draw a perpendicular to the length giving cab. The line cab represents the edge view of the triangle which fits between the planes and measure the dihedral angle.

(4) Rebat the triangle onto the horizontal plane by rotating vertex c as shown. Edge ab is perpendicular to the plan of the line of intersection.

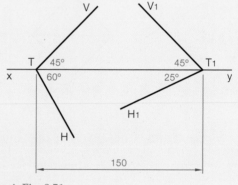

▲ Fig. 8.51

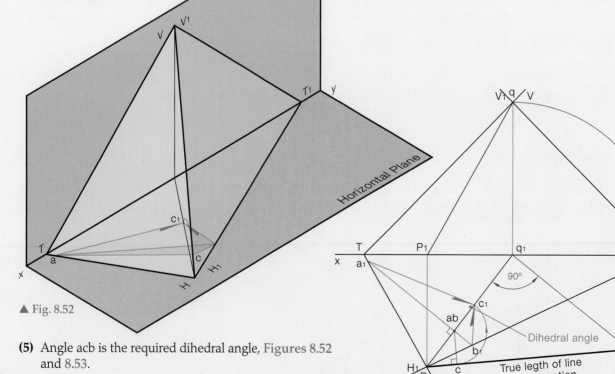

▲ Fig. 8.52

(5) Angle acb is the required dihedral angle, Figures 8.52 and 8.53.

▲ Fig. 8.53

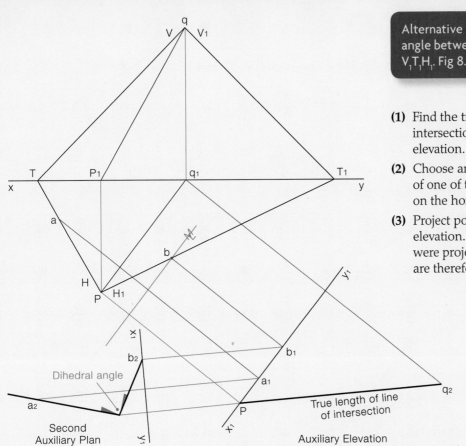

HIGHER LEVEL

Alternative method of finding the dihedral angle between two oblique planes VTH and $V_1T_1H_1$. Fig 8.54

(1) Find the true length of the line of intersection, pq, by using an auxiliary elevation.

(2) Choose any point 'a' on the horizontal trace of one of the planes and choose any point 'b' on the horizontal trace of the other plane.

(3) Project points a and b onto the auxiliary elevation. Both points rest on the x_1y_1 as they were projected from the horizontal trace and are therefore on the horizontal plane.

▲ Fig. 8.54

(4) Project a second auxiliary plan viewing along the true length which will show pq as a point view.

(5) In the diagram the distances for the second auxiliary plan are taken from the measuring line back to the points in the plan.

To draw the traces of a plane VTH given the inclination to the horizontal plane as 60° and the inclination to the vertical plane as 45°. Fig. 8.55.

(1) Draw a circle having its centre on the xy line.

(2) Draw a cone in elevation of base angle 60°, tangential to this sphere. Draw the cone in plan.

(3) Draw a cone in plan of base angle 45° tangential to the sphere.

(4) The traces of the required plane will pass through the vertex of each cone and be tangential to the base of each cone.

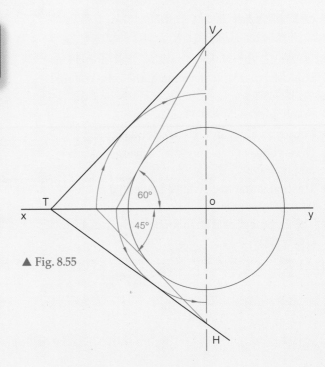

▲ Fig. 8.55

Given the projections of a line AB. Find the traces of the oblique plane that contains line AB and is inclined at 70° to the horizontal plane. Fig. 8.56.

(1) Draw the plan and elevation of the line as given.

(2) Draw the plan and elevation of a cone of base angle 70°, resting on the horizontal plane and having its vertex at A.

(3) Draw a similar cone having B as vertex.

(4) The HT line will be tangential to the cones in plan.

(5) The VT line is found by projecting the vertex of either cone parallel to the HT as far as the xy line. Then project vertically and across horizontally in elevation to find a point on the VT which can then be drawn in, Fig. 8.57.

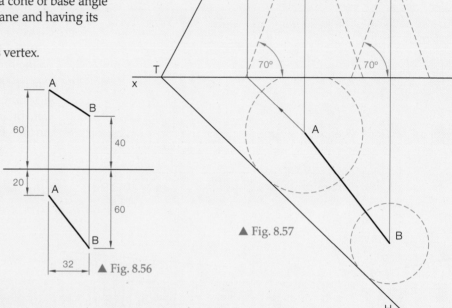

▲ Fig. 8.57

▲ Fig. 8.56

Fig. 8.58 shows the projections of a right square-based pyramid resting on the horizontal plane as shown. The pyramid is to be cut by an oblique plane which is inclined at 60° to the horizontal plane and passes through points A and B. Draw the projections of the cut pyramid. Pyramid base = 60 mm, altitude = 75 mm.

▲ Fig. 8.58

(1) Draw the plan and elevation of the solid resting on its base.

(2) Rotate the solid onto its side.

(3) Locate points A and B in plan and elevation.

(4) Draw cones of base angle 60° having A as apex and B as apex.

(5) The horizontal trace will be tangential to the base circles in plan.

(6) The vertical trace is then found in the usual way, Fig. 8.59.

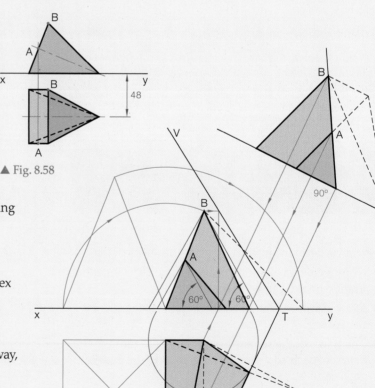

▲ Fig. 8.59

Spatial Coordinates

All points in space can be defined by their coordinates. When dealing with three dimensions it is necessary to define a point using three coordinates, x, y and z. With reference to Fig. 8.60 we can see how point P can be established relative to a datum line, the horizontal plane and the vertical plane.

The first coordinate, coordinate x, refers to the distance to the right of the datum line. The second coordinate, coordinate y, refers to the distance the point P is above the horizontal plane. The third distance, coordinate z, refers to the distance point P is in front of the vertical plane.

Since we can define points in space using coordinates we can also define lines and planes using the same method.

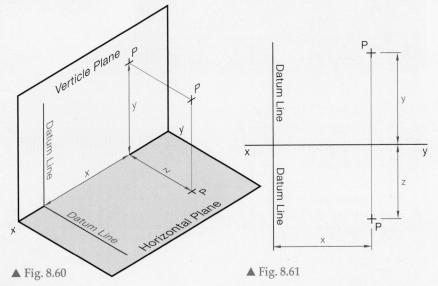

▲ Fig. 8.60   ▲ Fig. 8.61

Given the coordinates of a laminar surface. To draw the plan and elevation of that surface. Fig. 8.62.

		x	y	z
A	=	120	48	12
B	=	72	15	30
C	=	84	43	54

(1) Draw the xy line and a vertical reference line.

(2) To find point A measure 120 mm to the right of the reference line and draw a light vertical.

(3) Measure 48 mm above the xy line and mark A in elevation.

(4) Measure 12 mm below the xy line and mark A in plan.

x	y	z
120	48	12
→	↑	↓

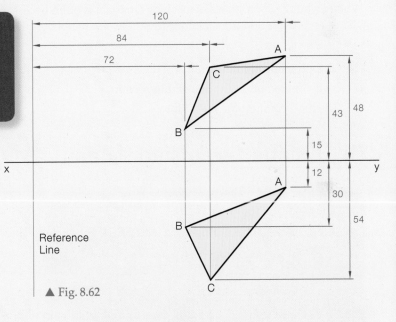

▲ Fig. 8.62

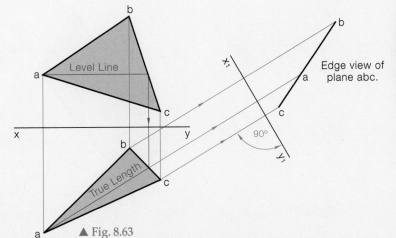

▲ Fig. 8.63

Given the coordinates of a laminar plane abc to find its edge view. Fig. 8.63

a	=	45	30	60
b	=	96	63	12
c	=	114	9	30

(1) Draw the plan and elevation of the triangle.

(2) Draw a level line in elevation and project to plan.

(3) The level line in elevation will project as a true length in plan. View in the direction of the true length and project an auxiliary elevation. The plane will appear as an edge view.

HIGHER LEVEL

Given the coordinates of a laminar plane abc, to find its true shape. Fig. 8.64

a	=	33	33	6
b	=	66	8	8
c	=	108	45	36

(1) Draw the plan and elevation.

(2) Find an edge view of the plane.

(3) Draw x_2y_2 parallel to the edge view and project the three points.

(4) The distances for the second auxiliary plan are found by measuring from x_1y_1 back to the plan or from a measuring line which is parallel to the x_1y_1 back to the plan.

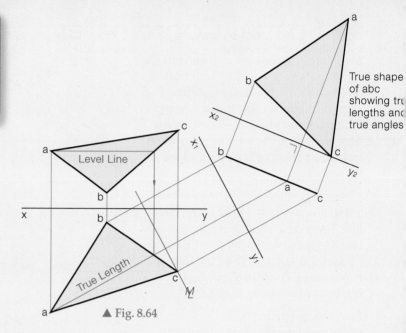

True shape of abc showing true lengths and true angles

▲ Fig. 8.64

Line of Intersection and Dihedral Angles for Triangular Lamina

When given the coordinates of meshing lamina it is often necessary to find the line of intersection between the planes and hence find the dihedral angle between the planes. There are three possible ways this problem can be presented:

(1) Given the line of intersection.

(2) Given one point on the line of intersection.

(3) Given no point on the line of intersection.

(1) Given the line of intersection

Given the coordinates for two planes ABC and ABDE. Determine the dihedral angle between the planes, Fig. 8.65.

A	=	35	5	115	B	=	90	20	45
C	=	105	45	80	D	=	70	75	10
E	=	15	50	90				

Here we are given the line of intersection.

(1) Project an auxiliary view from plan showing the true length of the line of intersection between the planes. View perpendicular to AB in plan.

(2) Project from this auxiliary viewing down along the true length. The x_2y_2 will therefore be perpendicular to the true length found. Both planes will be seen as edge views thus showing the dihedral angle. Note that the distances for the second auxiliary are taken from the x_1y_1 back to the plan or from a suitable measuring line.

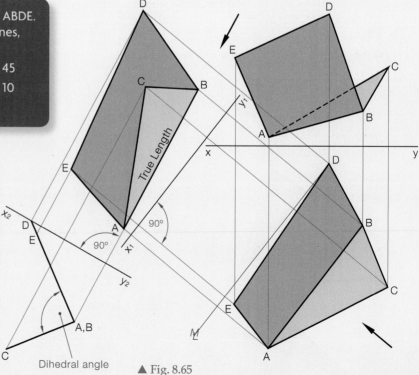

▲ Fig. 8.65

(2) Given one point on the line of intersection

See worksheets 8.6 and 8.7

Given the coordinates of two planes ABC and ADE. Determine the line of intersection and the dihedral angle between the planes. Fig. 8.66.

Point A is a shared point and therefore must be on the line of intersection

(1) Draw a horizontal cutting plane in elevation to cut both planes. In Fig. 8.66 this cutting plane gives points 1 and 2 on plane ABC and points D and 3 on plane ADE.

(2) Find these points in plan giving lines 1,2 and D,3. Where these two lines cross is a point on the line of intersection, i.e. a shared point. Thus find the line of intersection Ai in plan and elevation. The line of intersection must stop when it hits the edge of a plane. The dihedral angle follows as before.

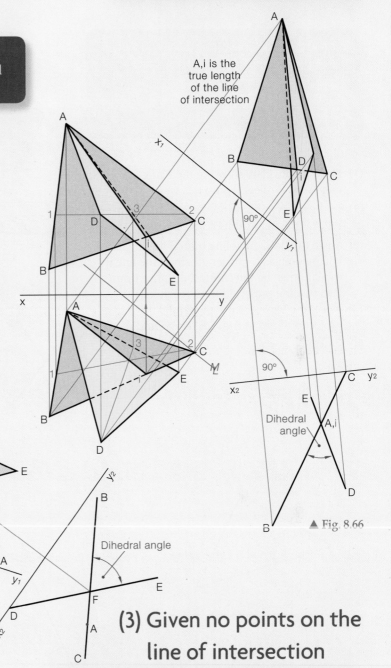

▲ Fig. 8.66

▲ Fig. 8.67

(3) Given no points on the line of intersection

Given the coordinates of two planes ABC and DEF to find the line of intersection and the dihedral angle between the planes. Fig. 8.67

| A = 140 | 5 | 80 | B = 95 | 90 | 25 | C = 30 | 25 | 55 |
| D = 80 | 10 | 15 | E = 130 | 55 | 95 | F = 20 | 70 | 35 |

This method is the same as in the previous example except that two separate horizontal cutting planes are used. These horizontal cutting planes can be drawn at any level as long as they cut both planes.

See worksheets 8.8

HIGHER LEVEL

Note 1: Line E,3 in plan will be parallel to 4,5. Also line 1,2 will be parallel to C,6 in plan.

Note 2: If the lines do not intersect they are extended until they do intersect.

> To draw the shortest horizontal line to a plane from a given point P outside it, Fig. 8.68.
>
> A = 75   75 10   B = 20   50 90
> C = 40   5   115   D = 95   20 45
> P = 110   45 80

(1) Draw an auxiliary showing the plane as an edge view. Project P onto this view.

(2) In the auxiliary draw the horizontal line from P to hit the plane at i. Project i to plan.

(3) Since the horizontal line from P to i in plan will be seen as a true length, then the line iP in plan must be the shortest distance from P to the line projected from the auxiliary elevation. Draw from P perpendicular to the projection lines to the auxiliary to find i.

(4) iP will be horizontal in elevation.

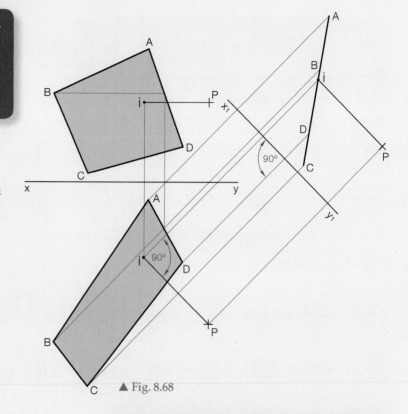

▲ Fig. 8.68

> To draw the perpendicular to a plane ABC from a point P outside it. Fig. 8.69
>
> A = 120   88 2   B = 50   50 94
> C = 160   20 84   P = 148   76 96

(1) Draw an auxiliary elevation showing the plane as an edge view and project point P onto this view.

(2) In the auxiliary, draw the perpendicular from P to the plane finding point q.

(3) It should be noted that **a perpendicular to a plane will appear perpendicular to the traces of that plane.** We can therefore draw the required line Pq in plan as it will appear perpendicular to the level line on the plane. The level line will be parallel to the HT line.

(4) Line Pq can be found in elevation as shown in Fig. 8.69.

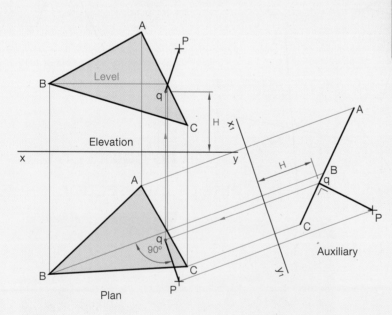

▲ Fig. 8.69

(1) This problem is solved under the principle that any line generator on the surface of a right cone will have the same inclination to the horizontal plane as the cone base angle. Furthermore all generators on a right cone will have the same length. Draw an auxiliary showing ABCD as an edge view. Project point E onto this view.

(2) Draw a cone in this view having E as apex, base angle of 45° and side length of 90 mm.

(3) Where the base of the cone is cut by the plane will give the required line when projected back.

To draw the projections of a line drawn from a point E outside a plane that will touch the plane at a distance of 90 mm from E and that shall be inclined at an angle of 45° to the horizontal plane. Fig. 8.70

A = 125   55 5   B = 165   15 85   C = 205 50 90
D = 185   80 40   E = 110   100 45

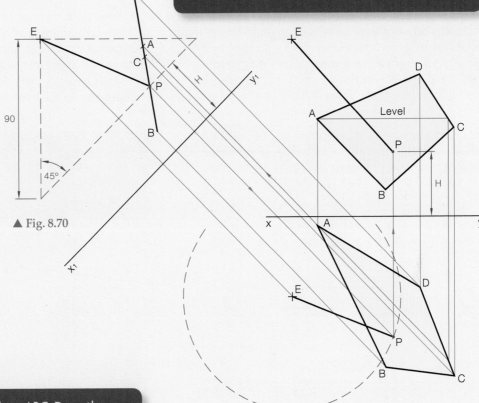

▲ Fig. 8.70

Given the coordinates of a plane ABC. Draw the projections of a line on the plane ABC, that passes through A and makes an angle of 60° with the edge BC. Fig. 8.71.

A = 125   85 30   B = 170   10 100   C = 80   75 65

(1) Draw the plan and elevation of the plane.

(2) Get an edge view of the plane in the usual way.

(3) By viewing perpendicular to the edge view we can project a true shape of the lamina.

(4) On the true shape draw the required line. Project point p back through the views to find the line in plan and elevation as shown in Fig. 8.71.

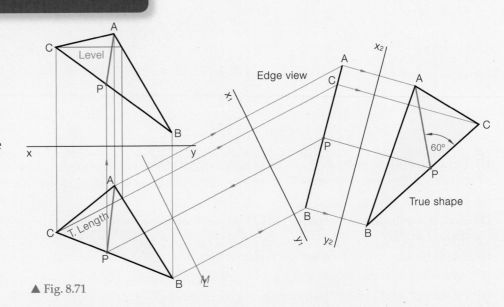

▲ Fig. 8.71

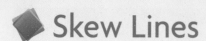

Skew Lines

Definition: Two lines are called skew lines if they are neither parallel nor intersecting.

In many practical areas of engineering, the shortest level distance between skew lines or the shortest perpendicular distances between skew lines, is often required. For example, in pipework, mining, structural frames etc., it is often necessary to connect two skew pipes with another new pipe; two mining shafts with another new tunnel; or two skew members of a frame with another new member. In cases like these it is of great advantage to know the shortest horizontal distance, or the shortest perpendicular distance, between the two elements. At a later stage we will apply the principles learned here about skew lines to solve problems on mining and on the hyperbolic paraboloid.

If we produce a plane that contains one of the lines and has an edge that is parallel to the other line, then an edge view of that plane will show both lines as parallel.

To find the shortest horizontal distance between two skew lines AB and CD. Fig. 8.72.

A = 45 55   5   B = 105 80   40
C = 30 100 45 D = 85 15   15

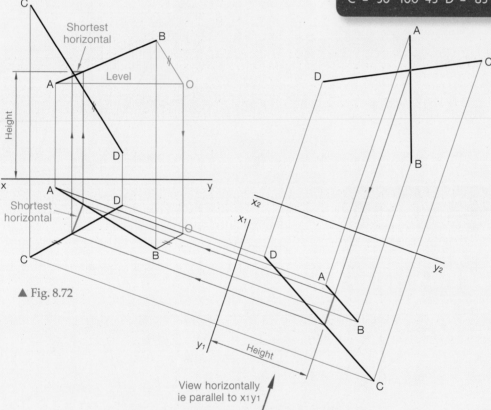

▲ Fig. 8.72

(1) Draw the plane to contain AB and be parallel to CD. Draw a level line from A in elevation. From B draw a line parallel to the other skew line CD. These two lines intersect at O. This completes the plane in elevation.

(2) Drop O to plan.

(3) From B in plan draw a line parallel to CD in plan. This line intersects the line dropped from O in elevation to give point O in plan.

(4) Join O back to A thus completing the plan of the plane.

(5) An auxiliary elevation viewing along AO will show both lines as parallel.

(6) Project a second auxiliary plan by projecting horizontally, i.e. parallel to the x_1y_1. Both lines appear to cross. Where they appear to cross is the location of the shortest horizontal line.

(7) Project the line back through the views as shown.

To find the shortest distance (shortest perpendicular distance) between two skew lines. Fig. 8.73.

A = 170 5   55   B = 250 20   65
C = 175 55   90   D = 230 25   30

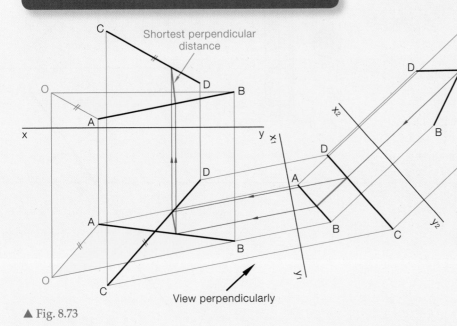

▲ Fig. 8.73

(1) The initial part of this problem is solved in the same way as the previous example up to the stage of projecting an auxiliary showing the two lines appearing parallel.

(2) A view is taken of this auxiliary which is perpendicular to the two parallel lines.

(3) The second auxiliary shows the two lines appearing to cross. Where they appear to cross is the location of the required line. The line is projected back to all views.

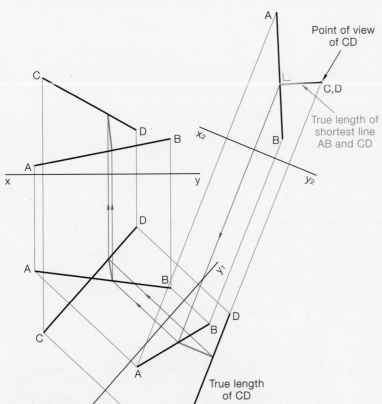

▲ Fig. 8.74

Alternative Method: Line Method

Given the same problem.

(1) Project an auxiliary from plan that will show one of the lines as a true length. Fig. 8.74 shows x_1y_1 drawn parallel to CD thus showing line CD as a true length in the auxiliary elevation.

(2) Project a second auxiliary viewing along the true length line. This new auxiliary shows CD as a point view.

(3) The shortest line between two skew lines will always appear as a true length in a view that shows one of the lines as a true length. When projected back to the first auxiliary the shortest line must therefore be parallel to the x_2y_2 line.

(4) Project back to all views.

See worksheet 8.9

HIGHER LEVEL

Given the coordinates of the centre lines of two 15 mm diameter pipes. Determine the clearance between them using the line method. Fig. 8.75.

A = 125 55   80 B = 175 101 0
C = 100 25   10 D = 165 75   50

The construction is as in the previous example. The pipes need only be drawn in the secondary auxiliary view.

(1) Draw the plan and elevation of the centre lines.

(2) Find the true length of one of these, e.g. CD, by auxiliary projection.

(3) Project a second auxiliary viewing along the true length CD.

(4) A point view of centre line CD is found. Draw in the pipe details which will show clearly the clearance between the pipes.

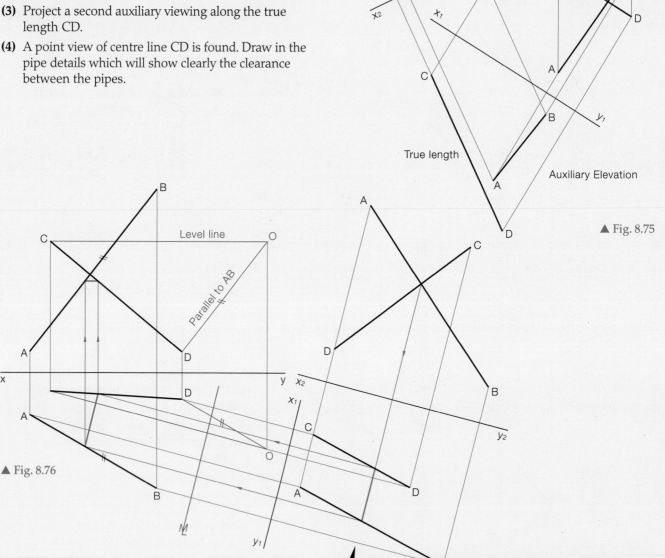

▲ Fig. 8.75

▲ Fig. 8.76

(1) Using the plane method project the auxiliary which shows the two lines appearing parallel.

(2) View parallel to x_1y_1 (horizontally) for the second auxiliary. The lines appear to cross which is the location of the required brace.

(3) Project back through the views.

Given the coordinates of two struts. Show the projections of the shortest horizontal brace strut between them. Fig. 8.76.

A = 30 8   16 B = 80 70 44
C = 38 50   7 D = 90 8   10

Activities

Dihedral angle

Q1. Given two planes VTH and $V_1T_1H_1$. Find the line of intersection between the planes. Determine the dihedral angle between the planes using the triangle method, Fig. 8.77.

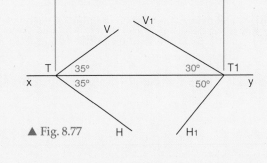

▲ Fig. 8.77

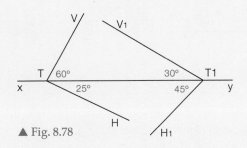

▲ Fig. 8.78

Q2. Given two planes VTH and $V_1T_1H_1$. Find the line of intersection between the planes. Determine the dihedral angle between the planes using the point view method, Fig. 8.78.

Q3. Draw the traces of a plane VTH given the inclination to the vertical plane as 40° and the inclination to the horizontal plane as 70°.

Q4. Draw the traces of a plane VTH given the inclination to the vertical plane as 45° and the inclination to the horizontal plane as 55°.

Q5. Given the projection of a line AB. Find the traces of the plane that contains line AB and is inclined at 55° to the HP, Fig. 8.79.

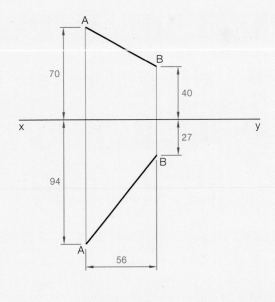

▲ Fig. 8.79

Q6. Fig. 8.80 shows the plan and elevation of a prism with a square base of 60 mm side which has been cut by an oblique plane. The cut surface abcd is inclined at 45° to the horizontal plane and the edge ab is inclined at 20° to the horizontal plane.

   (i) Draw the plan and elevation of the cut solid.

   (ii) Find the traces of the oblique plane.

   (iii) Determine the plane's inclination to the VP.

   (iv) Find the dihedral angle between surface S and the oblique plane.

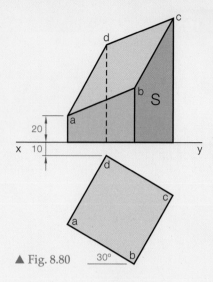

▲ Fig. 8.80   30°

Laminar surfaces

Q7. Given the coordinates of two planes ABC and ABD.

A = 220 15 10   B = 270 35 90
C = 260 65 15   D = 230 60 75

   (i) Determine the dihedral angle between the planes.

   (ii) Determine the projections of a perpendicular from D to the plane ABC.

Q8. Given the horizontal and vertical projections of two planes ABC and ABD.

A = 130 90 10   B = 215 15 95
C = 165 100 100   D = 245 70 25

   (i) Determine the dihedral angle between the planes.

   (ii) Show the projections of a line drawn from C to the line AD and which shall be perpendicular to AD.

Q9. Given the horizontal and vertical projections of two planes ABC and ADE.

A = 225 25 90   B = 220 95 50
C = 175 35 20   D = 240 60 10
E = 140 60 15

   (i) Determine the line of intersection between the planes.

   (ii) Determine the dihedral angle between the planes.

   (iii) Determine the inclination of the line AD to the plane ABC.

Q10. Given the coordinates of two planes ABC and DEF.

A = 130 60 5   B = 210 10 90
C = 200 80 25   D = 240 20 30
E = 155 85 5   F = 130 45 60

   (i) Determine the line of intersection between the planes.

   (ii) Determine the dihedral angle between the planes.

   (iii) Find the horizontal and vertical trace of DEF and find its true inclination to the vertical plane.

Q11. Given the coordinates of two skew lines AB and CD.

A = 125 85 30   B = 170 10 100
C = 75 20 105   D = 180 70 70

Show the projections of the shortest distance between them using the point view method.

Q12. Given the coordinates of two skew lines AB and CD.

A = 160 90 20   B = 225 5 10
C = 130 25 70   D = 235 30 25

Show the projections of the shortest horizontal line joining them.

AREA 4

INTERSECTION AND DEVELOPMENT OF SURFACES

9 Intersection of Solids

Syllabus Outline

Areas to be studied:

- Intersection of surfaces of prisms, pyramids[1] and spheres, their frustra and composite solids and development of same.
- *Intersection of right and oblique solids and their surface development.*

1 Pyramid and prism are taken to include the cone and cylinder respectively.
2 Principal planes of reference refers to the horizontal and vertical planes.

Learning Outcomes

Students should be able to:

Higher and Ordinary levels
- Find the intersection of given lines and planes with given planes and curved surfaces.
- Establish the surface intersections of prisms, pyramids, spheres, their frustra and composite solids, where the intersecting solids have their axes parallel to at least one of the principal planes of reference[2].

Higher Level only
- *Complete the intersection details of regular and oblique solids wherein their axes are parallel to one of the principal planes of reference.*

 Interpenetrations

Everyday life throws up numerous examples of solids joining into other solids. When these solids join we get a line of interpenetration. The line of interpenetration will be either straight or curved depending on the types of solids joining together.

Solids made up of flat or plane surfaces penetrated by a similar solid, will produce straight lines as join lines. Solids with curved surfaces, penetrated by other solids, will produce curved lines of penetration. In this chapter we investigate various methods of finding the lines of intersection between solids.

Method One: Limits Method

For some of the less complex interpenetrations, involving solids with plane surfaces, this is the best method. The solids involved will produce an interpenetration line made up of straight lines. If we can find the start, bend points and finish of each penetration line, we can find the full line of interpenetration.

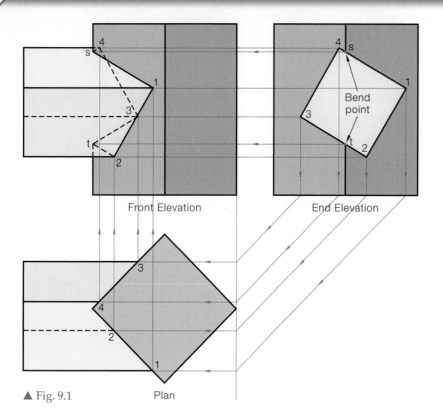

▲ Fig. 9.1

Front Elevation

End Elevation

Plan

Bend point

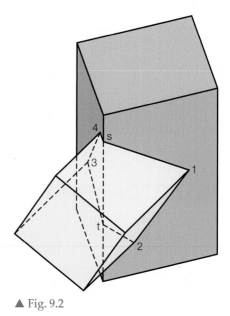

▲ Fig. 9.2

The orthographic projection shown in Fig. 9.1 is a good example of the use of this method. Two square-based prisms are joined and the line of intersection between them is to be found. Information is found from the end elevation and the plan to complete the front elevation. The penetration points of edges 1, 2, 3 and 4 can be clearly seen in plan and are projected to elevation. Where a penetrating surface straddles two surfaces, the line of intersection will have a bend in it. An example of this is the surface containing 2 and 3. The bend point is found in the end view and is point t. The penetration line goes from '2' to 't' to '3'. The pictorial, Fig. 9.2, may help in the visualisation of this.

Given the plan and end elevation of two intersecting solids, a hexagonal prism and a triangular prism. Draw the given views and complete the front elevation of the solids, Fig. 9.3.

(1) Draw the given views. Both the plan and end view are complete and provide the necessary information for the front elevation.

(2) Identify the bend points r, s, t and u in the end elevation. Project these across to the front elevation.

(3) The end points for edges 1 and 2 are seen in plan and projected up to the front elevation.

(4) Edge 3 does not make contact with the triangular prism.

(5) It is important to use indexing in this type of question, Fig. 9.4.

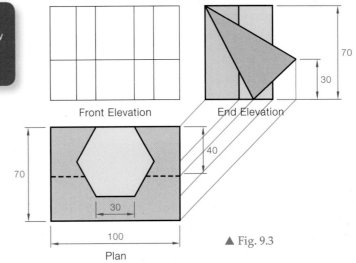

▲ Fig. 9.3

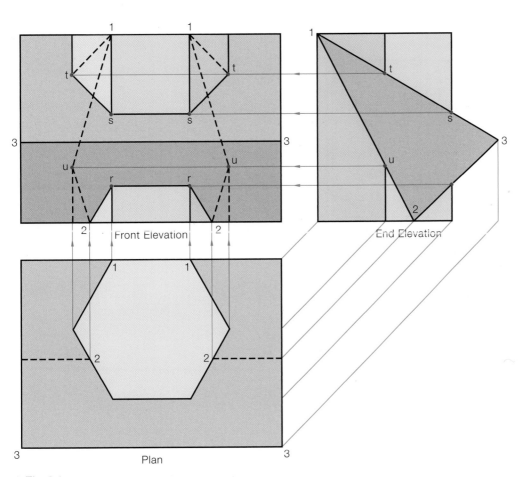

▲ Fig. 9.4

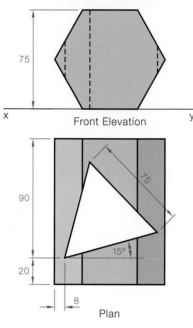

Given the plan and elevation of a hexagonal prism with an equilateral triangular hole cut through it. Draw the given views and project an end view of the solid, Fig. 9.5.

(1) Draw the plan and elevation as given. Both of these views are complete.

(2) By projecting points from both of these views onto the end view we can build it up.

(3) Note the bend points p, q, r and s where one of the cutting planes crosses two or more planes.

(4) When all the points are found they are joined up in order. The order in which they are joined is best seen in the plan. 1 → p → q → 2 → r → 3 → s → 1, Fig. 9.6.

▲ Fig. 9.5

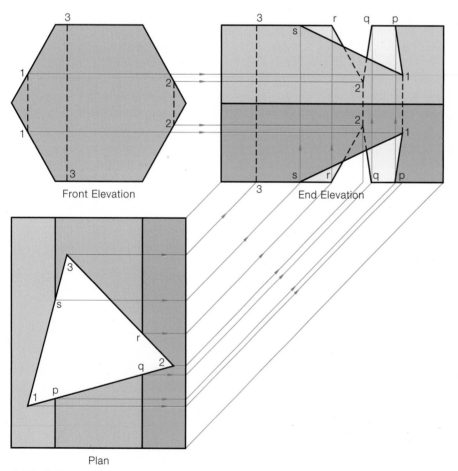

▲ Fig. 9.6

Given the plan and end view of two intersecting prisms. Draw the given views and project the front elevation, Fig. 9.7.

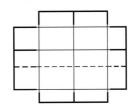

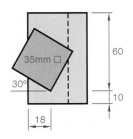

(1) Draw the given views.

(2) The edge, 1, of the square prism intersects the triangular prism in two places. Similarly for edge 2 and edge 3 of the square prism. It can be seen from the end view that edge 4 does not intersect the triangular prism. All six of these points are found in plan and projected to elevation.

(3) The bend points p, q, r and s are seen in end view and projected across to the front elevation.

(4) The sequence of joining the points is found from the end elevation, s, 1, p, 2, q, 3, r, 3, 2, 1, s, Fig. 9.8.

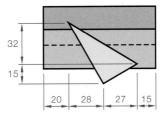

▲ Fig. 9.7

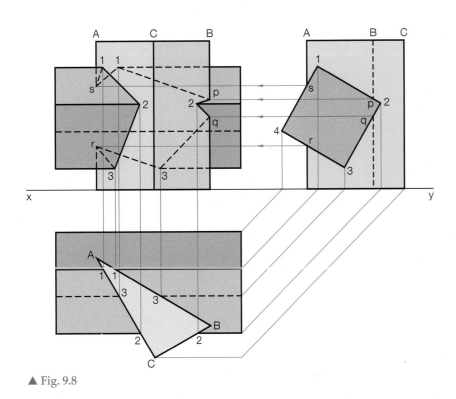

▲ Fig. 9.8

See worksheet 9.1

Method Two: Radial Elements Method

This method can be very useful when cones or pyramids are being penetrated by other solids. The limits method used in the previous examples will not work for these types of solid.

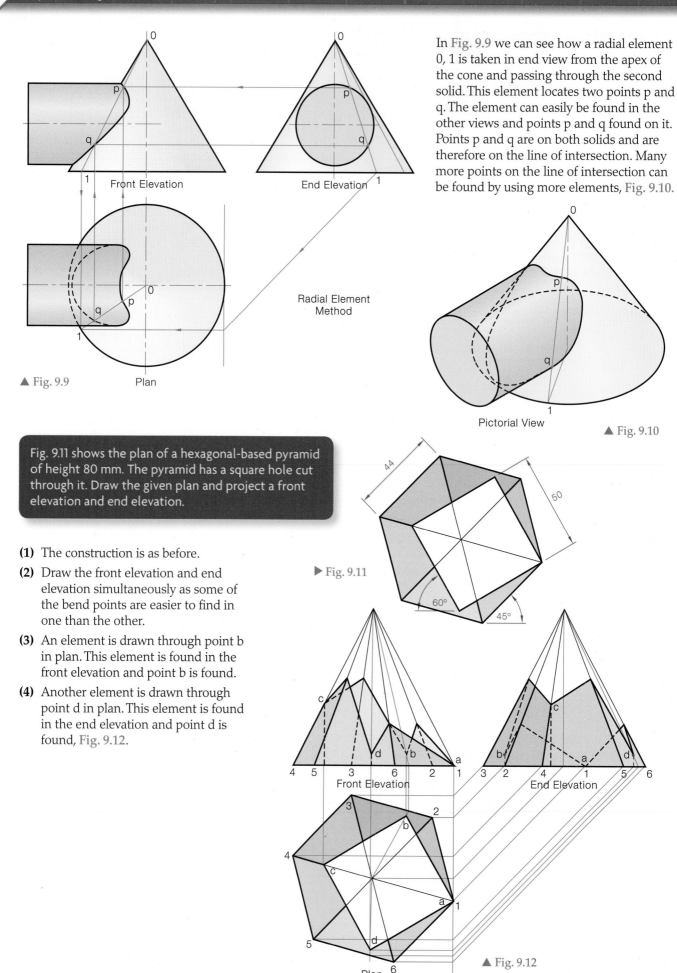

In Fig. 9.9 we can see how a radial element 0, 1 is taken in end view from the apex of the cone and passing through the second solid. This element locates two points p and q. The element can easily be found in the other views and points p and q found on it. Points p and q are on both solids and are therefore on the line of intersection. Many more points on the line of intersection can be found by using more elements, Fig. 9.10.

▲ Fig. 9.9   Plan

Front Elevation

End Elevation

Radial Element Method

Pictorial View

▲ Fig. 9.10

Fig. 9.11 shows the plan of a hexagonal-based pyramid of height 80 mm. The pyramid has a square hole cut through it. Draw the given plan and project a front elevation and end elevation.

(1) The construction is as before.

(2) Draw the front elevation and end elevation simultaneously as some of the bend points are easier to find in one than the other.

(3) An element is drawn through point b in plan. This element is found in the front elevation and point b is found.

(4) Another element is drawn through point d in plan. This element is found in the end elevation and point d is found, Fig. 9.12.

▶ Fig. 9.11

Front Elevation

End Elevation

Plan

▲ Fig. 9.12

Method Three: Horizontal Sections

The use of horizontal planes is a very useful method, particularly when dealing with spheres, cones and cylinders. The horizontal section of each of these solids produce circles, Figures 9.13 and 9.14.

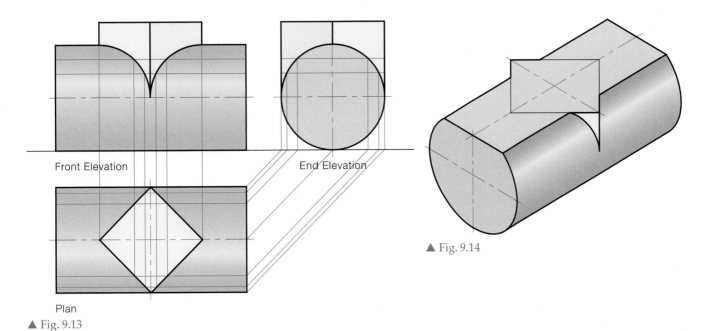

Front Elevation

End Elevation

Plan

▲ Fig. 9.13

▲ Fig. 9.14

Given the plan and elevation of a sphere and a cone which intersect each other. Draw the given views and find the line of interpenetration, Fig. 9.15.

(1) Draw the plan and elevation as given.

(2) It is advisable to space the horizontal sections at equal intervals each side of the sphere centre line.

(3) The intersections of the cone sections in plan with their corresponding sphere sections gives the points for the curve on the plan.

(4) Project these points of intersection to their corresponding horizontal sections to obtain the curve points on the front elevation, Fig. 9.16.

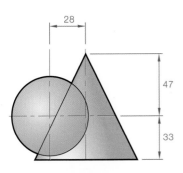

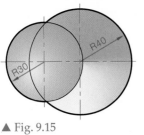

▲ Fig. 9.15

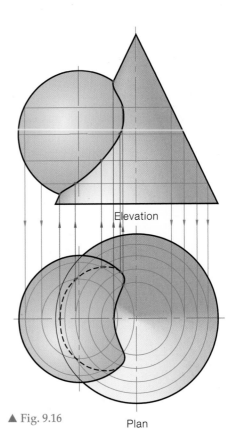

Elevation

▲ Fig. 9.16

Plan

See worksheet 9.2

Method 4: Vertical Sections

The method used here is exactly the same as that for horizontal sections. A series of vertical sections are taken at intervals through both solids and the line of intersection is built up, Figures 9.17 and 9.18.

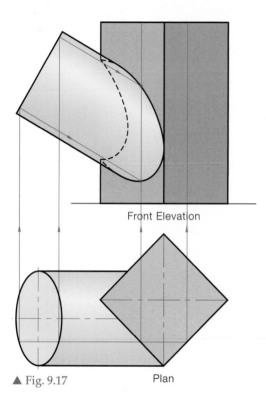

Front Elevation

Plan

▲ Fig. 9.17

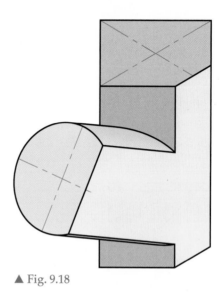

▲ Fig. 9.18

(1) Set up the plan and elevation.

(2) Vertical sections will produce intersecting straight lines as shown in Fig. 9.20. Ensure that one of the vertical sections taken is through the centre of the cylinder. The points found using this section, points r and s, are the transition points for the line of intersection from front to back.

Given the plan and incomplete elevation of a cylinder and a square prism intersecting. Draw the given views and find the line of interpenetration, Fig. 9.19.

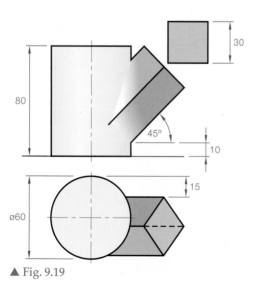

▲ Fig. 9.19

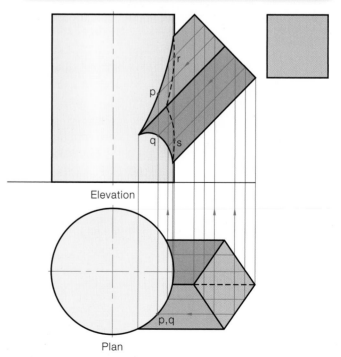

Elevation

Plan

▲ Fig. 9.20

Given the plan and incomplete elevation of a sphere intersecting a triangular prism. Draw the given plan and complete the elevation, Fig. 9.21.

(1) This problem could be solved by using horizontal or vertical cutting planes.

(2) It is advisable to take the cutting planes equidistant each side of the sphere centre line as this will reduce the number of sectional circles needed in elevation.

(3) One of these sectional circles forms part of the interpenetration line to the back of the two solids, Fig. 9.22.

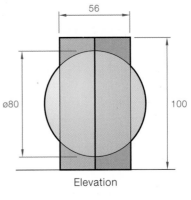

Elevation

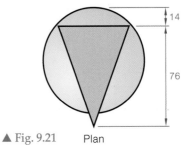

▲ Fig. 9.21   Plan

See worksheet 9.3

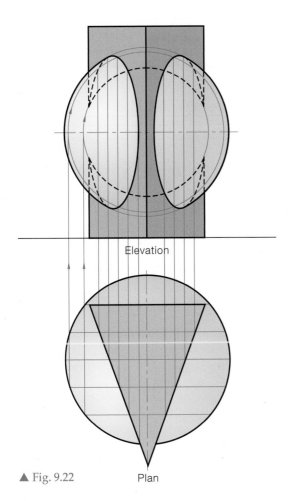

Elevation

▲ Fig. 9.22   Plan

Development and Interpenetration

Given the plan and incomplete elevation of two intersecting cylinders. Find the line of interpenetration and draw a surface development of the curved surfaces, Fig. 9.23.

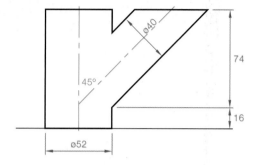

Plan ▲ Fig. 9.23

Development

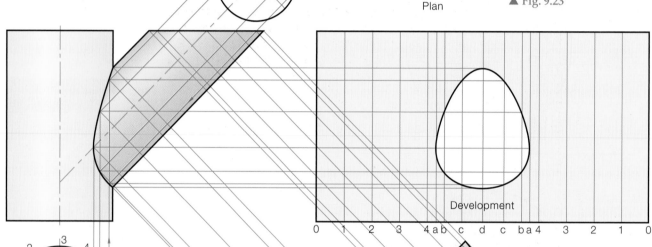

0 1 2 3 4 a b c d c b a 4 3 2 1 0

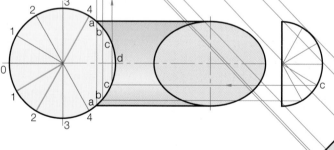

▲ Fig. 9.24

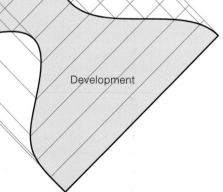

Development

(1) Vertical sections are used to find the line of interpenetration.

(2) A section of the inclined cylinder is drawn on the extended axis in plan and elevation. This section is divided into parts as shown.

(3) The vertical sections are drawn through these division lines giving the line of interpenetration as shown.

(4) The developments are projected from the elevation because the elevation shows true lengths of all elements on the cylinders, Fig. 9.24.

See worksheet 9.4

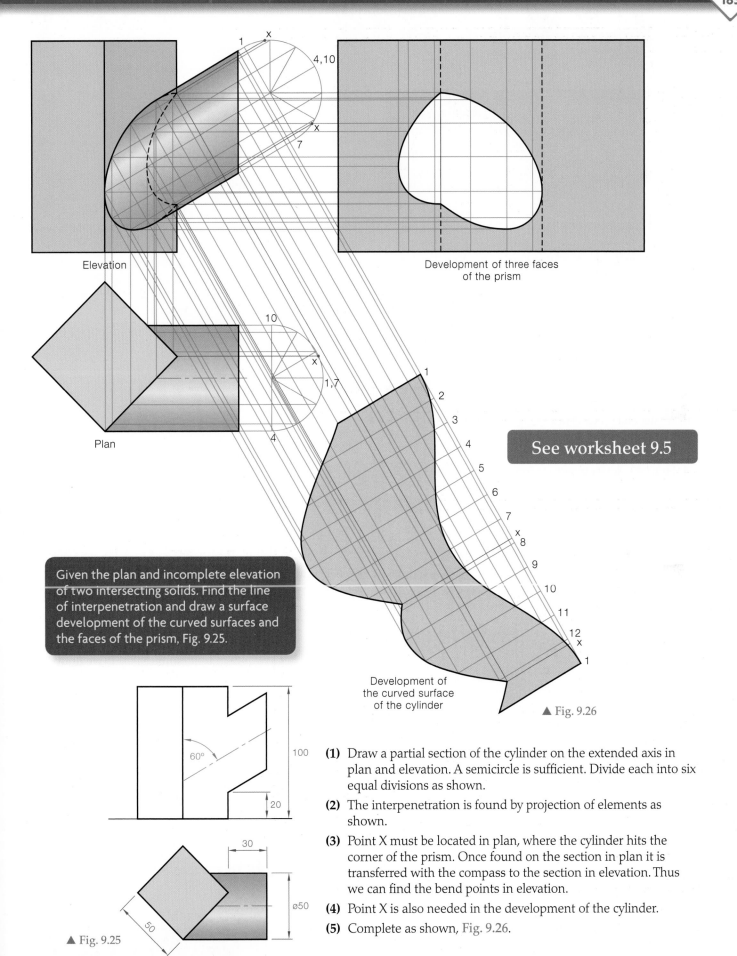

Elevation

Development of three faces
of the prism

Plan

See worksheet 9.5

Given the plan and incomplete elevation
of two intersecting solids. Find the line
of interpenetration and draw a surface
development of the curved surfaces and
the faces of the prism, Fig. 9.25.

Development of
the curved surface
of the cylinder

▲ Fig. 9.26

▲ Fig. 9.25

(1) Draw a partial section of the cylinder on the extended axis in plan and elevation. A semicircle is sufficient. Divide each into six equal divisions as shown.

(2) The interpenetration is found by projection of elements as shown.

(3) Point X must be located in plan, where the cylinder hits the corner of the prism. Once found on the section in plan it is transferred with the compass to the section in elevation. Thus we can find the bend points in elevation.

(4) Point X is also needed in the development of the cylinder.

(5) Complete as shown, Fig. 9.26.

Use of Auxiliary Plans

Fig. 9.27 shows the projections of a square-based prism of 50 mm side. This solid is being intersected by an equilateral triangular-based prism of 50 mm side. Draw the projections of the solids showing all lines of interpenetration

(1) Draw the square prism in plan and elevation.

(2) Details for the lowest line of the inclined triangular prism are given. Draw this line in elevation. Extend this line to the right and construct the equilateral section as given.

(3) Index the corners and project back to elevation.

(4) Project the corners of the section triangle perpendicularly to the prism axis thus finding d_1 and d_2.

(5) Details of one of the triangular prism edges is given in plan. This edge must be edge 1. Step distances d_1 and d_2 in plan to find the other two edges.

(6) An auxiliary plan is drawn, viewing down along the triangular prism's axis. This auxiliary shows which faces are intersected and finds bend points p, q, r and s.

(7) From the auxiliary, corner 2 penetrates surface ABCD and AABB.

AABB is seen as an edge view in plan and the penetration point is seen in plan and projected to elevation.

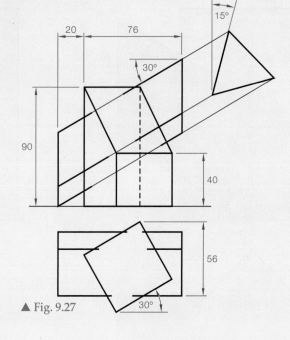

▲ Fig. 9.27

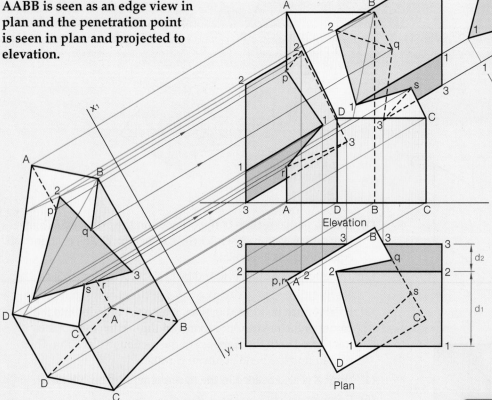

▲ Fig. 9.28

HIGHER LEVEL

(8) To find point 2 on surface ABCD we draw a line from one of the corners through 2, e.g. from B through 2 to hit edge AD. Find this line in elevation. Point 2 is on this new line in elevation and on line 2,2 so therefore is pinpointed at these lines' intersection point. Similar construction for point 1 on surface ABCD, Fig. 9.28.

See worksheet 9.6

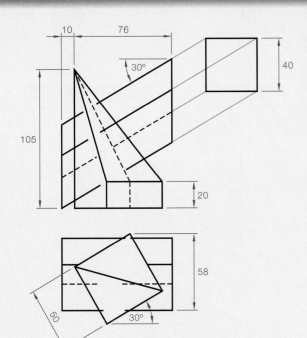

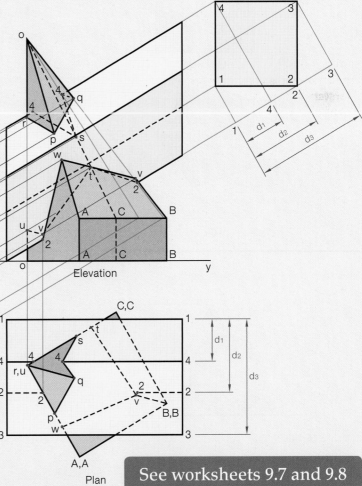

Fig. 9.29 shows the incomplete projections of an oblique pyramid with a 50 mm square base. This solid is penetrated by a square-based prism of 40 mm side. Draw the projections of the solid.

(1) Draw the oblique pyramid in plan and elevation.

(2) Draw the lowest line of the penetrating square prism as given. Extend this line and draw the square section as shown.

(3) Index the corners and project them back to the elevation.

(4) Find distances d_1, d_2 and d_3 from the sectional view by projecting the corners of the section perpendicular to the prism axis.

(5) One of the prism edges is given in plan. This must be edge 3, because edge 1 is appearing as a dotted line in elevation and is therefore at the back.

(6) Using distances d_1, d_2 and d_3, locate the other edges of the prism in plan.

(7) Draw the auxiliary plan.

(8) The auxiliary shows all bend points. Index these and project them back to elevation and plan.

(9) Edges 1 and 3 do not make contact with the pyramid.

(10) Edge 2 hits the vertical surface 0,0,AA. This surface is an edge view in plan and therefore shows the penetration point clearly.

(11) Edge 2 also makes contact with edge OBC. Draw a line from 0 through 2 to hit the edge BC. Find this line in elevation. Edge 2 makes contact with the surface where this line crosses line 2,2.

(12) Similar construction for edge 4.

(13) Join up the points. The order in which they are joined is found from the auxiliary, Fig. 9.30.

▲ Fig. 9.29

Sequence of
joining points
p,q,4,s,4,r,p
w,2,v,t,u,2,w

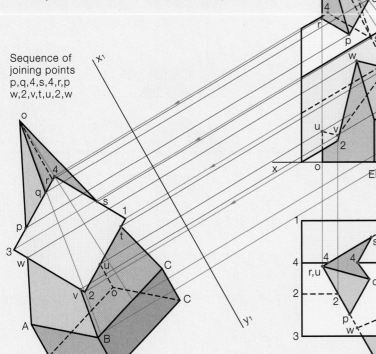

▲ Fig. 9.30   Auxiliary Plan

See worksheets 9.7 and 9.8

Activities

Find the line of intersection between the following solids. In each case draw a front elevation, end elevation and plan of the solids.

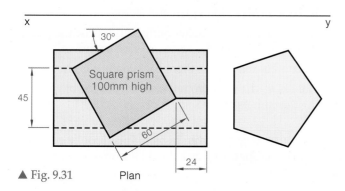

▲ Fig. 9.31   Plan

Q1.   Fig. 9.31

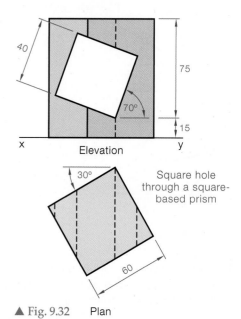

Q2.   Fig. 9.32

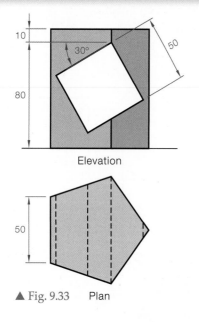

▲ Fig. 9.33   Plan

Q3.   Fig. 9.33

Q4.   Fig. 9.34

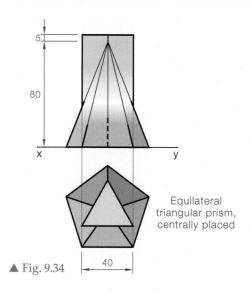

▲ Fig. 9.34

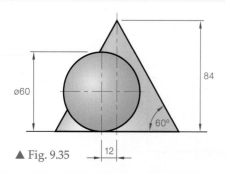

▲ Fig. 9.35

Q5.   Fig. 9.35

Solve the following questions using vertical sections. In each case draw a front elevation, end elevation and plan showing all lines of intersection.

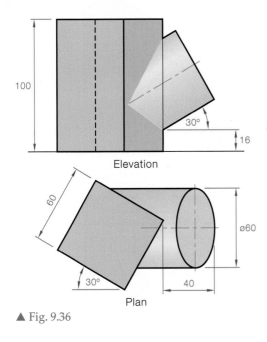

▲ Fig. 9.36

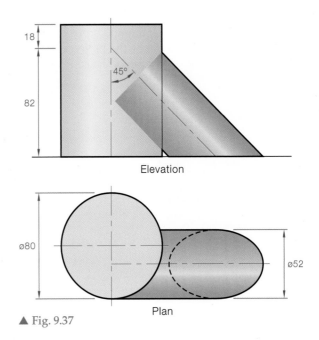

▲ Fig. 9.37

Q6. Fig. 9.36

Q7. Fig. 9.37

Determine the line of intersection between the solids A and B. Develop the surfaces of solid A.

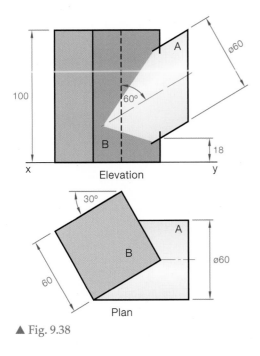

▲ Fig. 9.38

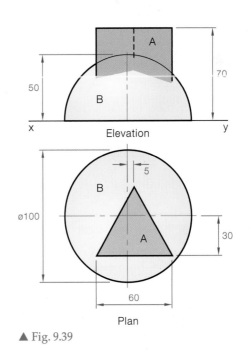

▲ Fig. 9.39

Q8. Fig. 9.38

Q9. Fig. 9.39

Q10. Fig. 9.40 shows the incomplete plan and elevation of a truncated equilateral triangular prism of 100 mm side resting on the horizontal plane. This solid is penetrated by a 60 mm side equilateral triangular prism which is inclined at 30° to the HP. Draw the projections of the solids showing all interpenetration lines.

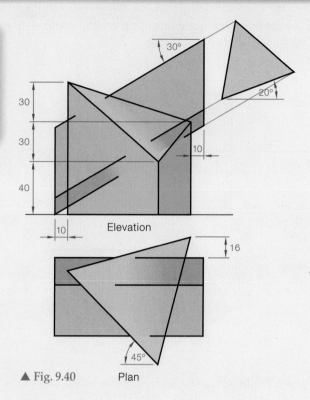

Elevation

Plan

▲ Fig. 9.40

10 Developments and Envelopments

Syllabus Outline

Areas to be studied:
- Surface development and envelopment of right solids.
- *Surface development and envelopment of oblique solids.*

Learning Outcomes

Students should be able to:

Higher and Ordinary levels
- Develop and envelop of right regular solids, their composites and frustra.
- Determine and project true distance lines between specified points on the surfaces of solids.

Higher Level only
- Develop and envelop the surfaces of oblique prisms and pyramids.

 Developments

The development of a surface is that surface laid out on a plane. The faces or surfaces of an object are unfolded onto a single plane. Fold lines are indicated by dashed lines.

A large number of industries rely on developments; for example, cardboard cartons are used for packaging and marketing manufactured goods. These cartons are usually made from a single sheet of cardboard. Sheet metalworkers continuously use developments, as does the clothes industry.

In a development all lines are true lengths and all surfaces are true shapes.

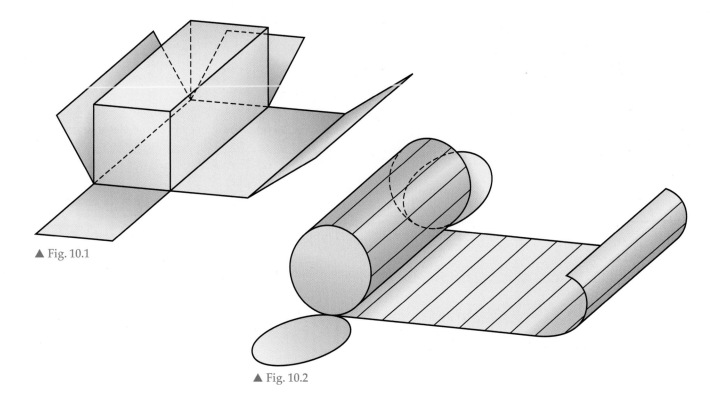

▲ Fig. 10.1

▲ Fig. 10.2

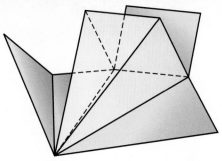

▲ Fig. 10.3

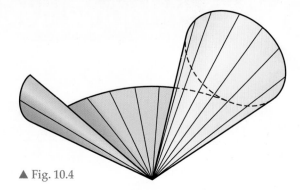

▲ Fig. 10.4

Given the plan and elevation of a rectangular prism. To draw the complete surface development. Fig. 10.5.

(1) Project lines from the elevation to obtain the heights of the sides.

(2) Step-off the lengths of the sides with a compass taking distances from the plan, 2–3, 3–4, 4–1, 1–2.

(3) Point 2 appears twice in this example because it forms the seam. The size of both top and bottom matches those of the plan. Dotted lines represent fold lines.

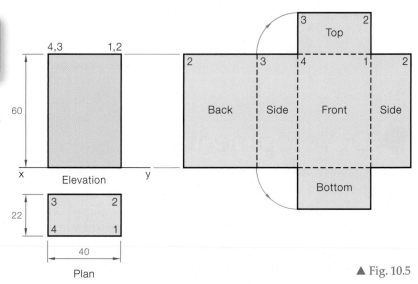

▲ Fig. 10.5

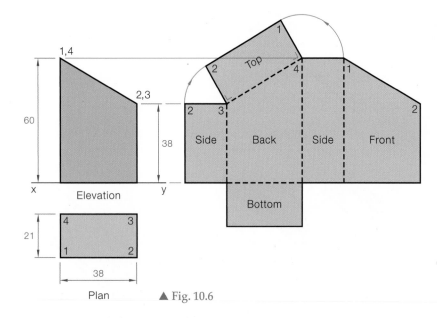

▲ Fig. 10.6

To draw the development of a truncated prism given its plan and elevation. Fig. 10.6.

(1) Project lines from the elevation to obtain the heights for the sides.

(2) The width of each face is taken from plan.

(3) The length of the top surface must match that of the sloped surface on the front or back.

(4) Project lines perpendicularly to one of these sloped lines and complete the top as shown in Fig. 10.6.

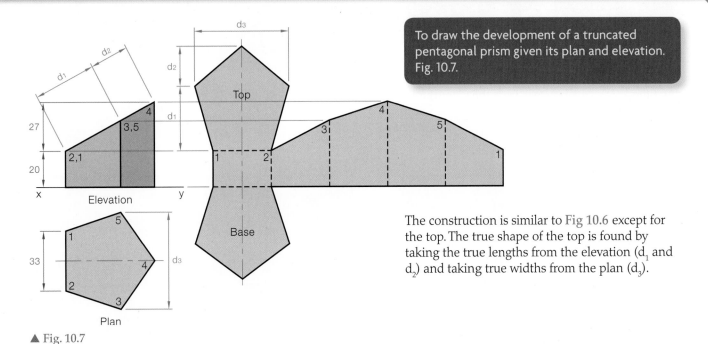

To draw the development of a truncated pentagonal prism given its plan and elevation. Fig. 10.7.

The construction is similar to **Fig 10.6** except for the top. The true shape of the top is found by taking the true lengths from the elevation (d_1 and d_2) and taking true widths from the plan (d_3).

▲ Fig. 10.7

Given the plan and elevation of a hexagonal prism which has been cut at the top as shown. Draw the complete surface development of the prism. Fig. 10.8.

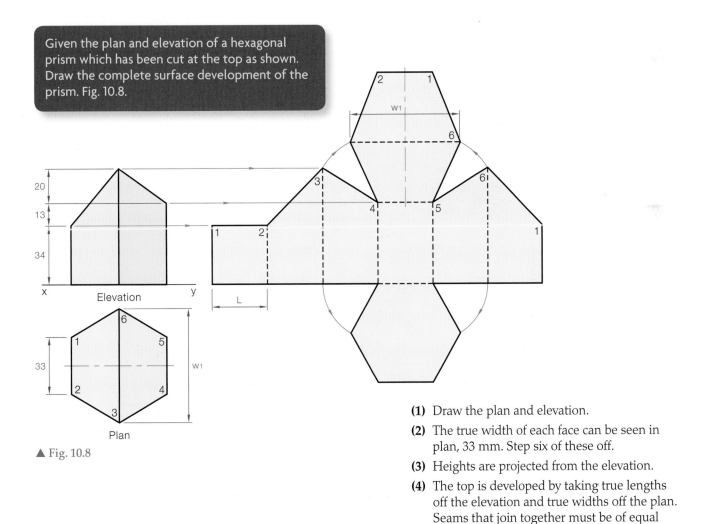

▲ Fig. 10.8

(1) Draw the plan and elevation.

(2) The true width of each face can be seen in plan, 33 mm. Step six of these off.

(3) Heights are projected from the elevation.

(4) The top is developed by taking true lengths off the elevation and true widths off the plan. Seams that join together must be of equal length.

(1) Divide the circumference of the circle in plan into twelve equal parts in the usual way.

(2) Project the top and bottom of the elevation across to obtain the height of the development.

(3) Step-off the twelve steps from the plan (the circumference).

(4) It does not matter where the top and bottom circles are added on the top and bottom lines.

To draw the development of a cylinder. Fig. 10.9.

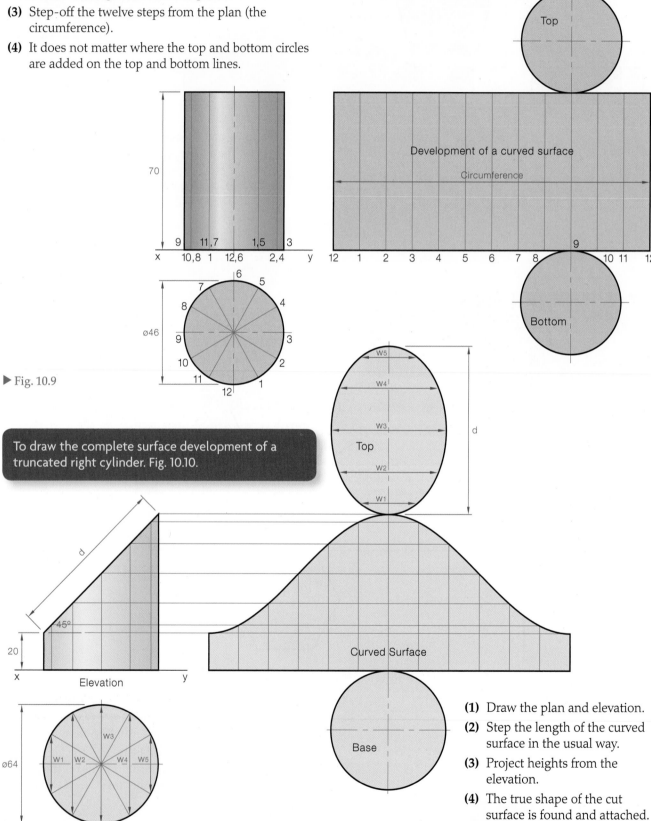

▶ Fig. 10.9

To draw the complete surface development of a truncated right cylinder. Fig. 10.10.

(1) Draw the plan and elevation.

(2) Step the length of the curved surface in the usual way.

(3) Project heights from the elevation.

(4) The true shape of the cut surface is found and attached.

▲ Fig. 10.10

See worksheet 10.1

This method, sometimes called the radial method, is applied to pyramids and cones. The true length of an edge is found. This length is used as the radius of an arc which is the basis of the construction.

(1) Find the true length of edge OC by rotating it parallel to the xy in plan and projecting it to elevation.

(2) Choose a point O for the development and scribe an arc having the true length of OC as radius.

(3) Step the length of the base around the arc four times.

(4) Complete the development by attaching the base.

> To draw the complete surface development of a square-based pyramid given its plan and elevation. Fig. 10.11.

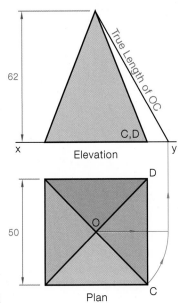

▲ Fig. 10.11

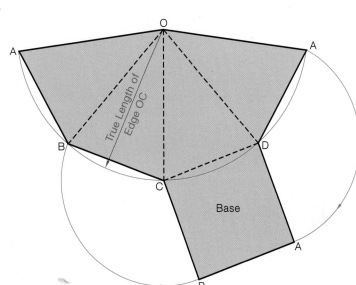

(1) The true length of an edge is first found as shown in plan and elevation.

(2) This true length is used to draw the arc for the development.

> To draw the surface development of a truncated hexagonal pyramid given its plan and elevation. Fig. 10.12.

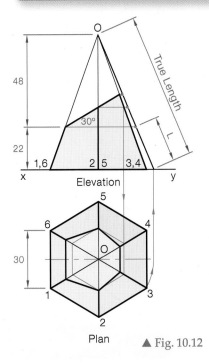

Plan ▲ Fig. 10.12

(3) Step the six hexagon sides around this arc and thus complete the development of the pyramid as if it has not been cut.

(4) The true length of each cut edge is now found and stepped-off on the development.

(5) The cut surface itself is found in the usual way.

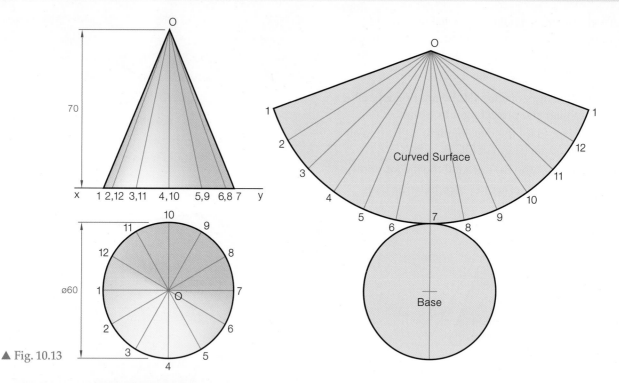

▲ Fig. 10.13

To develop the complete surface development of a cone given its plan and elevation. Fig. 10.13.

(1) A cone is developed in exactly the same way as a pyramid.

(2) The plan is divided into twelve equal pieces giving twelve generators.

(3) These generators are found in elevation.

(4) Generator O1 or O7 shows the true length of the generators and it is this true length that is used to draw the arc for the development.

(5) Complete the development in the usual way.

To draw the complete surface development of a truncated right cone given its plan and elevation. Fig. 10.14.

(1) Like the development of the truncated pyramid (Fig. 10.12) we develop the surface of the cone before it is cut.

(2) The true length of each cut generator must be found by projecting the cut end of each generator over to the side of the cone which will show it as a true length.

(3) Each length is then marked on the development and rotated about O onto the appropriate generator.

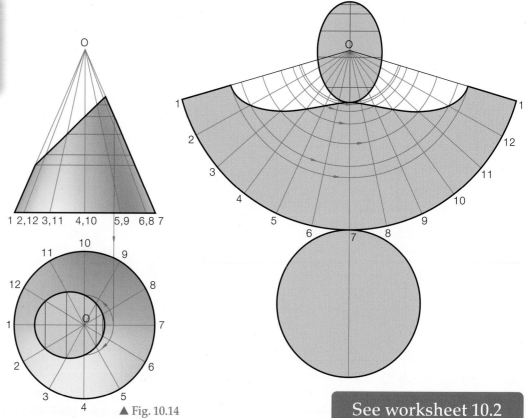

▲ Fig. 10.14

See worksheet 10.2

Worked examples

The elevation and plan of a right pentagonal prism of sides 30 mm with a ø25 mm hole passing centrally through it. Draw the given views and develop the surface of the prism. Fig. 10.15.

(1) Develop the prism as before.

(2) Divide the circle into 12 equal parts. Project these down to plan where the edge 3,4 is seen as a true length.

(3) w_1, w_2 and w_3 can then be transferred onto the development.

(4) Project across from the elevation to intersect perpendiculars from w_1, w_2 and w_3 and join to give a fair curve.

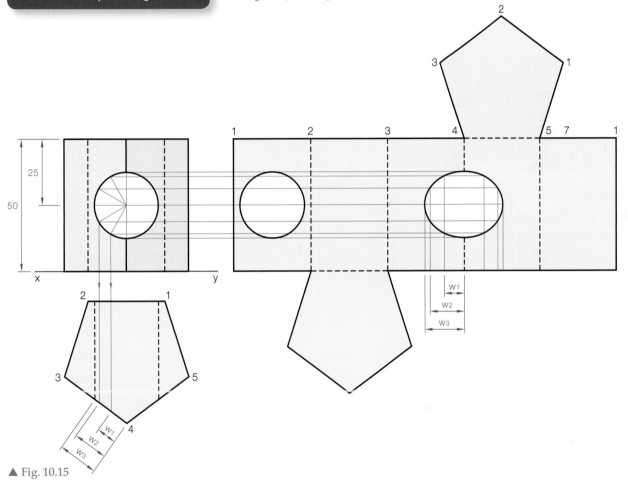

▲ Fig. 10.15

The drawing shows a right hexagonal prism with a square hole. Draw the development of the pyramid. Fig. 10.16.

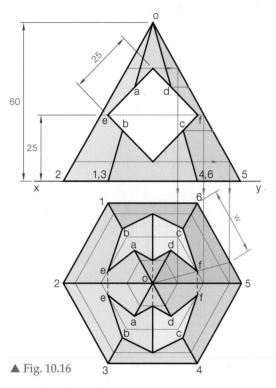

(1) The square hole in plan is found by taking horizontal sections. Each horizontal section gives a hexagon in plan on which a vertex is located. The points a and b can be projected directly onto edge 1,o and 3,o. Similarly c and d are projected to edge 6,o and 4,o.

(2) Develop the surface of the pyramid. All points are brought across to edge 5,o on the elevation to find true distances.

(3) These true distances are swung around on the development and the points are located as shown. The development of the base is not shown.

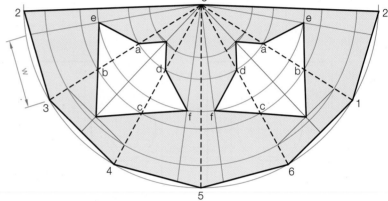

▲ Fig. 10.16

Activities

Q1 to Q3

Figures 10.17 to 10.19 show pictorial views of solids. In each case draw a plan and elevation and a complete surface development.

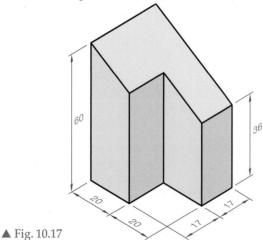

▲ Fig. 10.17

▲ Fig. 10.18

Q1. Fig. 10.17

Q2. Fig. 10.18

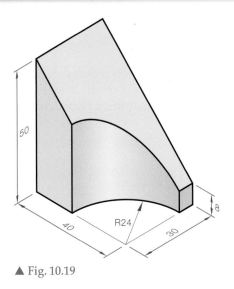

▲ Fig. 10.19

Q3. Fig. 10.19

Q4 to Q6

Figures 10.20 to 10.23 show the plans and elevations of prisms and cylinders. In each case draw the given views and draw the surface development of the solids.

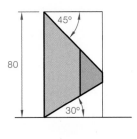

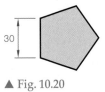

▲ Fig. 10.20

Q4. Fig. 10.20

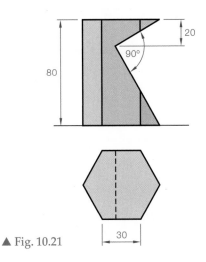

▲ Fig. 10.21

Q5. Fig. 10.21

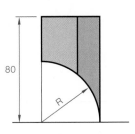

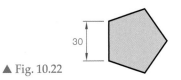

▲ Fig. 10.22

Q6. Fig. 10.22

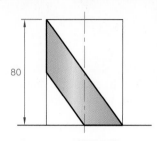

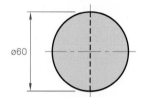

▲ Fig. 10.23

Q7.   Fig. 10.23

Q7 to Q12

Figures 10.24 to 10.28 show incomplete plans and elevations of pyramids and cones. In each case complete the given views and draw the surface development of the solid.

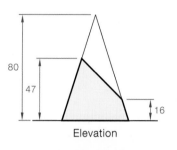

Elevation

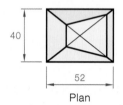

▲ Fig. 10.24   Plan

Q8.   Fig. 10.24

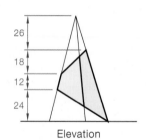

Elevation

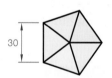

▲ Fig. 10.25   Incomplete Plan

Q9.   Fig. 10.25

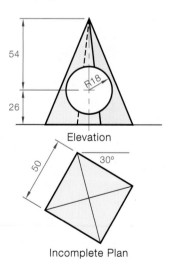

Elevation

▲ Fig. 10.26   Incomplete Plan

Q10.   Fig. 10.26

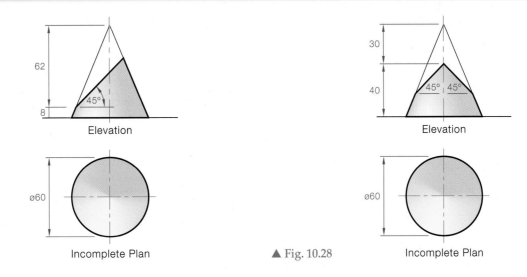

▲ Fig. 10.27   Incomplete Plan

▲ Fig. 10.28   Incomplete Plan

Q11. Fig. 10.27

Q12. Fig. 10.28

 # Envelopments

As explained earlier, the word 'development' describes the process of opening out the surfaces of an object. 'Envelopment' can be seen as the opposite; the closing over of a development to create the object.

Given the incomplete development of a solid. Draw the front elevation, end elevation and plan of the solid and complete the development. Fig. 10.29.

▲ Fig. 10.29

(1) The base must be rectangular as alternate sides are equal in length. The solid must also be a prism as the development is made up of parallel height lines.

(2) Decide which face of the development will form the front of the object. Draw the front elevation in line with the development.

(3) Project the plan which will equal the base in size.

(4) Draw the end elevation and complete the development, Fig. 10.30.

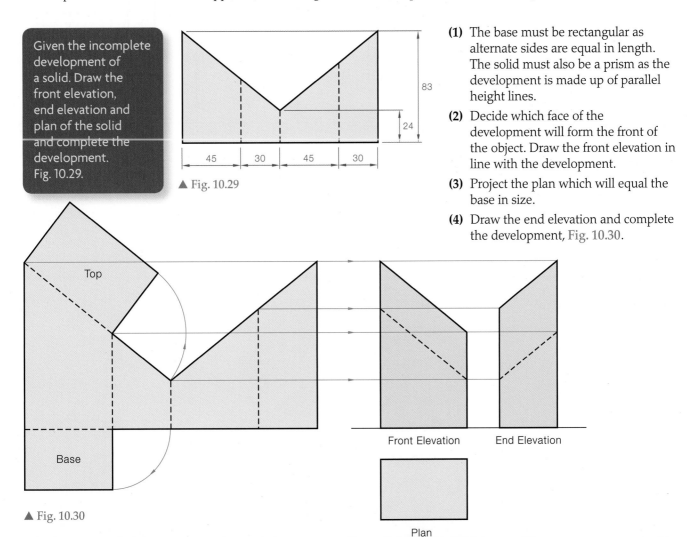

▲ Fig. 10.30

Given the partial development of a solid. Draw the front elevation, end elevation and plan of the solid. Complete the development. Fig. 10.31.

The solid must be a pentagonal prism because it has five equal sides and parallel height lines. The prism must also be truncated because of the variation in heights.

(1) Draw the development.

(2) Draw the base of the development and the plan.

(3) Project the elevation from the plan and from the development.

(4) Project the end view.

(5) Find the true shape of the cut surfaces by taking widths from the plan and lengths from the elevation, Fig. 10.32.

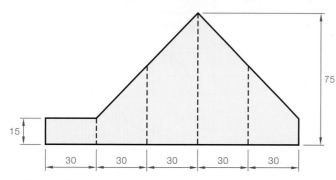

▲ Fig. 10.31

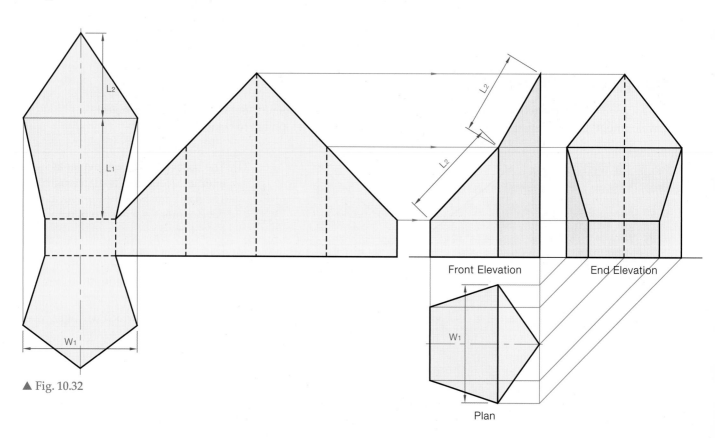

▲ Fig. 10.32

Front Elevation

End Elevation

Plan

The development of a cylinder which is open at both ends is shown. Draw a front elevation and plan of the object. Fig. 10.33.

(1) The length of the development must equal the circumference of the cylinder

$2\pi R = 180$ mm $\rightarrow$ R = 28.6 mm

(2) Draw the plan of the cylinder as a circle of radius 28.6 mm.

(3) Divide this circle into twelve.

(4) Divide the development into twelve equal parts.

(5) Complete by projection, Fig. 10.34.

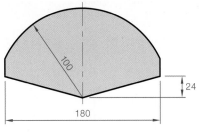

▲ Fig. 10.33

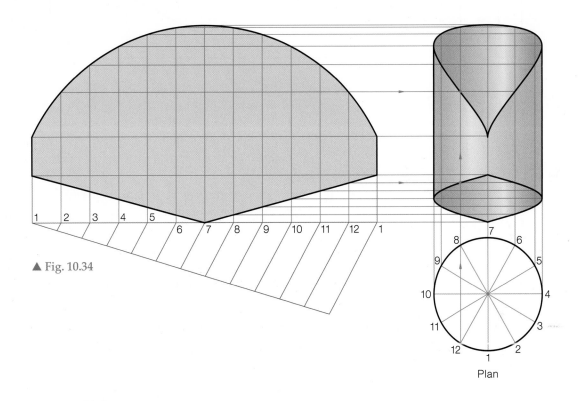

▲ Fig. 10.34

Plan

Partial Envelopments

A partial envelopment is when a label or sticker is wrapped around a solid. The label can be much more complicated in appearance when developed out than it would suggest when wrapped around the jar or bottle.

Given a label, draw it in position wrapped around a pentagonal prism. Fig. 10.35.

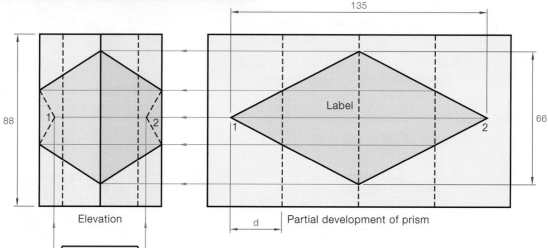

Elevation

Partial development of prism

▲ Fig. 10.35   Plan

(1) Draw the label and the prism.

(2) Draw a partial development of the prism over the label.

(3) All points may now be projected from the development onto the elevation.

(4) Points 1 and 2, the ends of the label, must first be found in the plan and then projected to the elevation.

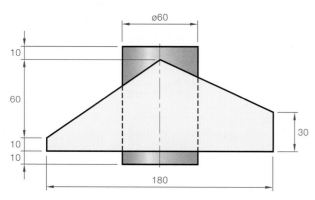

▲ Fig. 10.36

Given the projection of a cylinder and a label. Draw the elevation of the cylinder when the label is wrapped around it. Fig. 10.36.

(1) Draw the given view and draw the plan.

(2) Draw the stretched-out label in plan.

(3) Divide the plan into twelve equal parts.

(4) From the centre line of the label step-off the divisions to the left and right and index.

(5) Draw the generators in elevation.

(6) Project across the heights from the label to the generators in elevation.

(7) The ends of the label must be found in plan first and then in elevation, Fig. 10.37.

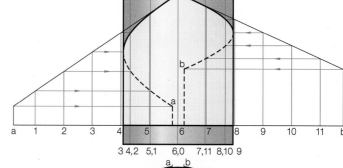

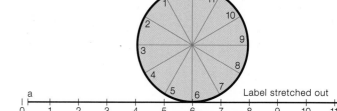

▲ Fig. 10.37

See worksheet 10.3

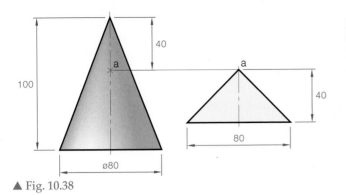

▲ Fig. 10.38

Given the projection of a cone and the development of a triangular label. Draw the elevation and plan of the cone when the label is wrapped around it. Fig. 10.38.

(1) Develop the surface of the cone and place the label in position.

(2) The label crosses the generators in the development. These generators are true lengths. Transfer the distances from the generators in the development to the side of the cone and project horizontally.

(3) The plan is projected from elevation, Fig. 10.39.

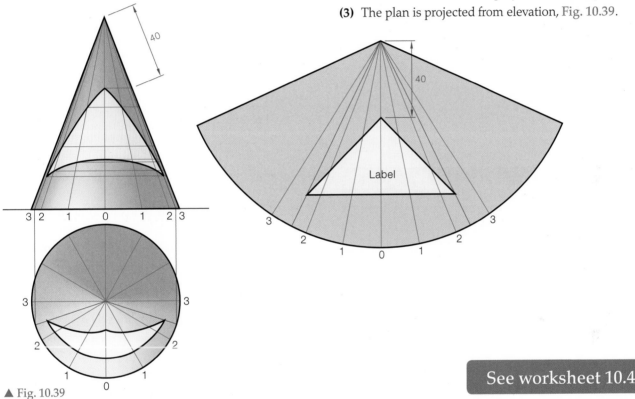

▲ Fig. 10.39

See worksheet 10.4

Shortest Distance

The shortest distance between two points on the same plane is a straight line. When the two points are on different surfaces of the same solid and we wish to find the shortest distance between them along the surface of the solid, we develop the surface of the solid and join the points with a straight line. This straight line can then be found on the projections of the solid.

Given the plan and elevation of a cylinder and two points p and q on its surface. Draw the projection of the shortest distance between these two points along the surface of the cylinder. Fig. 10.40.

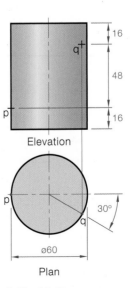

▲ Fig. 10.40

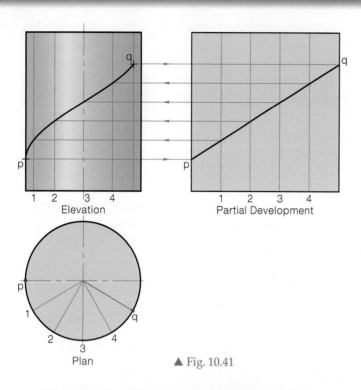

Elevation   Partial Development

p

1   2   3   4

Plan

▲ Fig. 10.41

(1) Develop the surface of the cylinder between p and q.

(2) Project p and q onto the development and join with a straight line.

(3) Project this line back to elevation. The line joining p and q in elevation forms part of a helical curve, Fig. 10.41.

The front elevation and plan of a solid are shown in Fig. 10.42. Also shown are two points p and q on the surface of the solid. Draw the path of the shortest distance between these two points along the surface of the solid.

(1) Draw the given plan and elevation and locate points p and q on its surface.

(2) Develop the surface of the solid and locate p and q on the development.

(3) Join p and q with a straight line on the development.

(4) Distances Oa, Ob, Oc and Od are true lengths on the development and are stepped down on generator Op in elevation because it too is a true length.

(5) The elevation and plan are finished by projection, Fig. 10.43.

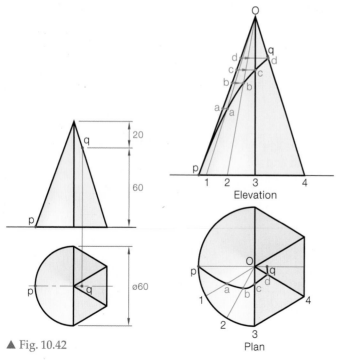

▲ Fig. 10.42

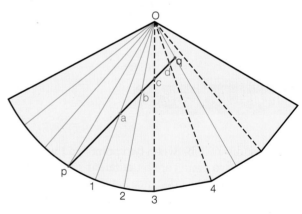

Elevation

Plan

▲ Fig. 10.43

Activities

Envelopments

Q1 to Q3

Figures 11.44 to 11.46 show the incomplete developments of prisms. Draw the front elevation, end elevation and plan of each solid and complete the development

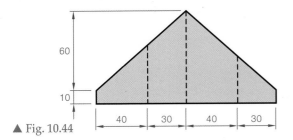

▲ Fig. 10.44

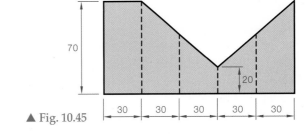

▲ Fig. 10.45

Q1. Fig. 10.44

Q2. Fig. 10.45

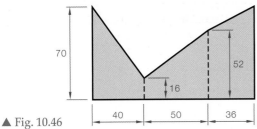

▲ Fig. 10.46

Q3. Fig. 10.46

Q4 to Q5

Figures 10.47 and 10.48 show the development of cylinders that are open at both ends. Draw a plan and elevation of the cylinder.

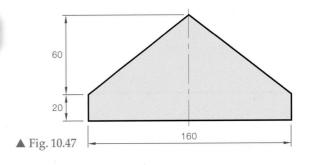

▲ Fig. 10.47

Q4. Fig. 10.47

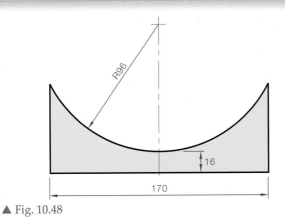

▲ Fig. 10.48

Q5. Fig. 10.48

Partial envelopments

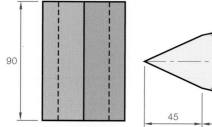

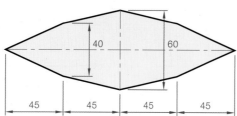

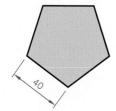

Q6. Given the plan and elevation of a pentagonal prism and the development of a label. Draw the plan and elevation of the prism when the label is wrapped around it, Fig. 10.49.

▲ Fig. 10.49

Q7. Given the plan and elevation of a cylinder and the development of a label. Draw the elevation of the cylinder when the label is wrapped around it, Fig. 10.50.

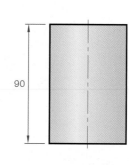

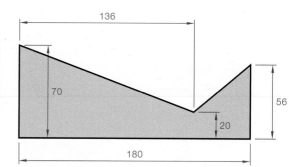

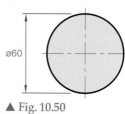

▲ Fig. 10.50

Development of Oblique Solids

To draw the development of an oblique pentagonal prism. Fig. 10.51.

(1) Draw the plan and elevation.

(2) The edge lines are true length lines in elevation. Project the ends of these lines perpendicularly.

(3) Choose a starting point for edge 1.

(4) With radius 36 mm, the length of the side of the pentagon in plan, swing an arc from point 1 to locate edge 2 and so on.

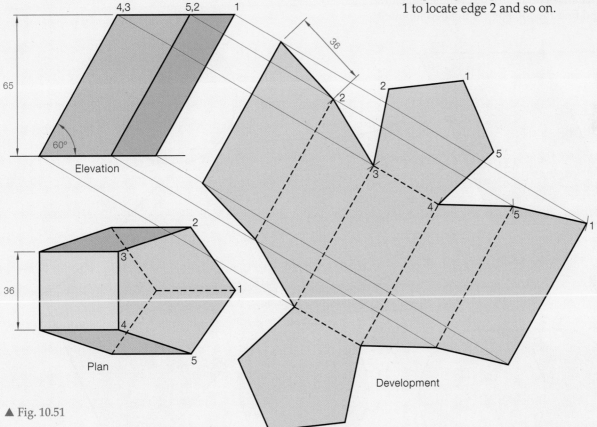

▲ Fig. 10.51

To draw the surface development of an oblique cylinder. Fig. 10.52.

(1) Draw the plan and elevation.

(2) Divide the base circle into 12 equal parts.

(3) Project these points to elevation and draw in the generators.

(4) Project out the ends of each generator at right angles.

(5) Choose a starting point 1.

(6) Take distance d from plan and swing an arc from point 1 to locate point 2.

(7) Continue in this manner to locate the other points.

(8) Construct lines parallel to the cylinder edge from each point and find the top edge of the development.

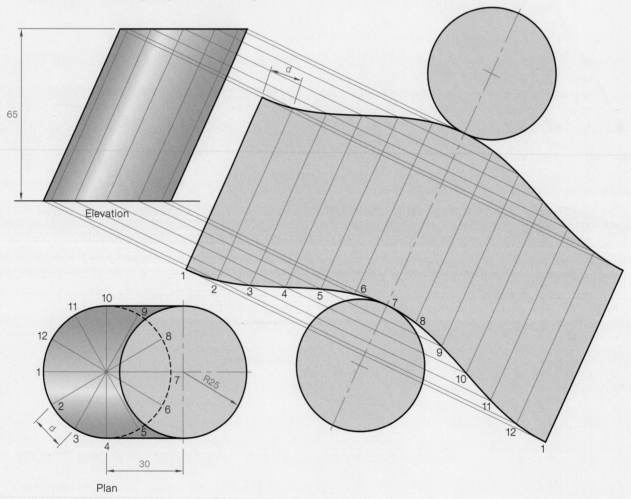

▲ Fig. 10.52

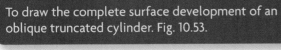

To draw the complete surface development of an oblique truncated cylinder. Fig. 10.53.

The construction is as Fig. 10.52.

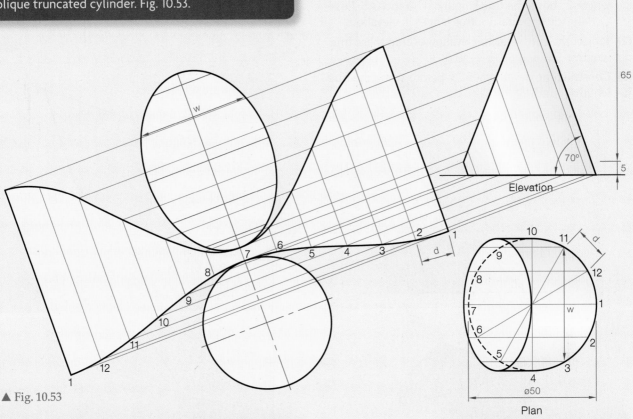

▲ Fig. 10.53

To develop the surface of a square-based oblique pyramid. Fig. 10.54.

See worksheet 10.5

All edges in a development are true lengths. We must therefore first find the true length of the edges of the pyramid.

(1) Rotate edge O,2 about O until it is horizontal in plan.

(2) Project to elevation, giving true length 1 which is the true length of O,2 and O,3.

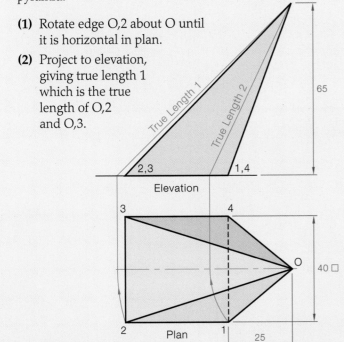

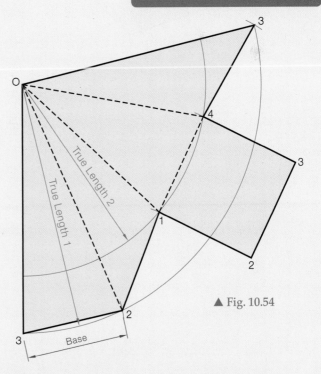

▲ Fig. 10.54

(3) Find the true length of O,1 in a similar way.

(4) Choose a starting point O for the development.

(5) Swing two arcs using the true lengths.

(6) Step the length of the base around and add the base.

HIGHER LEVEL

(1) Find the true length of all the edges. True length 1 shows the true length of edges O,3 and O,4. True length 2 shows the true length of O,2 and O,5. Edge O,1 already appears as a true length in elevation.

(2) Project the cut points in elevation over to these true lengths.

(3) Construct the development as before, using the true lengths found.

To develop the surface of a pentagonal-based oblique pyramid. Fig. 10.55.

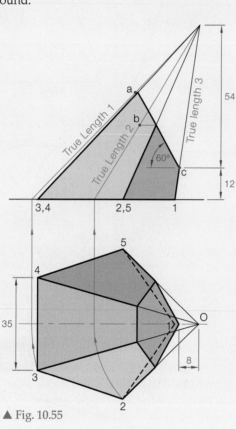

▲ Fig. 10.55

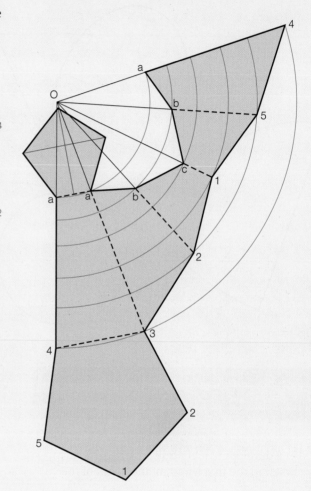

(1) Divide the base circle and draw in the radians.

(2) Find the true length of each radian. Radian O,1 and O,7 are already shown as true lengths.

(3) Start the development with radian O,1.

(4) With the true length of O,2 as radius and O as centre, scribe an arc. With chord length 1,2 as radius and point 1 as centre, scribe an arc to cut the previous arc giving point 2 on the development.

(5) Continue in this way to complete the development.

To develop the surface of an oblique cone. Fig. 10.56.

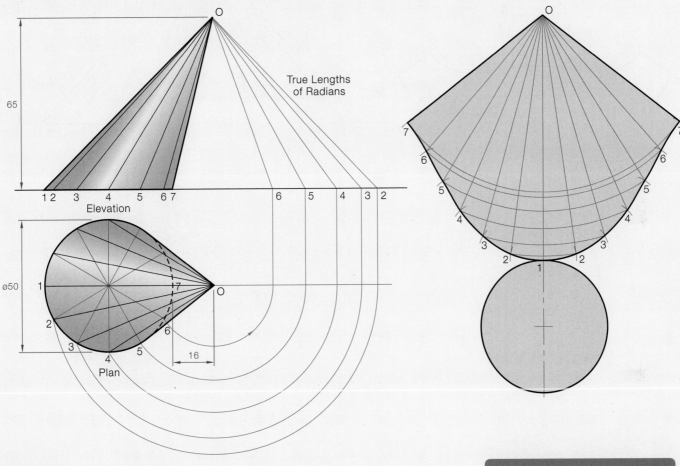

True Lengths of Radians

65

ø50

16

Elevation

Plan

▲ Fig. 10.56

See worksheet 10.6

To develop a truncated oblique cone. Fig. 10.57.

(1) Develop the full cone as above.

(2) Transfer the cut length of each radian in elevation across to its true length.

(3) Transfer these true lengths to the development.

(4) Add the true shape of the cut surface.

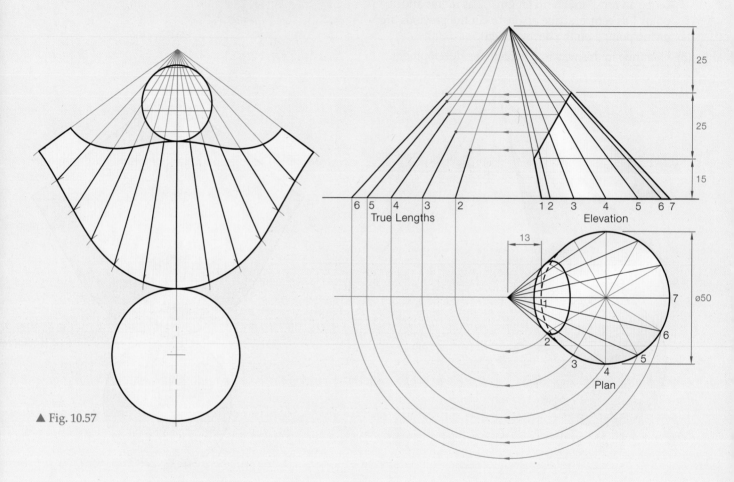

True Lengths

Elevation

Plan

25

25

15

13

ø50

▲ Fig. 10.57

Given the plan and elevation of an oblique pentagonal prism and the development of a label that is to be wrapped around it. Draw the plan and elevation of the prism when the label is in position. Axis ab on the label is to be placed centrally on edge 1,1 of the prism. Fig. 10.58.

(1) Develop the surface of the prism as described earlier.

(2) Place the label in position on the development.

(3) All corners and fold points are easily projected back, except for corners c and d.

(4) On the development, point d is projected parallel to the edges onto 2,3 which is a true length. Point q is found on 2,3 in plan which is also a true length.

(5) Draw line qq in plan and elevation. It will run parallel to the edges. Corner d is now projected onto line qq.

(6) Similar construction for point c.

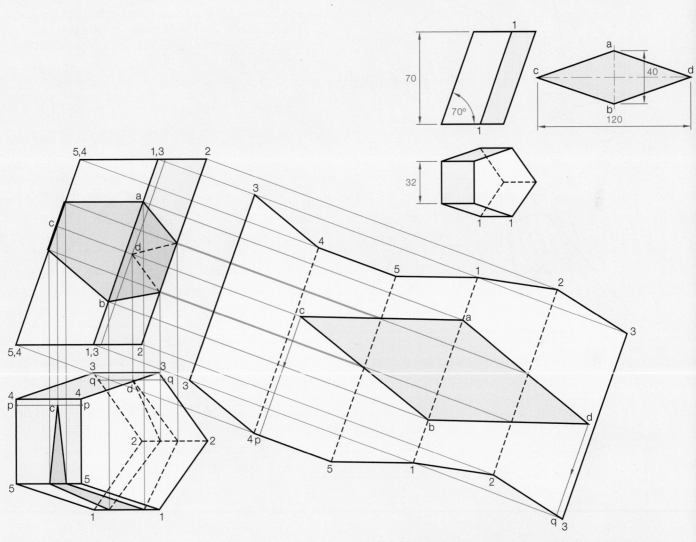

▲ Fig. 10.58

See worksheets 10.7 and 10.8

Given the plan and elevation of a pentagonal-based oblique pyramid and the development of a label. Draw the plan and elevation of the pyramid when the label is wrapped around it. Point p on the label is to be placed on point p on the pyramid, and the axis pq is to be placed on the edge O,1. Fig. 10.59.

(1) Develop the surface of the pyramid as explained earlier. Place the label in position on the development.

(2) Transfer distances Op and Oq onto the true length of O,1 and project across to the elevation.

(3) Points on O,5 on the development are transferred to the true length of O,5 and projected over to the elevation.

(4) Points on O,2 in the development can be transferred directly to O,2 in the elevation as this is a true length.

(5) Points r and s are found by drawing a line from the apex in the development through them, to lines 4,5 and 2,3 respectively. These lines can be found in plan. Find their true lengths. Transfer Or and Os from the development to the true lengths, then project to elevation and plan, Fig. 10.60.

▲ Fig. 10.59

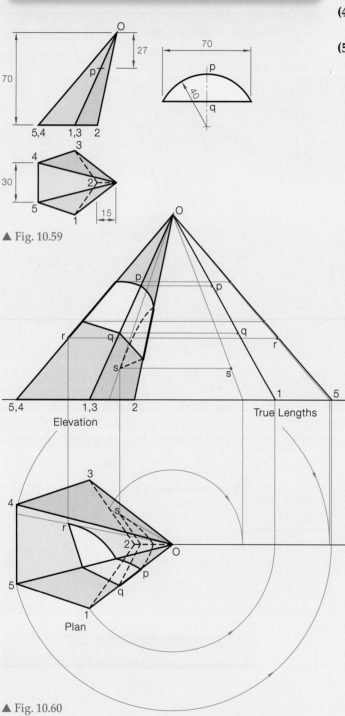

▲ Fig. 10.60

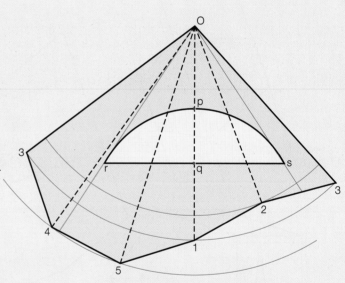

Development with label in position

Activities

Q1 to Q2

Develop the surfaces of the oblique prisms shown in Figures 10.61 and 10.62.

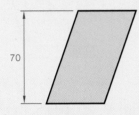

70

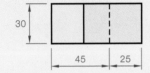

30

45   25

▲ Fig. 10.61

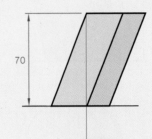

70

30

▲ Fig. 10.62

Q1. Fig. 10.61

Q2. Fig. 10.62

Q3 to Q4

Develop the surfaces of the oblique pyramids shown in Figures 10.63 and 10.64.

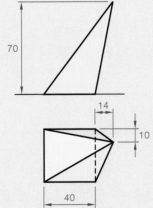

70

14

10

40

▲ Fig. 10.63

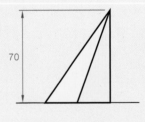

70

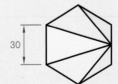

30

▲ Fig. 10.64

Q3. Fig. 10.63

Q4. Fig. 10.64

HIGHER LEVEL

Q5 and Q6

Develop the surface of the oblique cylinders and oblique cones shown in Figures 10.65 and 10.66.

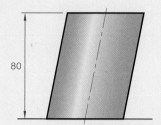

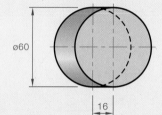

▲ Fig. 10.65

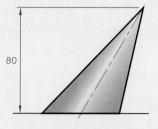

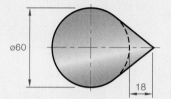

▲ Fig. 10.66

PART 2

COMMUNICATION
OF DESIGN

11 Communication of Design

Syllabus Outline

Areas to be studied:

- Drawing conventions, symbols and standards.
- Presentation methods and layout.
- Design drawings and associated processes.
- Pictorial and orthographic working and assembly drawings.
- Balloon extraction detailing.
- Exploded pictorial views.
- Dimensioning and notations.
- Schematic diagrams.

Learning Outcomes

Students should be able to:

Higher and Ordinary levels

- Use graphical symbols as necessary to convey a design to the correct drawing standards.
- Create drawings and layouts that make appropriate use of materials available to achieve a pleasing presentation.
- Use graphics, both orthographic and three-dimensional, to explain design function and methods of assembly.
- Produce drawings which can be used by a third party to produce an artefact.
- Use standards pertaining to dimensioning and notation.
- Design schematic diagrams to explain familiar operations.

Higher Level only

- *Present drawing work in a manner that will make maximum use of materials available to achieve a pleasing layout.*
- *Design schematic diagrams to explain familiar operations.*

Once a design has been formulated, has passed through the rough sketches phase and is ready for production/manufacture, it is important that a full set of working drawings is produced. These drawings must convey the information necessary for the complete manufacture of all parts and for the assembly of these parts. Furthermore, these drawings must be presented in a format that is readily understandable to anybody who is required to read them. In this chapter we will examine what is required to produce such working drawings.

 # Presentation

Paper Size

The size of the piece of paper used will obviously have an effect on the amount of information that can be placed on each sheet and on the selection of scale used for the drawings. Fig. 11.1 shows the relationship between the sheet sizes of the A series of drawing sheets. An A1 sheet is half the size of an A0 sheet, an A2 sheet is half the size of an A1 sheet and so on. Most of our drawings are done on A2 or A3 sized paper.

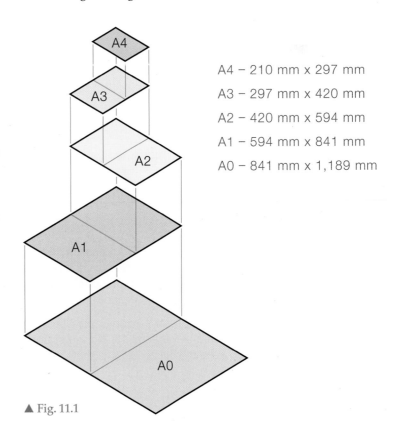

A4 – 210 mm x 297 mm

A3 – 297 mm x 420 mm

A2 – 420 mm x 594 mm

A1 – 594 mm x 841 mm

A0 – 841 mm x 1,189 mm

▲ Fig. 11.1

Sheet Layout: Title Block

Regardless of what is to be drawn on the sheet and what sheet size is to be used, it is important that the work is laid out neatly and that the sheet has a margin and a title block. The margin is usually 10 mm in from the edge of the page and the title block is placed in the lower right corner, Fig. 11.2. This title block can take many forms but it would usually have spaces to accommodate the following:

- The name of the part(s) being represented.

- The scale being used.

- The date the drawing was produced.

- The name of the draughtsperson.

- The drawing number.

- A parts list.

- A revision list.

Not all sheets will require so many subcategories and the title block can be adapted to suit. The lettering must be clear and neat. The size of the lettering will vary. Items of greater importance are indicated by larger lettering and/or heavier lettering, Fig. 11.3.

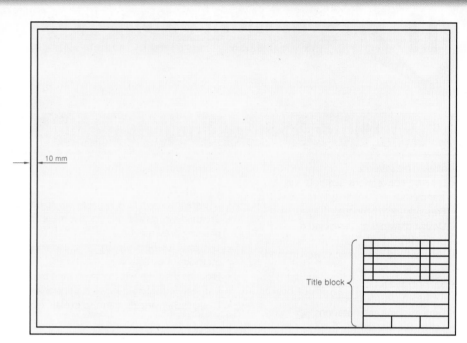

▲ Fig. 11.2

4	Table	1	Steel
3	Clamp shoe	1	Steel
2	Housing	1	Steel
1	Table	1	Aluminium
No.	Name	Reqd	Material

Checked by:

Drawn by: JOHN SMITH

GRINDER VICE ASSEMBLY

| Scale 1:2 | 20-6-05 | Sh. 2 of 3 |

▲ Fig. 11.3

Parts List

A parts list is an itemised list of the parts represented on the drawing. These are generally in order of size or importance with the larger/more important listed first. The number given to each part on the list will also be written down beside the drawing of that part. Additional information for each part, like the number required and the material to be used in manufacture, will also be placed in the parts list.

Standard parts such as bolts, screws, springs, pins, bearings, washers, keys, etc., often will not be drawn in the detail drawings but will be listed in the parts list. No extra information is given by drawing these standard parts in a detail drawing but they do need to be listed so that they can be identified from the assembly drawing.

Lines and Linework

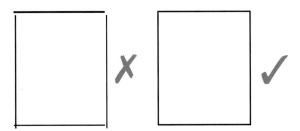

 X   ✓

Good presentation requires good linework. There should be consistency on the sheet with regard to line tone and line thickness. A number of different line types may be used in the drawing but there must be no variation within each line type. Figures 11.4 and 11.5 show inconsistent and consistent linework and Fig. 11.6 shows line types.

▲ Fig. 11.4   ▲ Fig. 11.5

Line	Name	Use
————	**Thick continuous**	Visible outlines and edges.
————	**Thin continuous**	Dimensions and leader lines. Hatching. Fictitious outlines and edges. Outlines of revolved parts.
– – – –	**Short dashes**	Hidden outlines and edges.
—— – — – —	**Chain**	Centre lines. Extreme positions of moveable parts.
—— – — – —	**Chain line thickened at ends and at changes in direction**	Cutting/section planes.
∼∼∼∼∼	**Wavy continuous**	Limits of partial views or sections.

▲ Fig. 11.6

 Symbols

It is common practice to use a number of symbols in drawings both to save space on the drawing and to save time.

First- and Third-angle Projection Symbol

The more usual system of projection in Europe is first-angle projection. The projection symbol should be shown on all drawings, Figures 11.7 and 11.8.

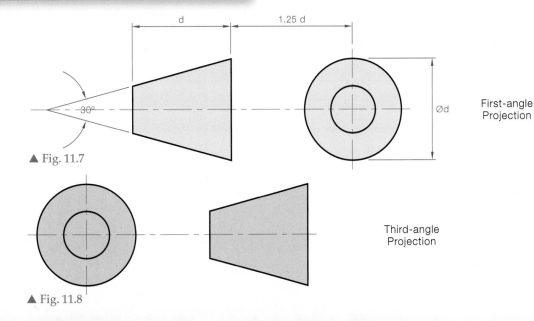

d   1.25 d

30°

Ød

First-angle Projection

▲ Fig. 11.7

Third-angle Projection

▲ Fig. 11.8

Abbreviations

Abbreviation	Meaning	Sketch Explanation
A/C	Across corners	
A/F	Across flats	
HEX HD	Hexagon head	
ASSY	Assembly	
CRS	Centres	
℄ or CL	Centre line	
CHAM	Chamfer	
CH HD	Cheese head screw	
CSK	Countersunk	
C'BORE	Counterbore	
CYL	Cylinder or cylindrical	
DIA	Diameter – in a note	
Ø	Diameter – in a dimension	
R	Radius – in a dimension	
DRG	Drawing	
FIG	Figure	
LH	Left hand	
LG	Long	
MATL	Material	
NO.	Number	

Abbreviation	Meaning	Sketch Explanation
PCD	Pitch circle diameter	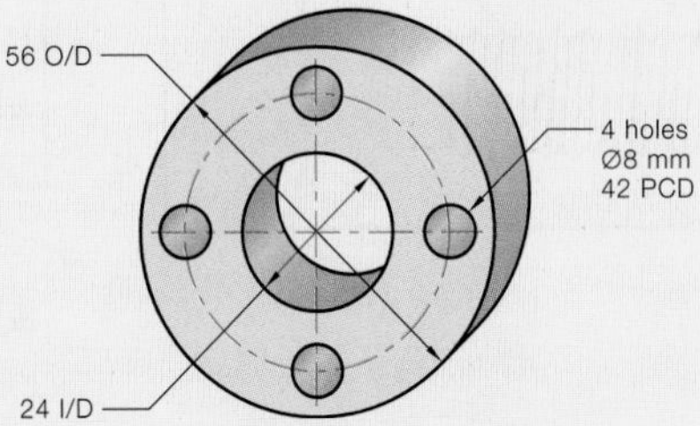
I/D	Inside diameter	
O/D	Outside diameter	56 O/D 4 holes Ø8 mm 42 PCD 24 I/D
RH	Right hand	
RD HD	Round head	
SPEC	Specification	
SQ	Square – in a note	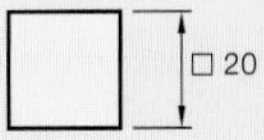 □ 20
□	Square – in a dimension	
STD	Standard	
U'CUT	Undercut	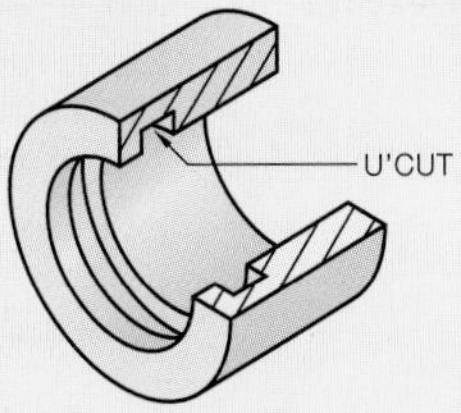 U'CUT
MM	Millimetres	
NTS	Not to scale	
RPM	Revolutions per minute	

▲ Fig. 11.9

Conventional Representation of Common Features

There are many components commonly used in designs such as bolts, bearings and springs which in themselves are complicated to draw in full. Many of these may be represented in a simplified form to save drawing time.

A line parallel to the side represents the screw thread. The distance between the two lines approximately equals the depth of thread. A broken circle in the end view represents the thread, Fig. 11.11.

External thread

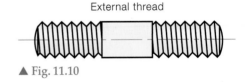

▲ Fig. 11.10

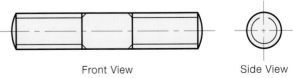

Front View   Side View

▲ Fig. 11.11

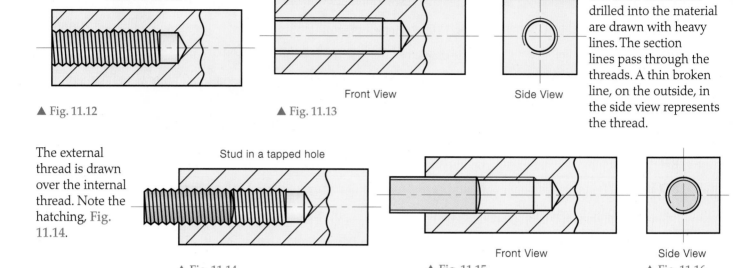

Internal thread

▲ Fig. 11.12

Front View   Side View

▲ Fig. 11.13

The sides of the hole drilled into the material are drawn with heavy lines. The section lines pass through the threads. A thin broken line, on the outside, in the side view represents the thread.

The external thread is drawn over the internal thread. Note the hatching, Fig. 11.14.

Stud in a tapped hole

▲ Fig. 11.14

Front View

▲ Fig. 11.15

Side View

▲ Fig. 11.16

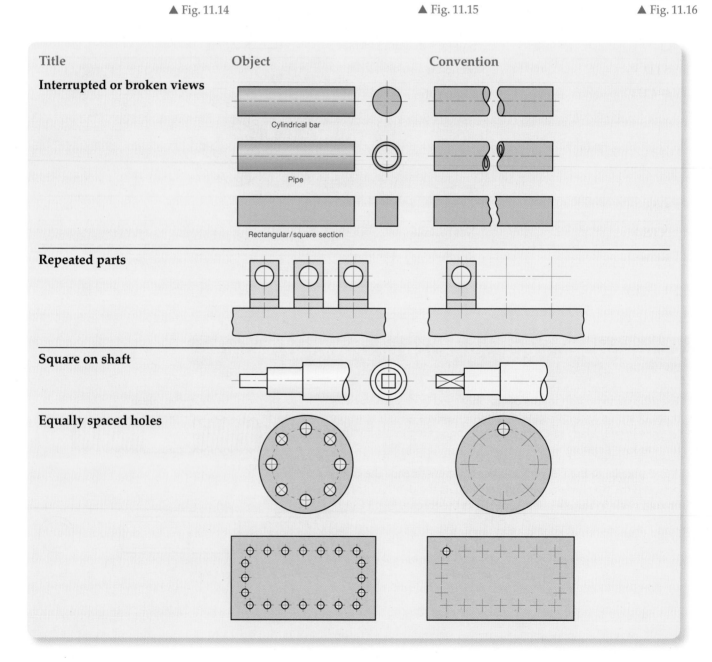

Title	Object	Convention
Interrupted or broken views	Cylindrical bar	
	Pipe	
	Rectangular/square section	
Repeated parts		
Square on shaft		
Equally spaced holes		

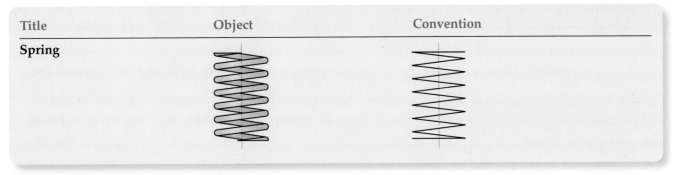

Title	Object	Convention
Spring		

▲ Fig. 11.17

Materials

Wood that has been planed/machined		Rough wood	
Plywood		Particle board, e.g. chipboard, MDF, etc	
Blockboard		Glass, clear perspex	
Concrete		Stone	
Sheet metal		Thick metal	

▲ Fig. 11.18

Learning to Dimension

When applying dimensions to a drawing or a number of drawings on a sheet, it is important to follow certain rules. These rules help to keep the presentation both neat and regular in appearance. They also ensure that the drawing and the dimensions remain clear and legible. These rules will be outlined below.

Dimension Lines

A dimension line is a thin, dark, solid line which usually ends with arrowheads. The dimension line indicates the direction and extent of a measurement. It should be placed at least 10 mm from the object outline. The spacing of dimension lines should be uniform throughout the drawing.

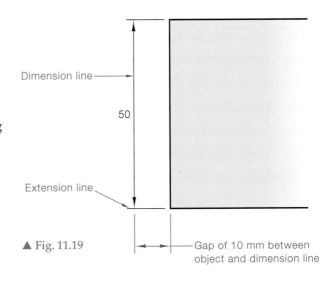

Dimension line

50

Extension line

▲ Fig. 11.19

Gap of 10 mm between object and dimension line

Extension Lines

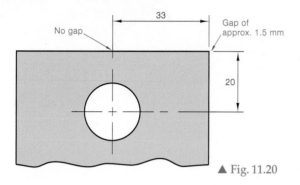

▲ Fig. 11.20

An extension line is a thin, dark, solid line which 'extends' from the point on the object to which the dimension refers. A gap of approximately 1.5 mm should be left between the start of the extension line and this point. If a centre line is being used as an extension line there should be no gap left at the object outline, Fig. 11.20.

The arrowheads indicate the extent of dimensions. They are drawn freehand and should have a length to width ratio of 3:1. They must be uniform in size and style throughout the drawing. Long slender arrowheads look best, Fig. 11.21.

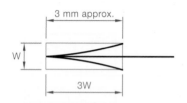
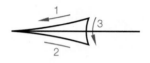

▲ Fig. 11.21

Placement of Dimension Lines and Extension Lines

There are several basic rules that should be followed:

(1) Shorter dimensions are placed nearest to the object, Fig. 11.22.

(2) Dimension lines should not cross extension lines, Fig. 11.23.

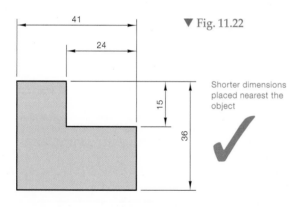

▼ Fig. 11.22

Shorter dimensions placed nearest the object

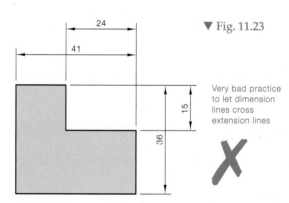

▼ Fig. 11.23

Very bad practice to let dimension lines cross extension lines

(3) Extension lines should not be shortened as shown in Fig. 11.24.

(4) Where possible, dimensions should be outside the object, should not cross and should not form a continuation of a line/outline of the drawing, Fig. 11.25.

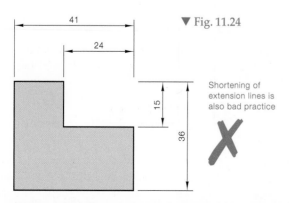

▼ Fig. 11.24

Shortening of extension lines is also bad practice

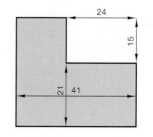

▼ Fig. 11.25

Placing dimensions inside the object and lining up with the object outline gives a very unclear result

(5) Where possible the dimensions should be grouped together at the same level, Fig. 11.26. They should not vary in height, Fig. 11.27.

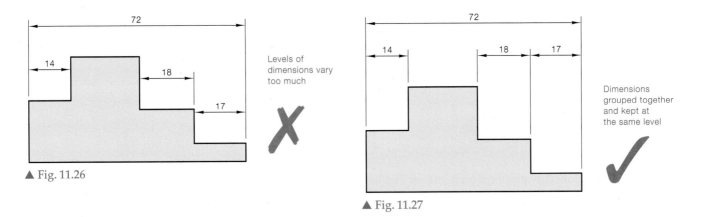

▲ Fig. 11.26

Levels of dimensions vary too much

Dimensions grouped together and kept at the same level

▲ Fig. 11.27

Dimensioning Arcs and Fillets

Arcs and circles are dimensioned in the view in which they are seen as true shapes. The centre of the arc/circle should be indicated with a small cross except where they are either very small or unimportant. The dimension should be radial and where practical should be placed inside the curve, Fig. 11.28.

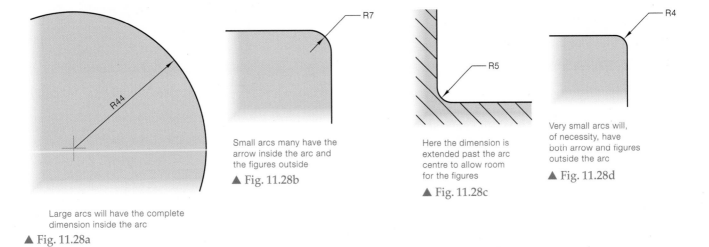

Small arcs many have the arrow inside the arc and the figures outside

▲ Fig. 11.28b

Here the dimension is extended past the arc centre to allow room for the figures

▲ Fig. 11.28c

Very small arcs will, of necessity, have both arrow and figures outside the arc

▲ Fig. 11.28d

Large arcs will have the complete dimension inside the arc

▲ Fig. 11.28a

For fillet radii, which may often be of similar size throughout a drawing, it is neater to print a note rather than dimension each fillet. A note such as: 'All fillet radii are 6 mm unless otherwise specified' is ideal.

Leaders

A leader is a thin, continuous line which starts from a note or dimension and ends with an arrow or a dot. If an arrow is used it should touch the part to which the note/dimension refers, e.g. the outline of the object or the side of a hole. If a dot is used it should be within the object.

The leader should be inclined and should extend from the beginning or end of a note. A leader referring to an arc or circle should be radial so that if extended it would pass through the centre, Fig. 11.29.

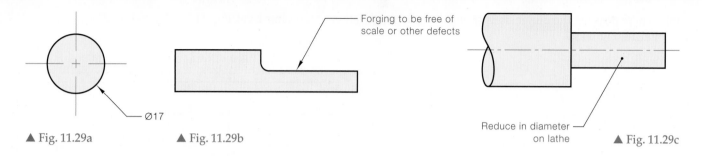

Forging to be free of
scale or other defects

Ø17

▲ Fig. 11.29a   ▲ Fig. 11.29b

Reduce in diameter
on lathe   ▲ Fig. 11.29c

Chamfers and Angles

Angles are dimensioned by means of coordinates, Fig. 11.30, or by degrees, Fig. 11.31, or with a combination of both, Fig. 11.32. Using coordinates is a more accurate method than using degrees.

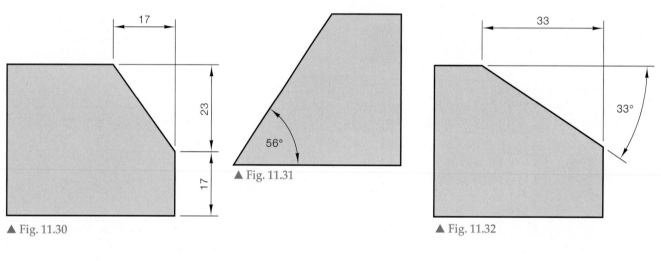

17

23

17

▲ Fig. 11.30

56°

▲ Fig. 11.31

33

33°

▲ Fig. 11.32

Chamfers can often be very small and difficult to dimension in the normal way. If they are all the same size a note will be sufficient, otherwise they can be dimensioned as shown in Fig. 11.33.

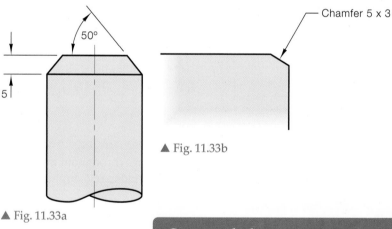

50°

5

▲ Fig. 11.33a

Chamfer 5 x 3

▲ Fig. 11.33b

See worksheets 11.1 and 11.2

 # Working Drawings

Full working drawings may include assembly drawings, detailed drawings, isometric views, exploded views or whatever views are necessary to clearly communicate the project. The drawings should be neatly and clearly presented and use recognised drawing standards. We will look at the preparation of a set of working drawings for a simple object like an adjustable set-square.

Detailed Drawings

Note the use of **detail extraction** to allow the clear dimensioning of the holes for a quite complicated area. The detail is drawn at three times full scale and is removed out of the way so that it does not interfere with the other dimensioning.

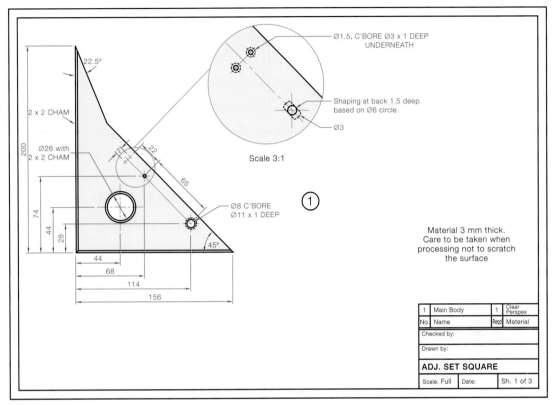

▲ Fig. 11.34

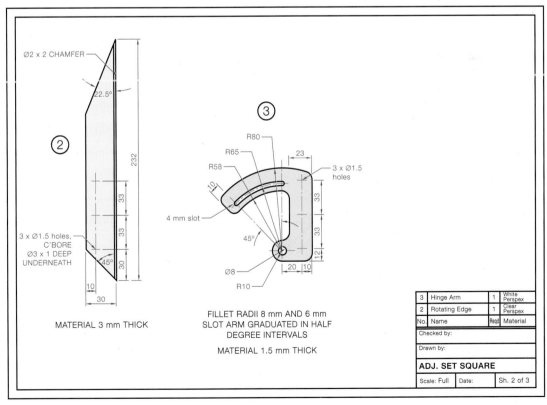

▲ Fig. 11.35

Note: In sheet 3 the components are drawn using an enlarging scale to give clear information on small parts.

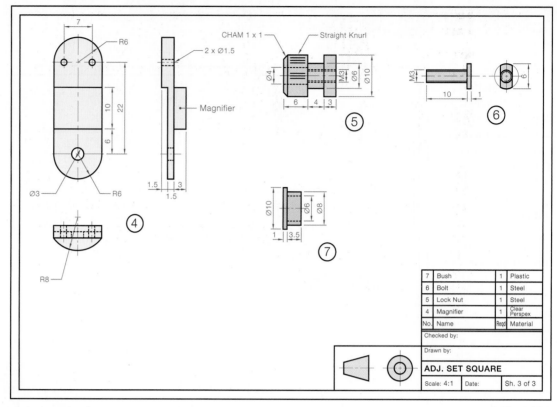

▲ Fig. 11.36

Assembly Drawing

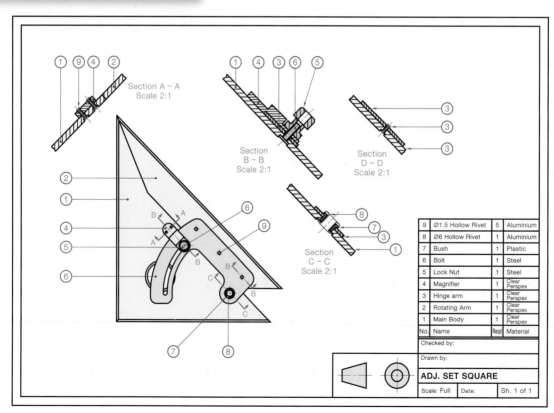

▲ Fig. 11.37

The assembly drawing shows all the parts shown in the detail drawings put together in the correct order. Standard parts used in the assembly usually are not drawn and are listed in the parts list. In this example the hollow rivets have not been shown in the detail drawings but are shown in the assembly drawing. The parts in the assembly are balloon-referenced. These numbers refer to the parts list on the sheet or to corresponding numbers on the detail drawings. There is no necessity to dimension the parts in the assembly drawing as the sizes of each individual piece are given in detail in the detail drawings. Overall heights, widths and thicknesses of the assembled object are sometimes given.

The use of a sectional view often clarifies an assembly detail. In this example they are drawn to twice full size. When balloon-referencing, care should be taken to place the circles in line and not to draw the leaders crossing each other.

Exploded Pictorial Views

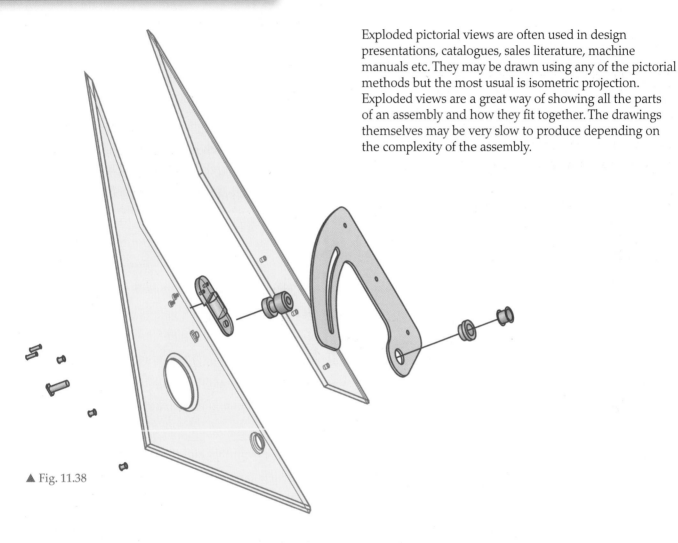

Exploded pictorial views are often used in design presentations, catalogues, sales literature, machine manuals etc. They may be drawn using any of the pictorial methods but the most usual is isometric projection. Exploded views are a great way of showing all the parts of an assembly and how they fit together. The drawings themselves may be very slow to produce depending on the complexity of the assembly.

▲ Fig. 11.38

Activities

Q1. Using notes and/or diagrams explain the following abbreviations:

- CSK
- O/D
- U'CUT
- RPM
- STD
- NTS
- Ø
- CHAM

- CYL
- A/C
- CRS
- SQ
- DRG
- I/D
- RH
- HEX HD

- RD HD
- SPEC
- C'BORE
- MATL
- CH HD
- A/F
- PCD

Q2. Draw in conventional form, having M15 screw thread.

(i) A double-ended stud with a 20 mm non-threaded area in the centre.

(ii) A blind hole.

(iii) A stud in a tapped hole.

Q3. Make neat diagrams showing the following drawing conventions:

(i)
- a break in a circular pipe,
- a break in a solid cylindrical bar,
- a break in a solid rectangular bar.

(ii) A square end on a cylindrical shaft.

(iii) A coil spring.

Syllabus Outline

Areas to be studied:
- Materials for freehand drawing.
- Observation techniques.
- Representing shape, form, texture and material.
- Light and shade.
- Design sketching.
- Freehand detailing.
- The use of colour.

Learning Outcomes

Students should be able to:

Higher and Ordinary levels
- Use freehand sketching as a tool to explain an idea.
- Produce freehand drawings.
- Select the most suitable medium for producing and rendering sketches and drawings.
- Identify the surfaces of an object relative to each other in three-dimensional space.
- Use various methods of rendering and colouring to enhance a drawing.

Higher Level only
- *Analyse critically the texture and colour of a surface and choose suitable rendering media by which the surface can be accurately represented.*
- *Represent graphically the effects light and shade have on surface.*

Freehand sketching is the process of representing an object, a scene or an idea by making lines on a surface. This drawing is generally linear in nature but it may include other elements such as dots and brush strokes. Whatever form a drawing takes, it is the principal means by which we organise and express our visual thoughts and perceptions. It can be regarded as a form of artistic expression but also as a practical tool for formulating and working through design problems or graphics problems as presented in a subject like this one.

In design, the role of sketching expands to include recording what exists, working out ideas, as well as speculating and planning for the future. Throughout the design process we use drawing to guide the development of an idea from concept, to proposal, to constructed reality.

Materials for Freehand Drawing

Two of the most versatile media for sketching available to students are pencil and ink. Of the two, the pencil provides the best solution for quick sketches, sketching used to develop ideas, sketches of a non-permanent nature and sketches used to rough out an idea.

▲ Fig. 12.1

▲ Fig. 12.2

The use of ink can produce permanent and almost microscopically detailed drawings which can then be further improved using water colours, colouring pencils, etc. Ink as a medium, therefore, is usually reserved for the final presentation drawing.

There are many other drawing media which can be used for sketching purposes or to enhance sketches already produced in pencil or ink. These include felt-tipped markers, pastels, wax crayons, colouring pencils, charcoal, etc.

Throughout this chapter we will focus on building up skills with a pencil with the understanding that the skills learned are transferable to these other media.

Pencil Types

There are many different types of pencil to allow the drawing of lines of various weights and thicknesses. A pencil's grade is denoted by using the letters **H** and **B**, which refer to the pencil lead. H stands for hardness, while B stands for blackness. In general it is the softer pencils that are used for freehand sketching but of course any pencil may be used.

Dark lines		3B		Softer lead
		2B		
		B		
		HB		
		H		
		2H		
		3H		
Light lines		4H		Harder lead

▲ Fig. 12.3

Fine-line pencils and/or clutch pencils may also be useful. Because fine-line pencils hold leads of specific thickness, e.g. 0.3 mm, 0.5 mm, they do not need sharpening. The constant line thickness can, however, be restrictive, particularly when shading or applying tone and texture. Clutch pencils hold lengths of pencil lead which are available in a range of grades and as such can be sharpened and used in the same way as a pencil.

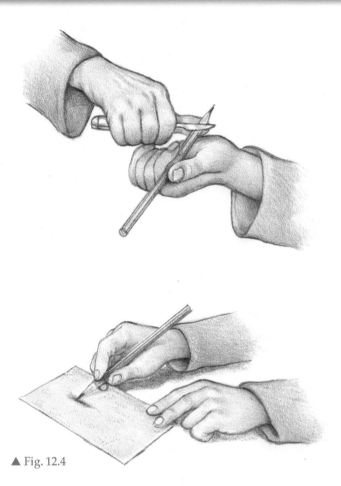

The tapered point produced by a pencil sharpener is perfectly satisfactory for most work. The lead point can be touched up using a sandpaper pad or a sheet of medium/smooth sandpaper. Another useful point type is the chisel point. Here the wood is usually whittled away with a sharp knife, taking care not to break the lead or reduce its size by too much, Fig. 12.4.

Then, holding the pencil in a normal drawing position, rub the point on some sandpaper until it is quite blunt. This point can now be used to make either a broad or a fine stroke, depending on how the pencil is held, Fig. 12.5.

▼ Fig. 12.5

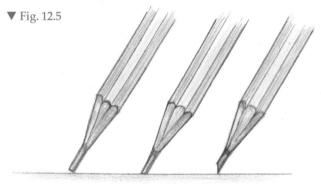

| Point may be used to give broad lines or fine lines. | Sandpaper to give chisel point. | Wood pared away. |

▲ Fig. 12.4

Holding the Pencil

How you position your hand depends on the drawing being done – whether it requires bold, sweeping strokes or more carefully executed lines. Most typically, the pencil is held as if for writing with the hand resting lightly on the table. For short lines and lines demanding considerable pressure you need little arm movement. Swing the hand at the wrist, or let the fingers alone perform the necessary motion, Fig. 12.6. For longer strokes the pencil is held back from the point. The entire forearm and hand are swung freely from the elbow and there is minimal wrist and finger movement, Fig. 12.7. For particularly unrestrained sketching hold the pencil at its unsharpened end. The pencil should be full length. Swinging the hand will produce rapid, bold lines, Fig. 12.8.

▲ Fig. 12.6

▲ Fig. 12.7

▲ Fig. 12.8

Sketching Practice

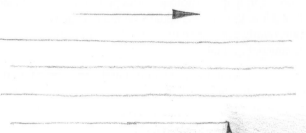

Horizontal Lines

Lock your wrist and fingers and use an arm movement to move the pencil. Your hand slides across the paper as you are sketching the lines.

Vertical Lines

Again an arm movement is used rather than a wrist or finger movement. It may prove easier to rotate the sheet by 90° and draw the lines as if they are horizontal.

▲ Fig. 12.9

Sketching with Short Overlapping Strokes

Rather than trying to draw long lines using one continuous stroke it can often be better to build up the line with short overlapping lines. Sketch a short line return to the middle of the first line and make a similar, second short line. Repeat this overlapping process until the line is as long as is needed.

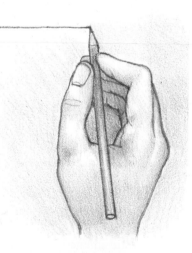

▲ Fig. 12.10

Squares and Rectangles

Continue to practise drawing horizontal, vertical and inclined lines and use these lines to build up squares and rectangles. These two-dimensional shapes will form the building blocks for many diagrams.

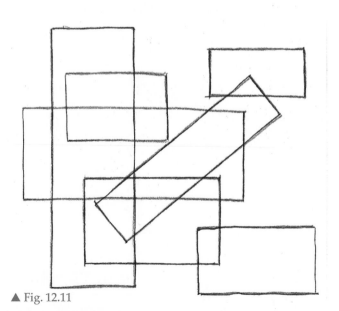

▲ Fig. 12.11

Circles

Before drawing a circle it is advisable to draw the square into which the circle is to fit. Divide the square into quarters. This gives the circle centre and four points on the circumference. When drawing the circle draw in one quarter at a time. Use the overlapping stroke technique and sketch lightly. Use your wrist as a pivot to help draw the curves. You will draw more naturally if your hand is inside the curve. When you are happy with the circle it can be darkened. The sheet can, of course, be rotated to any position to help you draw the curve.

For larger circles:

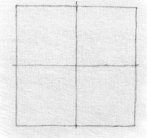

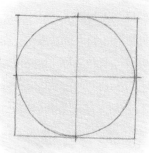

▲ Fig. 12.12

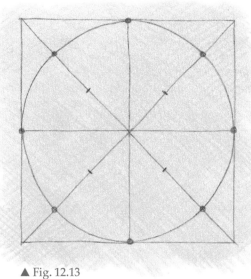

▲ Fig. 12.13

(1) Draw the square into which the circle is to fit.

(2) Sketch in the diagonals and lines to divide the square into quarters.

(3) If each half-diagonal is now divided into three equal parts (Fig. 12.13) then more points can be found on the circumference.

(4) Draw in the curve as before.

Ellipses

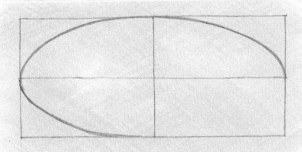

▲ Fig. 12.14

All ellipses will fit into rectangles just as circles fit into squares.

(1) Draw the rectangle into which the ellipse is to fit.

(2) Draw in the centre lines which form the major and minor axis of the ellipse.

(3) Sketch in the ellipse.

Large ellipses may be constructed using any of the methods discussed earlier in the book. The rectangle method is probably the most suitable as it is constructed solely using straight lines.

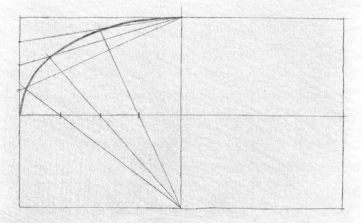

▲ Fig. 12.15

Sketching Pictorials

There are many different types of pictorial view. One of the quickest to sketch and the easiest to visualise is an isometric view. The sketches are built up using crating in a similar way as when producing isometrics using instruments. The idea behind crating is to break down an object into its component geometric parts, i.e. rectangular prisms, cylinders, cones, etc. Each component part is then crated in, on the sketch, and completed individually. Fig. 12.16 shows an example of this technique.

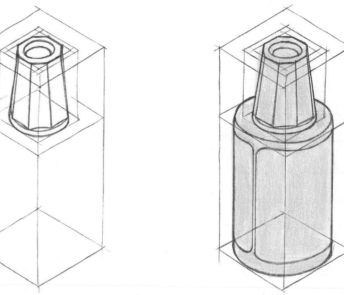

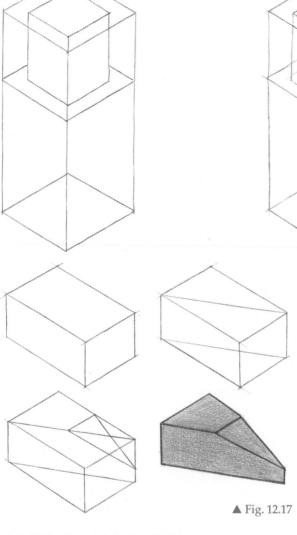

▲ Fig. 12.16

This procedure remains the same whether the object is simple or complex. What should be remembered, however, is that the larger masses should be outlined/ghosted in first, with more detail coming later. In this way it is easier to keep the sketch in proper proportion.

▲ Fig. 12.17

Circles in Pictorials

For smaller circles we start by drawing an isometric square into which the circle will fit. Then divide it into quarters. This gives the centre and four points on the circumference. The circle, which appears as an ellipse, is sketched in one quarter at a time.

▲ Fig. 12.18

For larger circles start by drawing, in isometric, the square into which the circle will fit. Sketch in the diagonals and lines parallel to the sides through the square's centre. Each half-diagonal is divided into roughly three equal parts in the same way as when drawing a circle. This provides eight points on the isometric circle's circumference. Sketch in the pictorial circle.

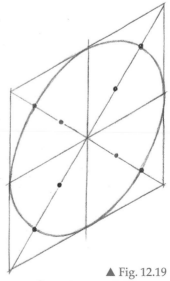

▲ Fig. 12.19

Worked Examples

Given the orthographic views of an object in Fig. 12.20. Produce a neat pictorial sketch of the solid. Choose a viewing orientation that gives a good view of the object's details.

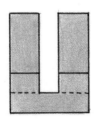
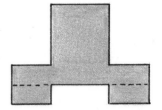

(1) Decide on the best angle to view the object.

(2) Sketch out the cage frame to the overall length, width and height.

(3) Rough in the object's features on the cage faces.

(4) Complete the shape and darken all visible lines, Fig. 12.21.

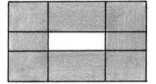

▲ Fig. 12.20

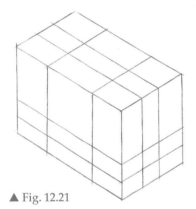
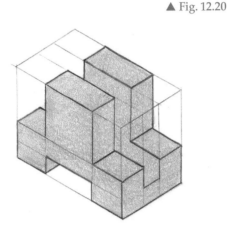

▲ Fig. 12.21

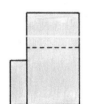
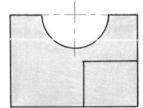

Given the plan, front elevation and end view of an object in Fig. 12.22. Make a neat freehand pictorial sketch of the object.

(1) Some objects are best divided into parts with a separate cage framework for each part.

(2) Locate the semicircle centre and complete the half square into which it will fit.

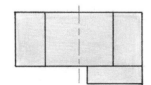

(3) Draw in the diagonals and centre lines.

(4) Draw in the curve.

▲ Fig. 12.22

(5) Darken all visible lines, Fig. 12.23.

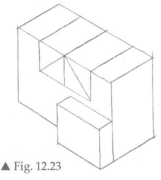
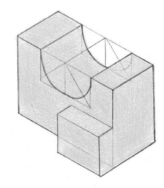

▲ Fig. 12.23

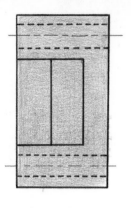

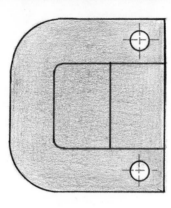

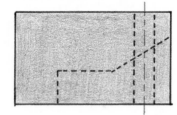

▲ Fig. 12.24

Given the orthographic views of an object in Fig. 12.24. Produce a neat pictorial sketch of the solid. Choose a viewing orientation that gives a good view of the object's details.

(1) Decide on the best orientation for the sketch.

(2) Box out the overall dimensions.

(3) Locate the main features and planes.

(4) Locate the centres of all circular features. Draw their centre lines and box out the general shape.

(5) Darken the visible shape, Fig. 12.25.

Note: The main outline may be thickened slightly to improve the visual impact of the drawing.

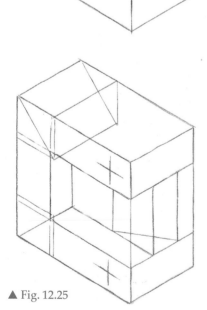

▲ Fig. 12.25

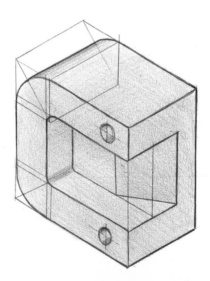

See worksheets 12.1 and 12.2

Given the plan and elevation of an object in Fig. 12.26. Produce a neat isometric sketch of the object choosing the most descriptive orientation.

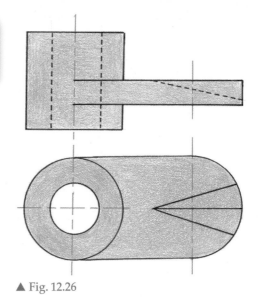

▲ Fig. 12.26

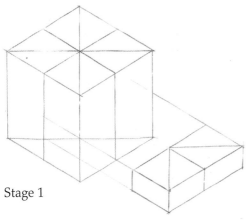

Stage 1

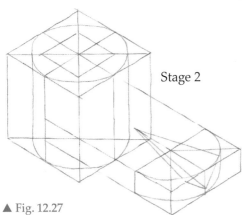

Stage 2

Stage 3

▲ Fig. 12.27

See worksheet 12.3

Given the front elevation and end elevation of an object in Fig. 12.28. Complete an isometric sketch of the object choosing the most descriptive orientation for your pictorial.

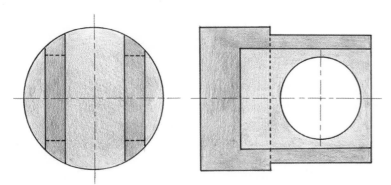

▲ Fig. 12.28

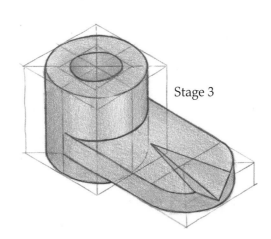

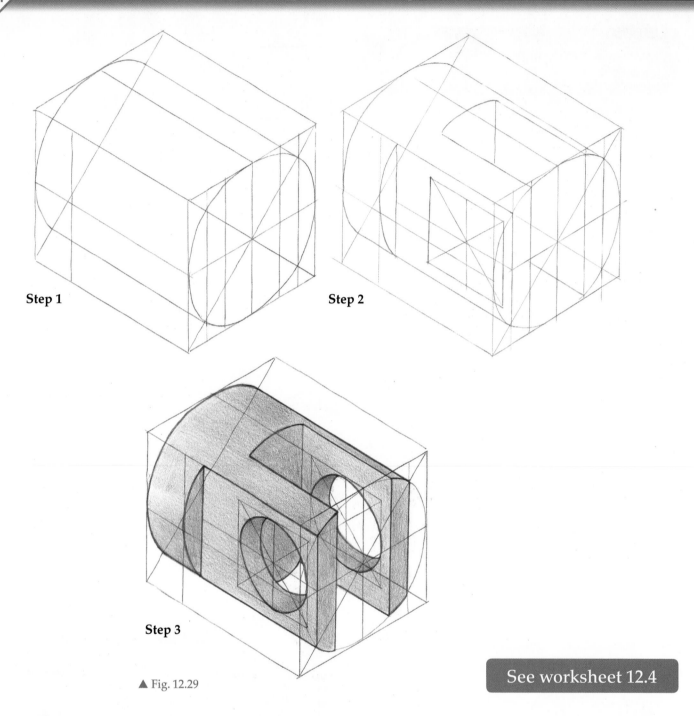

Step 1

Step 2

Step 3

▲ Fig. 12.29

Sketching in Orthographic

As we have seen elsewhere throughout this book, the fundamentals of orthographic projection are widely applied to most areas of technical drawing. Moreover, these fundamental principles are universally accepted and understood in most countries around the world. Sketching in orthographic can provide a quick method of conveying ideas and also provide more information than a pictorial sketch. Furthermore, orthographic sketches lend themselves better to dimensioning than do pictorials and it is with measurements and proportions that design ideas move from the drawing board into production.

All the practices observed when drawing orthographic views using instruments should be followed when sketching in orthographic. Position of views, projection lines, xy lines, etc. are all equally important in the sketch as in the drawing produced using instruments. An orthographic sketch which is technically inaccurate is of little value as it does not communicate the idea(s) properly.

See worksheet 12.4

Worked Examples

Given a pictorial view of an object. Make neat freehand orthographic views of this object showing all hidden detail.

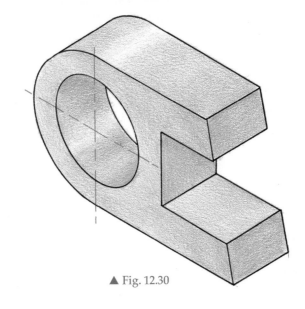

(1) Start by drawing in an xy line and boxing in the space for the front elevation and the plan directly beneath it.

(2) 'Project' these boxes around in the usual way to give the position and size of the end view.

(3) The circle and semicircle are sketched in by first drawing squares and fitting the circles into these squares.

(4) Thicken and darken all outlines and visible details, Fig. 12.31.

▲ Fig. 12.30

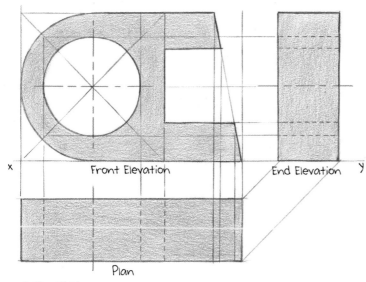

x   Front Elevation   End Elevation   y

Plan

▲ Fig. 12.31

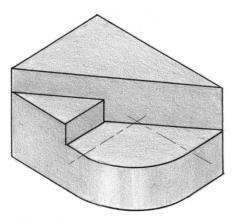

Given the pictorial of an object in Fig. 12.32. Make a neat three-view orthographic sketch of the object.

▲ Fig. 12.32

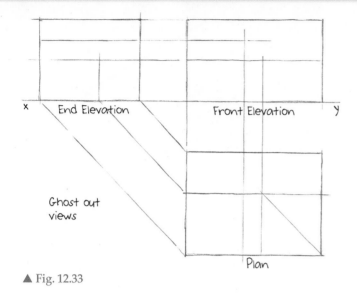

▲ Fig. 12.33

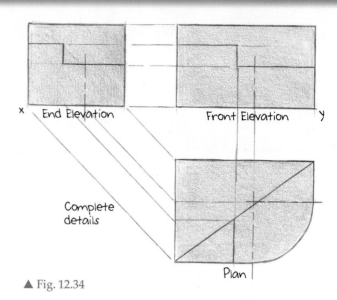

▲ Fig. 12.34

Given an isometric of a shaped solid in Fig. 12.35.
Make a neat, freehand sketch showing a front
elevation, end elevation and plan of this object.

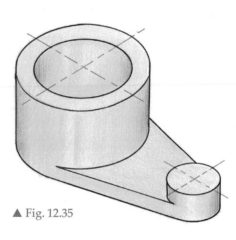

▲ Fig. 12.35

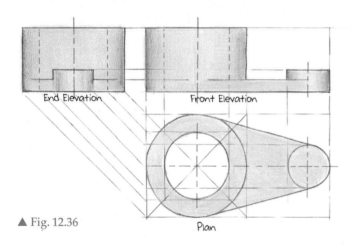

▲ Fig. 12.36

See worksheets 12.5 and 12.6

 # Perspective Sketching

One of the most popular types of pictorial sketches are perspective sketches. Many illustrators, designers and architects
use these almost exclusively because they present a drawing most like the image the camera records or the eye sees.
The perspective drawing is a pictorial projection that can take several forms depending on the vanishing points.
Unlike orthographic or isometric projections, which assume parallel lines of sight from the observer to the object,
the perspective uses lines of sight that converge at one, two, three or more points. Fig. 12.37 shows an upside-down
cardboard box drawn using one-point, two-point and three-point perspective.

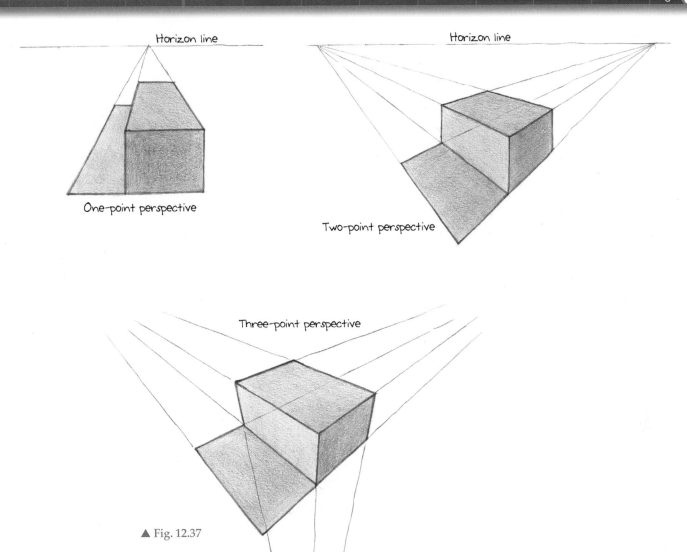

Horizon line

One-point perspective

Horizon line

Two-point perspective

Three-point perspective

▲ Fig. 12.37

The rules followed when drawing perspective views with instruments should also be followed when producing a perspective sketch.

- Horizontal lines vanish to vanishing points on the horizon.

- Parallel lines vanish to the same vanishing point.

- Lines and edges behind the picture plane appear shorter than their true length while lines/edges in front of the picture plane appear longer than their true length.

As with the isometric pictorial sketch, your first step is to establish the major points and lines by boxing in the object. The object is then broken into parts with the larger areas/planes being found first; then work towards the finer details.

Worked Examples

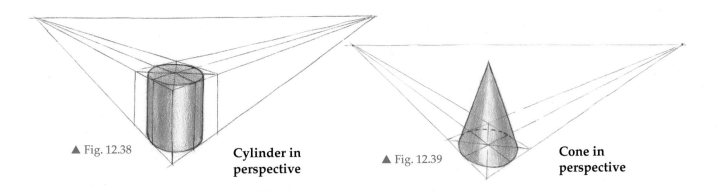

▲ Fig. 12.38   **Cylinder in perspective**

▲ Fig. 12.39   **Cone in perspective**

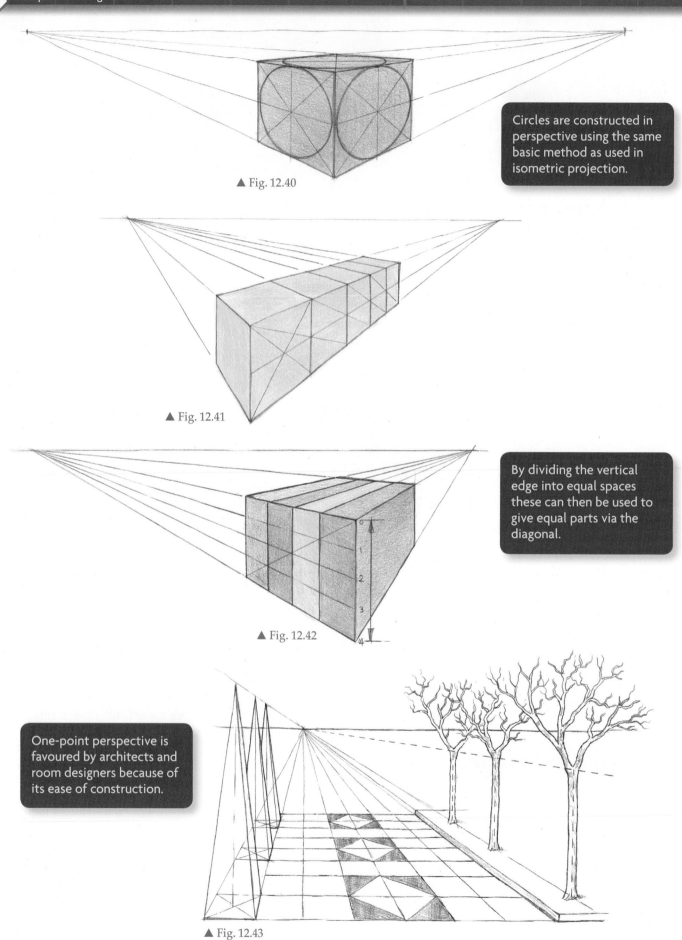

▲ Fig. 12.40

Circles are constructed in perspective using the same basic method as used in isometric projection.

▲ Fig. 12.41

By dividing the vertical edge into equal spaces these can then be used to give equal parts via the diagonal.

▲ Fig. 12.42

One-point perspective is favoured by architects and room designers because of its ease of construction.

▲ Fig. 12.43

Tone

Lines are obviously essential to outline shape, areas and contours. However, certain visual qualities of a surface cannot be fully described by lines alone. In order to improve our representation of such surfaces we must become skilful in the rendering of tonal values. Through the use of such rendering a good sense of light, mass and space are produced. Sketches can change from being flat and two-dimensional to being vibrant and three-dimensional.

Seeing patterns of light and dark is essential to our perception of objects. In a drawing it is tonal values that depict the lightness or darkness of an object, that describe the play of light on their forms and clarify their arrangement in space.

▲ Fig. 12.44

Apple	Pear	Plum
Dark Green	**Light Green or Yellow**	**Dark Purple**

Tonal value can also be used to depict colour. Fig. 12.44 shows an example of this. Tone is used both to indicate light and shade and also to show colour. It can be seen here that the drawing is completely drawn with pencil yet we can easily visualise the green apple, the light green or yellow pear, and the rich dark purple plum.

Techniques Used to Create Tonal Value

Using the traditional medium of pencil, there are several techniques for creating tonal values. These are:

- hatching • crosshatching • scribbling • stippling.

We will look at each of these separately.

▶ Fig. 12.45

Hatching

Hatching in sketching consists of a series of more or less parallel lines. These lines, drawn freehand, may be either long or short. Variation in tonal value is achieved in two ways:

- by varying the grade of lead used or increasing/decreasing the pressure with which we draw,
- by varying the spacing and density of the hatching.

The most flexible freehand technique for hatching uses relatively short, rapid, diagonal strokes. Start at the edges and work inwards. Strokes may overlap slightly. Apply a second or even a third layer of strokes at a slightly different angle to the first to build up the density and tonal value of an area. Hatching on a curved surface should curve to depict the contours of the surface.

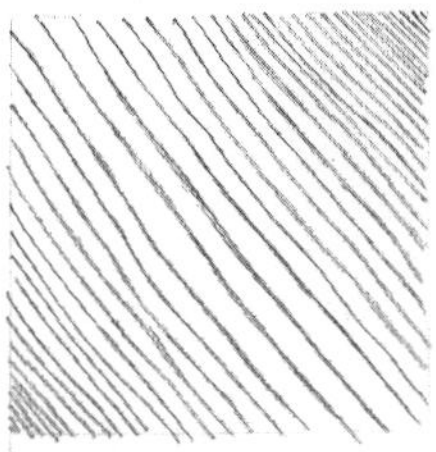

▲ Fig. 12.46

By varying the spacing of the hatching we can vary the tone.

▲ Fig. 12.47

Work inwards from the edges to produce crisp, clear, precise, edges.

▲ Fig. 12.48

By applying additional layers of strokes at a slightly different angle we can also vary the tone.

In this diagram the variation in tone is obtained by varying the spacing of the lines and by varying the line darkness.

▲ Fig. 12.49

Crosshatching

Crosshatching uses two or more sets of parallel lines to create tonal effects. The simplest type consists of two perpendicular sets of parallel lines, which gives a simple weave pattern. By adding more sets of lines, darker tonal values can be achieved. In practice, hatching and crosshatching are combined into a single technique. Simple hatching is used to provide the lighter tones and crosshatching is used to render the darker values, Fig. 12.50.

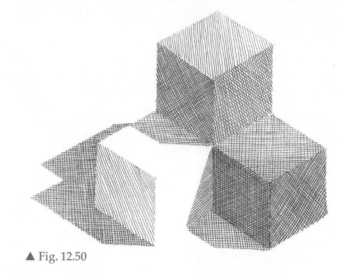

▲ Fig. 12.50

▲ Fig. 12.51

A simple crosshatch weave is very effective. The orientation of theweave will also give a different effect.

▲ Fig. 12.52

A tight weave mesh produces a strong tonal value.

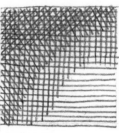

▲ Fig. 12.53

Variation in tone across a surface is achieved by varying the degree of hatching.

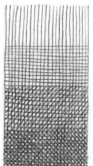

In this diagram it can be seen that the building up of the four layers of hatching increases the tonal value.

▲ Fig. 12.54

Scribbling

Scribbling is the fastest of the shading techniques and offers great flexibility during sketching. It involves the use of multi-directional lines with the pencil being lifted from the paper only occasionally to change direction. It is a less rigid and less formal method of shading than the previous two methods we have looked at. The lines are varied to suit the style required. They may be continuous, straight, curved, jagged, wavy. The scribbling may be single-layered or many-layered. By drawing the lines close together a dense, dark tonal value may be achieved.

The surface texture may also be conveyed using this technique, as can pattern and the surface quality.

▲ Fig. 12.55

▲ Fig. 12.56

Scribbling as a shading technique is fast and effective.

▲ Fig. 12.57

Different scribbling methods gives both tone and texture.

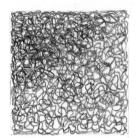

▲ Fig. 12.58

This scribbling technique relies on a completely freeform pattern.

Stippling

Stippling uses fine dots as a means of defining different tonal values. It is the slowest of the methods mentioned and requires patience. Stippling relies on the density of the dots to determine the tone; closely packed dots will produce a dark tone while well-spaced dots will produce a light tone. The size of the dots used on an area will affect the apparent texture of that surface. By using small dots a fine texture is portrayed, while by using larger dots a coarse texture appears. If, however, the dots are drawn too large the stippling loses its effectiveness.

The shapes are first drawn very lightly. Dots are used over these lines to define the objects' edges. Areas to be shaded are then covered with an even distribution of dots. This will produce a light tonal value. By adding more layers of stippling darker tones are attained.

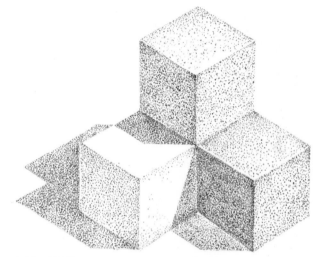

▲ Fig. 12.59

▲ Fig. 12.60

A dark tone with a fine texture is achieved by using small dots closely spaced.

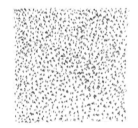

▲ Fig. 12.61

A medium tone with acoarse texture is achieved by using larger dots with medium spacing.

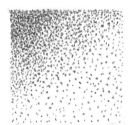

▲ Fig. 12.62

Variation in tone across an area can be achieved by varying the dot spacing.

See worksheet 12.7

Modelling Form

▲ Fig. 12.63

Modelling is the technique of making a two-dimensional drawing of an object or objects appear to have depth, volume and a relative position to each other in space. The two-dimensional drawing appears to gain three-dimensional status. This process is achieved by using shading and tonal values to transform a drawing of contours into forms in space.

The modelling of surfaces using light and shade can help us understand whether the surface is flat or curved or whether it is smooth or rough. Light patterns on curved surfaces such as cylinders, cones and spheres move gradually from light to dark. On planar solids such as cubes, prisms and pyramids there is a more abrupt change in shade/tonal value from plane to plane.

Gradual change from light to dark on the curved surface of the cylinder in comparison to an abrupt change from plane to plane on the pyramid.

▲ Fig. 12.64

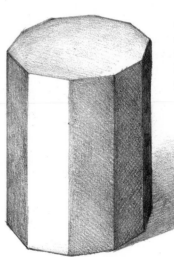

As the faces of an object turn away from the light their tonal value increases.

▲ Fig. 12.65

Light may be reflected off nearby objects and so lighten the tone of the shade.

Highlights occur on surfaces directly facing the light source.

▲ Fig. 12.66

Shadow is the dark area cast by the object onto a surface.

Shade refers to the comparatively dark values of surfaces away from the light.

See worksheet 12.8

 Colour

The use of colours when sketching can be a very effective tool. Colours can improve presentation, can identify materials being used, can highlight contrasts between two different parts of an object and/or can be used to draw attention to a particular part of a diagram. A note of caution here: the use of too much colour can confuse the viewer and can make a sketch fussy and distracting. The main function of sketches and diagrams in technical drawing is to convey an idea or to help solve a problem; they are not visual art in the same way as an artist's sketch or painting is.

Primary Colours

Red, yellow and blue are known as the primary colours and are shown on a colour wheel in Fig. 12.67.

All other colours can be achieved by mixing these primary colours. By mixing red and yellow, for example, orange is produced; yellow and blue mixed gives green; and blue and red mixed gives violet. Colours obtained by mixing two primary colours are called secondary colours. An even greater range of colours is found by mixing a primary colour with a secondary colour. These colours are termed tertiary colours.

Black and white are neutral colours and when mixed with other colours affect the tone of the colour.

The colour blue in Fig. 12.69 decreases in tone from left to right. This is achieved by allowing more of the white background to emerge through the colour.

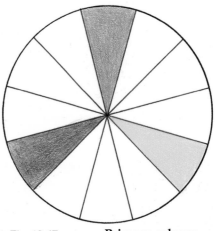

▲ Fig. 12.67   **Primary colours**

▲ Fig. 12.69

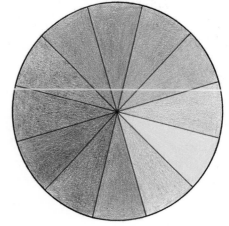

▲ Fig. 12.68   **Primary, secondary and tertiary colours**

Application of Colour

Colour may be applied to sketches using many different media:

- watercolour,
- felt-tipped pens,
- colouring pencils,
- coloured pens/biros, etc.

Each of these has its own characteristics.

Watercolour

Watercolours are used for shading large blocks or areas. They are usually used as a wash over a finished drawing rather than as a means of building up the drawing itself. They can cover a large area quickly but do not lend themselves to intricate detail with many colour changes.

▲ Fig. 12.70

Felt-tipped Pens

Felt-tipped pens are useful for block shading or where a coarse application of colour is adequate. They cannot be removed once applied, which may cause problems. The colours produced are very vibrant. Variations in tone are difficult to produce, Fig. 12.70.

Coloured Pens/Biros

These can be used very effectively using the methods described earlier for pencil sketching. Obviously it must be always remembered that the ink cannot be erased in the same way as a pencil.

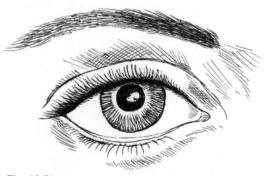

▲ Fig. 12.71

However, a biro/pen can give a more permanent feel to a sketch and will not be smudged when handled. By tracing over light pencil lines we can combine the advantages of sketching in pencil with the advantages of having sketches finished with ink, Fig. 12.71. The thickness of the lines produced cannot be varied when using biro but the line quality is very good. The range of colours available is also limited and they do not lend themselves to mixing colours, Fig. 12.72.

▲ Fig. 12.72

Colouring Pencils

Colouring pencils provide one of the best means of applying colour to a sketch or diagram. They come in a wide range of colours and also can be mixed by applying one layer over another. They can be sharpened in many ways to give different line widths and can be erased. Sketches may be drawn from start to finish using colouring pencils or they can be used to enhance a pencil or ink sketch.

▲ Fig. 12.73   **Pencil sketch with colouring pencil applied afterwards**

▲ Fig. 12.74   **Sketch done solely with colouring pencils**

See worksheet 12.9

 ## Tone and Texture

When we use hatching, stippling or scribbling to create a tonal value we are simultaneously creating texture. Furthermore, as we try to describe a material's texture with lines we are also creating tone. There is a constant relationship between tone and texture. We should therefore always be aware of this when attempting to produce either.

The texture of an object may be smooth or rough, high sheen or dull, hard or soft. When rendering tone on a sketch it is often possible to convey this texture quality through the use of different shading techniques. Large-scale strokes will produce a rough texture while small-scale strokes produce a fine-grained effect. Polished surfaces depend on the reflection of light to convey their texture. They reflect light brilliantly and appear sharply in focus. Matt surfaces absorb and diffuse light and therefore appear less sharp. Coarse surfaces cast shadow patterns on themselves, thus revealing their textural quality.

▲ Fig. 12.75

▲ Fig. 12.76a

Short strokes

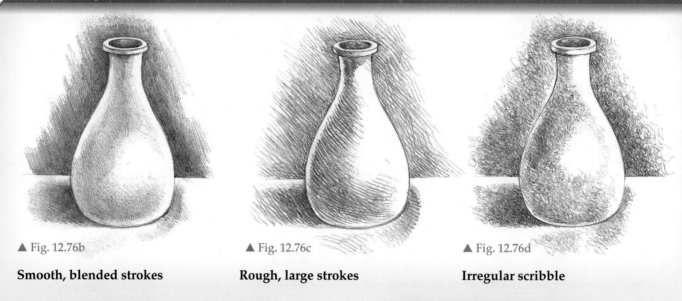

▲ Fig. 12.76b

Smooth, blended strokes

▲ Fig. 12.76c

Rough, large strokes

▲ Fig. 12.76d

Irregular scribble

Some Common Materials

See worksheet 12.10

By critical analysis of the texture and colour of various materials we should be able to accurately represent different materials in our sketching.

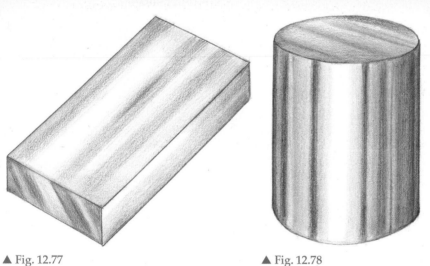

▲ Fig. 12.77

▲ Fig. 12.78

Metal

Metals have a smooth surface and are highly reflective of light. Shading on the surfaces is unidirectional and uses straight lines. Shading on the end is inclined. The shading is laid down in bands as shown in Figures 12.77 and 12.78. For highly polished surfaces it is important to catch the light high points and the reflections of other objects in the surface, Fig. 12.79. Blue/grey is best to represent steel while an orange/yellow best represents brass or gold.

▲ Fig. 12.79

Wood

Wood can have many variations both in colour and texture and also has the added interest of grain pattern. The faces of a rectangular block of wood will show quite different grain patterns but it should be remembered that the grain patterns are all interlinked. If a grain feature reaches an edge of a face it will continue in some form on the adjoining face. Some woods show very little grain pattern while for others the grain pattern dominates each face.

The colours used are generally light brown or orange as a base colour, with a darker brown or orange to show the grain.

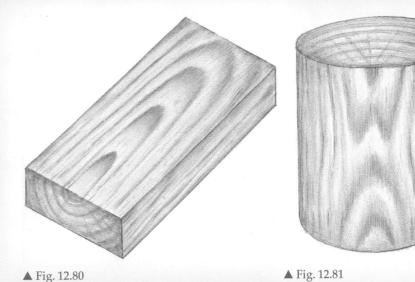

▲ Fig. 12.80

▲ Fig. 12.81

Plastic (opaque)

Opaque plastic is smooth and generally shiny with often strong colouring. Attention should be paid to the light high points and colour depth.

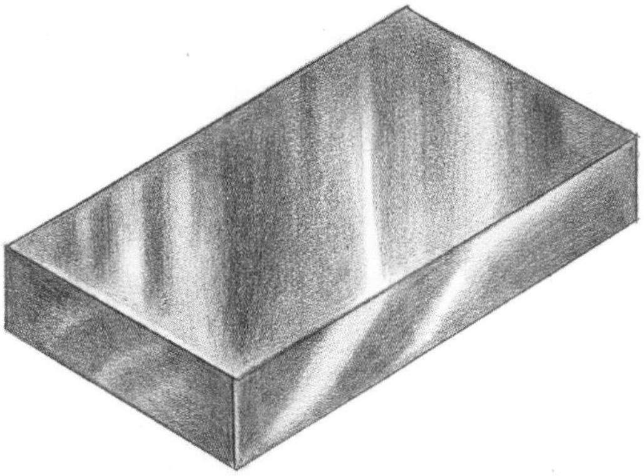

▲ Fig. 12.82

Clear plastic and glass

It can be difficult to depict a transparent or semi-transparent material. The standard way of representing colourless materials is to draw groups of parallel lines using a ruler. These lines are angled across the surface as shown in Fig. 12.83.

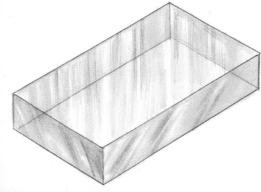
▲ Fig. 12.83

▲ Fig. 12.84

Because of the reflective nature of these materials when they are grouped together they will reflect light onto each other. Shade and shadow will not be uniform in value as a result of this bouncing light. Curved glass or plastic will also distort the image of an object seen through it, Fig. 12.84.

HIGHER LEVEL

Shade and Shadow

Many sketches need no shading yet all sketches may be shaded. The amount of effort put into shading depends on the purpose of the sketch, the subject being drawn, the type of drawing and the need for clarity. Most sketches are more pleasing to the eye if surfaces are emphasised and contrasts are indicated. Using shading and shadow to differentiate between vertical, horizontal and inclined surfaces makes the drawing easier to read. Pictorial sketches are regularly shaded but orthographic or working drawings are usually left unshaded.

There is one guiding principle in shading or rendering a drawing. The rendering must always make the drawing either clearer or more attractive. If it fails in these it is better to omit it. Rendering should not be used to hide inaccuracy or mistakes. It can only be successful if the basic drawing is correct.

Terminology

We must first define what we mean by shade and shadow because they are not two words for the same thing.

Shadow

A shadow is a relatively dark figure, cast by an opaque object or part of an opaque object onto a surface. It is caused by the object intercepting or blocking the light rays from a source.

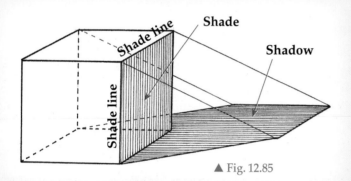

▲ Fig. 12.85

Shade

Shade refers to the varying amount of light that is reflected to an observer by the surfaces of an object. Shade will be at its darkest on areas turned away from the light and will vary in brightness as a surface turns toward the light, Fig. 12.85.

Shade line

A line on an object that separates an illuminated surface from one in shade. Also called the casting line.

Shadow line

The edge of the shadow cast on a receiving body.

 # Light Source

As has been mentioned earlier, for most sketching we assume that the light rays shining on the object are parallel, i.e. the source of light is very far away, e.g. the sun. This makes working out the shadow simpler than if the rays are non-parallel. The light source can be anywhere; behind, above, in front, to the left, below, etc. The position of the light source will affect the shade and the shadow, see Fig. 12.86.

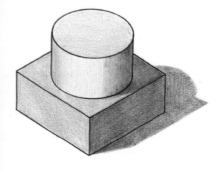
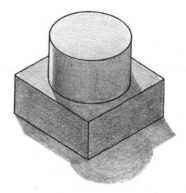

▲ Fig. 12.86

Worked Examples

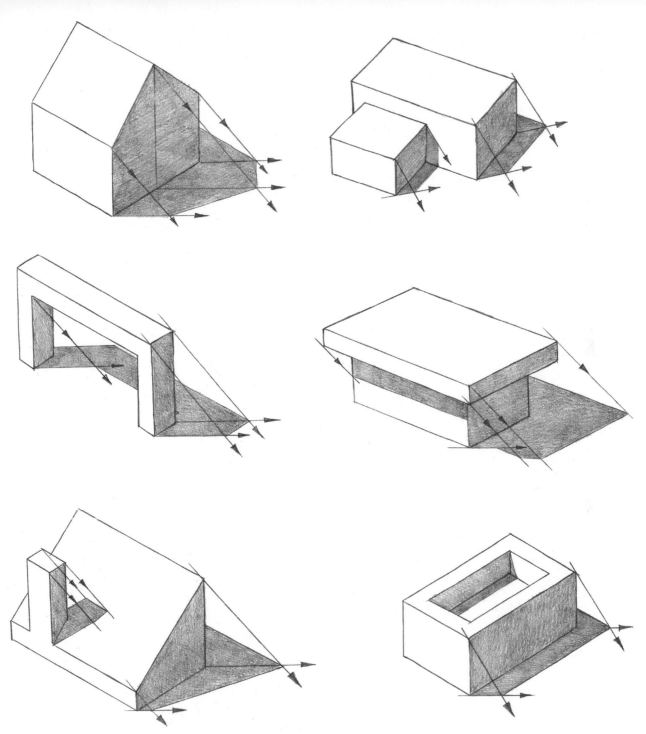

▲ Fig. 12.87

Activities

Q1. Make neat freehand sketches of the plane figures shown in **Figures 12.88, 12.89** and **12.90**.

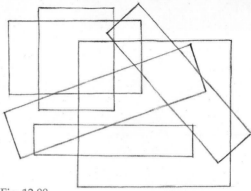

▲ Fig. 12.88

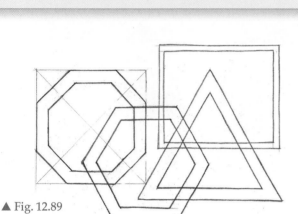

▲ Fig. 12.89

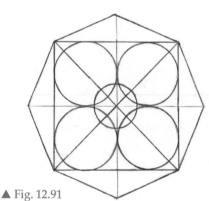

▲ Fig. 12.90

Q2. Sketch the diagrams shown in **Figures 12.91, 12.92** and **12.93**, which are based on circles.

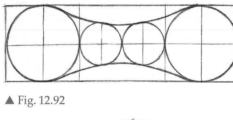

▲ Fig. 12.92

▲ Fig. 12.91

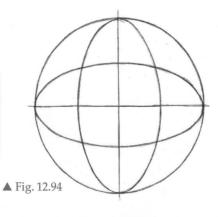

▲ Fig. 12.93

Q3. Make neat diagrams of the objects shown in **Figures 12.94** and **12.95**, which are based on ellipses.

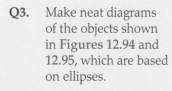

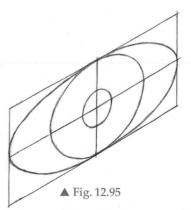

▲ Fig. 12.94   ▲ Fig. 12.95

Q4. Given the orthographic views of various objects, **Figures 12.96 to 12.100**. Make a neat freehand pictorial sketch of each object.

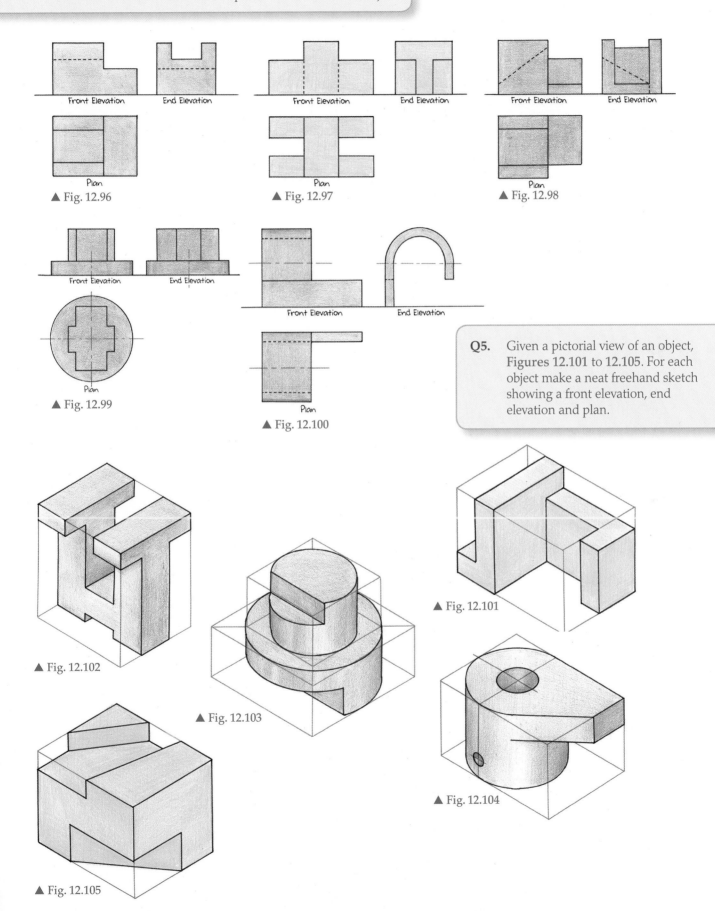

Front Elevation   End Elevation

Plan

▲ Fig. 12.96

Front Elevation   End Elevation

Plan

▲ Fig. 12.97

Front Elevation   End Elevation

Plan

▲ Fig. 12.98

Front Elevation   End Elevation

Plan

▲ Fig. 12.99

Front Elevation   End Elevation

Plan

▲ Fig. 12.100

Q5. Given a pictorial view of an object, **Figures 12.101 to 12.105**. For each object make a neat freehand sketch showing a front elevation, end elevation and plan.

▲ Fig. 12.101

▲ Fig. 12.102

▲ Fig. 12.103

▲ Fig. 12.104

▲ Fig. 12.105

Q6. Make neat two-point perspective sketches of the objects shown in **Figures 12.106** to **12.110**. Vary the height and position of the spectator to give different views.

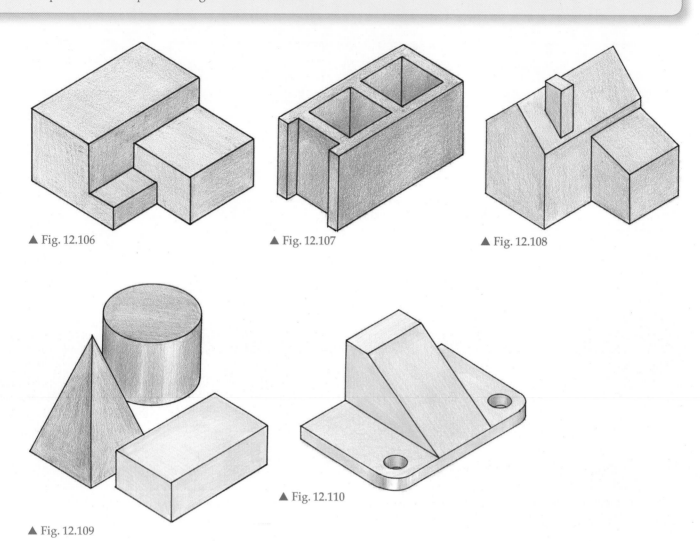

▲ Fig. 12.106   ▲ Fig. 12.107   ▲ Fig. 12.108

▲ Fig. 12.109

▲ Fig. 12.110

PART 3

APPLIED

GRAPHICS

Syllabus Outline

Areas to be studied (in an applied context):

- The common geometric loci: involutes, helices, conical spirals, Archimedean spirals, and *logarithmic spirals.*
- *Construction of loci defined by the movement of circles relative to lines and circles.*
- *Construction of tangents at a point on an involute, Archimedean spiral, cycloid, epicycloid, hypocycloid and trochoid.*
- Determination of loci from linkage mechanisms.
- *Construction of cam profiles and displacement diagrams depicting uniform velocity, simple harmonic motion, uniform acceleration and retardation for in-line knife-edge followers.*
- *Construction of cam profiles and displacement diagrams depicting uniform velocity, simple harmonic motion, uniform acceleration and retardation for roller and flat in-line followers.*

Learning Outcomes

Students should be able to:

Higher and Ordinary levels

- Construct the involute of a circle and regular polygons.
- Construct the helix and conical spiral from given data.
- Construct an Archimedean spiral.
- Use a trammel to solve problems on loci.
- Construct the locus of a point in a link mechanism.
- Construct radial plate cams of given uniform velocity, simple harmonic motion, uniform acceleration and retardation to in-line knife-edge followers.
- Construct cam profiles and displacement diagrams.
- Construct displacement diagrams for given cam profiles.
- Understand the applications for all the curves constructed.
- Construct standard cycloids.

Higher Level only

- *Construct epicycloids, hypocycloids and trochoids.*
- *Construct a tangent at a point on an involute, Archimedean spiral, cycloid, epicycloids, hypocycloid and trochoid.*
- *Construct radial plate cams of given uniform velocity, simple harmonic motion, uniform acceleration and retardation to roller and flat in-line followers.*
- *Construct involute and epicycloidal gear profiles.*
- *Construct a logarithmic spiral.*

Dynamic Mechanisms 1

- Involutes

- Helices

- Conical Spirals

- Archimedian Spirals

Involute

If a piece of string is wound around a plane figure, being kept taut at all times, the path the end of the string follows is called an involute.

Involute to a square

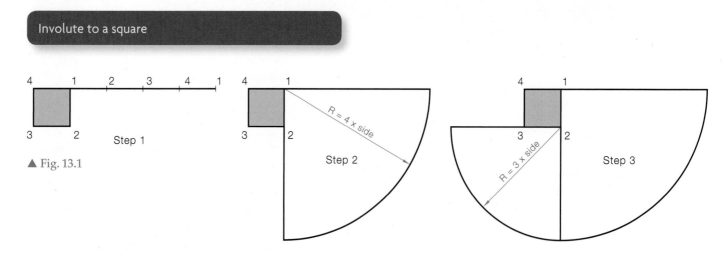

▲ Fig. 13.1

Extend one side and make it equal to the perimeter of the square. With corner 1 as centre, rotate the string until it runs along edge 1,2. The string now bends at corner 2 and pivots. With 2 as centre and radius to the end of the string, rotate until the string is in line with edge 2,3. Continue to complete the involute.

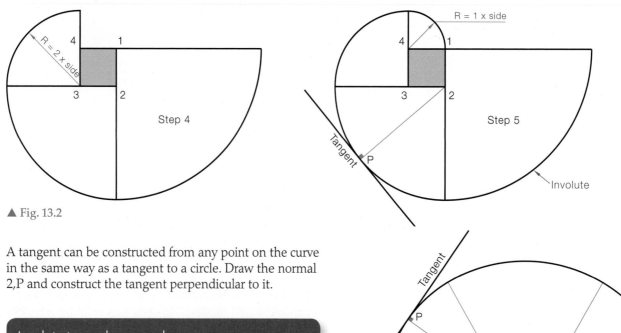

▲ Fig. 13.2

A tangent can be constructed from any point on the curve in the same way as a tangent to a circle. Draw the normal 2,P and construct the tangent perpendicular to it.

Involute to a polygon, e.g. hexagon.

Extend one side of the polygon and make it equal to the perimeter in Fig. 13.3. The involute is constructed as before. It pivots on a corner until it reaches the next corner and then proceeds to pivot on it. The path followed is therefore made up of portions of circles. Tangents are constructed as before.

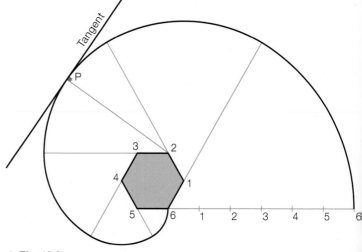

▲ Fig. 13.3

Involute to a circle.

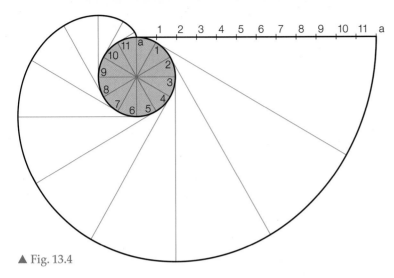

▲ Fig. 13.4

An involute to a circle is different from the previous examples because at no stage does the string pivot about a fixed point.

(1) Divide the circle into twelve equal parts and construct a tangent at the end of each division.

(2) Choose one of these and step-off the circumference as shown in Fig. 13.4.

(3) As the string is wrapped it shortens. By the time the string is wrapped to position 4 on the circle it is only eight divisions long because the remaining four divisions are around the circle. By the time the string reaches 10 on the circle it is only two divisions long because the remaining ten divisions are around the circle.

(4) The curve must be drawn freehand.

Involute to an irregular shape.

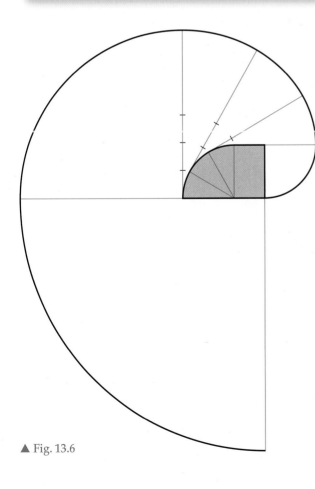

▲ Fig. 13.6

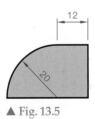

▲ Fig. 13.5

Draw the involute of the irregular shape in Fig. 13.5.

(1) Most irregular shapes can be broken up and seen as shapes made up of pieces of regular shapes. This particular shape is broken up as a rectangle and a quarter of a circle.

(2) The construction can be seen in Fig. 13.6 and follows the approach used in the involute to a square and the involute to a circle.

The Helix

A helix is the path of a point which moves around a cylinder at a constant rate while moving in the direction of the axis at a constant rate.

To draw a helix of one revolution.

Draw the plan and elevation of the cylinder. Divide the plan into 12 equal parts and project up to the elevation. Draw the development of the curved surface of the cylinder. The development of a helix is a straight line. The points on the development are projected back to the elevation as shown in Fig. 13.7. The helix can be left-handed or right-handed. Fig. 13.7 shows a left-handed helix.

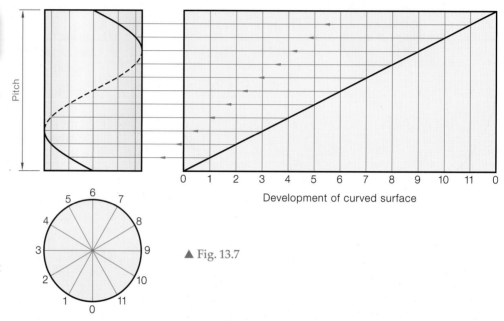

Development of curved surface

▲ Fig. 13.7

To draw a right-handed helix of 1½ revolutions given the cylinder in Fig. 13.8.

An alternative method to using a development is to divide the height of the cylinder into the required number of equal parts. If the plan is divided into 12 parts then we must divide the cylinder height into 18 equal parts to achieve 1½ revolutions. The right-handed helix shown in Fig. 13.9 is plotted by projection as shown.

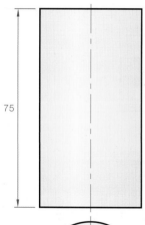

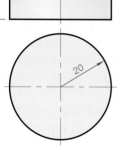

▲ Fig. 13.8

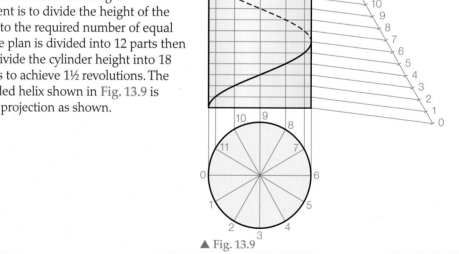

▲ Fig. 13.9

Screw threads and springs

Most screw threads are helices, as are coil springs, worm gears and spiral staircases.

To draw a right-hand screw thread (square) given the inside diameter, the outside diameter and the lead. Fig 13.11.

The lead is the advancement of the thread after one revolution.

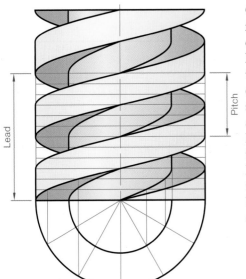

Double start right-hand thread

▲ Fig. 13.10

Construct two helices from the outside diameter, one running half a revolution behind the other. Similar construction for the small diameter. This is a single start thread. In a single start thread the pitch is equal to the lead. For a double start thread, Fig. 13.10, it can be seen that the pitch is equal to half the lead.

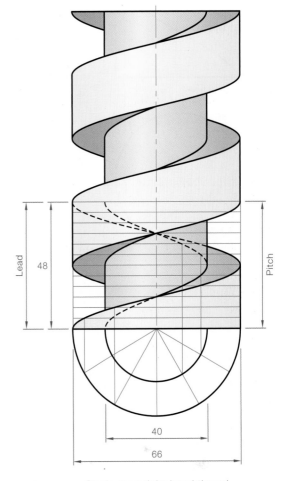

Single start right-hand thread

▲ Fig. 13.11

Given the plan and elevation of a cylinder with two points on its surface, A and B, Fig. 13.12. Draw a helix starting from the base of the cylinder and finishing at the top of the cylinder and passing through A and B.

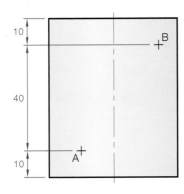

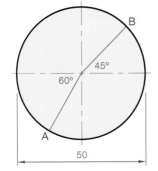

▲ Fig. 13.12

(1) Draw the plan and elevation.

(2) Divide up the plan, draw the generators in elevation and draw the development.

(3) Find points A and B on the development. Point A is on generator 2 and point B is halfway between generators 7 and 8.

(4) Draw a straight line between A and B, on the development, and extend to hit the top and bottom of the development at points t and s. The development of a helix is a straight line.

(5) From the development, project the points on the elevation.

(6) Points s and t must first be found on the plan before being found in elevation.

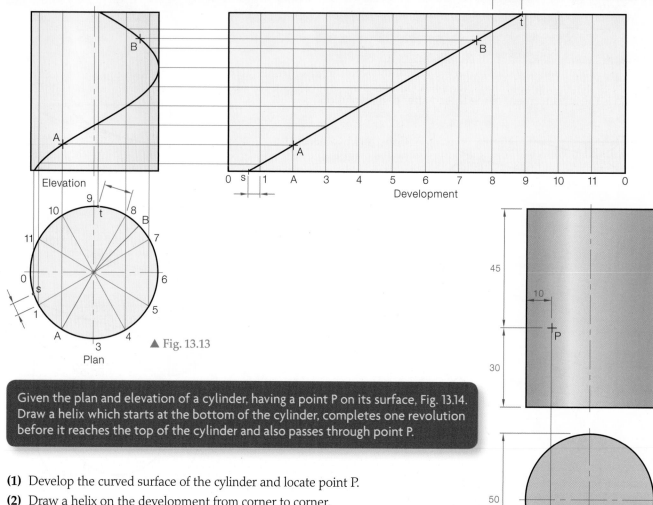

Elevation

Plan

Development

▲ Fig. 13.13

Given the plan and elevation of a cylinder, having a point P on its surface, Fig. 13.14. Draw a helix which starts at the bottom of the cylinder, completes one revolution before it reaches the top of the cylinder and also passes through point P.

(1) Develop the curved surface of the cylinder and locate point P.
(2) Draw a helix on the development from corner to corner.
(3) The required helix will run parallel to this helix.
(4) Project the helix back to the elevation.
(5) The start and finish of the helix are taken from the development to the plan and then to elevation.

▲ Fig. 13.14

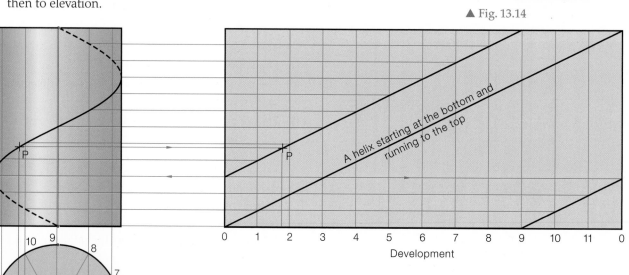

A helix starting at the bottom and running to the top

Development

▲ Fig. 13.15

Conical Spiral

A conical spiral is drawn in the same way as a helix except that the path moves from the base of a cone to its apex. Divide the plan into 12 equal divisions. Draw these generators in elevation. Divide the height of the cone into the same number of equal divisions as the plan. Plot the curve in elevation as shown in Fig. 13.16. Project to plan. The points in plan on generators 3 and 9 are found as shown. The curve produced in plan is an **Archimedean Spiral**.

Archimedean Spiral

An Archimedean spiral is the locus of a point which is moving at a uniform velocity along a straight line which itself is rotating about a fixed point, the pole, at a uniform angular velocity.

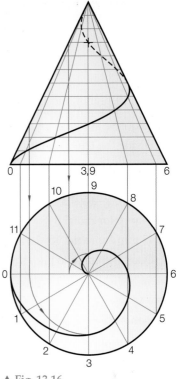

▲ Fig. 13.16

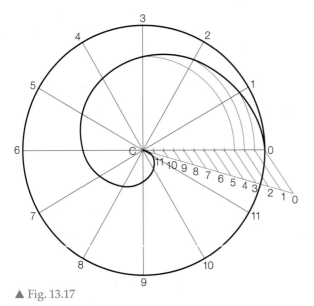

▲ Fig. 13.17

To draw an Archimedean spiral of one convolution given the longest radius vector as 50 mm and the shortest as 0 mm.

(1) Draw a circle having the radius equal to the longest radius vector. The spiral will start at a point on the circumference of this circle and after one convolution will reach the centre of the circle.

(2) Choose your starting point on the circumference, point 0. Divide the circle into twelve equal divisions from this point 0.

(3) Divide the radius C0 into twelve equal parts.

(4) Swing these points to cut the radials as shown in Fig. 13.17.

(5) Join these points with a freehand curve to form the spiral.

Draw an Archimedean spiral of 1 ¾ convolutions given the largest radius vector of 50 mm and the shortest of 15 mm. Fig. 13.18.

(1) Draw two concentric circles, one of 50 mm radius, the other 15 mm radius.

(2) Divide the circles into 12 equal parts.

(3) The distance between the two circles is divided into 21 equal spaces; twelve parts for a full convolution and nine for ¾ of a convolution.

(4) Plot the spiral as before.

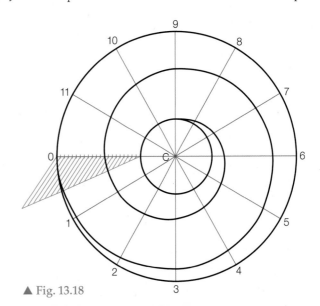

▲ Fig. 13.18

Construct one convolution of an Archimedean spiral given the shortest radius vector of 15 mm and an increase in vector length of 3 mm every 20º.

(1) Draw a 15 mm circle.

(2) Choose a starting point on the circumference.

(3) Divide the circle up into 20° sections from this point.

(4) For each radial measure the required distance outside the circumference of the 15 mm circle.

9 mm for radial 3 (3 × 3 mm)

24 mm for radial 8 (8 × 3 mm)

45 mm for radial 15 (15 × 3 mm)

(5) Draw the curve to pass through these points.

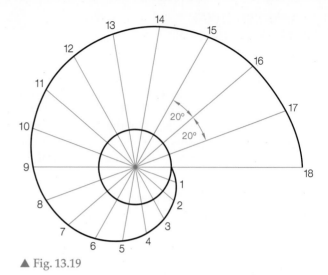

▲ Fig. 13.19

Cycloid

A cycloid is the path traced out by a point on the circumference of a circle as it rolls along a fixed straight line without slipping.

To draw a cycloid given the circle, the base line and the point on the circumference.

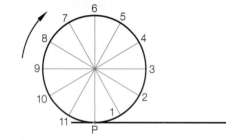

▼ Fig. 13.20

(1) Draw the circle, the base line and point P.

(2) Divide the circle into a number of equal parts, e.g. twelve parts.

(3) The circle is to make one revolution, so it will travel a distance equal to the circumference of the circle. Take one-twelfth of the circumference and step it off, from P, twelve times.

(4) Index the points as shown.

(5) As the circle rolls, the centre of the circle will travel parallel to the base line. We are going to look at the circle at twelve stages during its travel. Locate the centre point of the circle for each of these stages by erecting perpendiculars from 1,2,3 etc. on the base line.

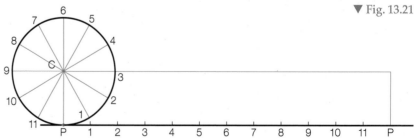

▼ Fig. 13.21

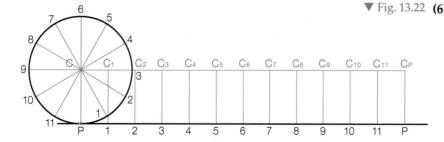

▼ Fig. 13.22

(6) As the circle rolls clockwise, point 1 on the circumference moves onto point 1 on the base line. At the same time the centre will have moved to C1. Point P will have moved also and can be located by triangulation. Take the distance from point 1 on the circumference to point P. Place the compass on the new point 1 on the base line and scribe an arc. Take a second distance from the circle centre to point P (the radius) and scribe an arc from C1 to intersect the first arc, giving the location of point P1 on the locus.

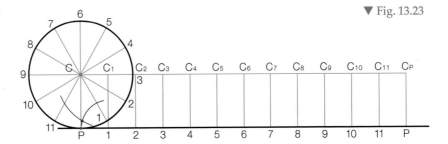

▼ Fig. 13.23

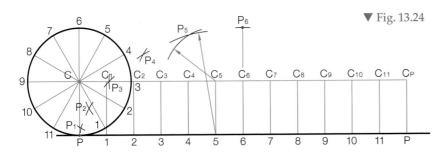

▼ Fig. 13.24

(7) Take a similar approach for the rest of the points. For example P5 is found by taking the distance from 5 on the circumference. Place the compass on 5 on the line and scribe an arc. Take a second distance from the centre of the circle to point P (the radius) and scribe an arc from C5. The intersection of the arcs gives P5, the fifth point on the cycloid.

(8) The right half is completed in the same way with the arcs swung to the right. Join the points up freehand to form a smooth curve, see Fig. 13.25.

To draw a cycloid given the base line, circle and the point P on the circle circumference. Point P does not fall on one of the twelve divisions.

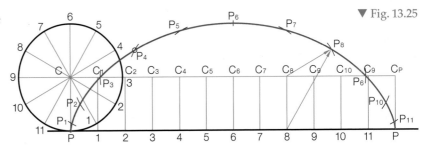

▼ Fig. 13.25

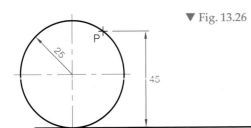

▼ Fig. 13.26

(1) Divide the circle into twelve equal parts and index.

(2) Take one-twelfth of the circumference and step along the base line twelve times.

(3) Find the twelve centres. Index both sets of points.

(4) Point P falls between 4 and 5 on the circumference and will therefore hit the base line between 4 and 5. It is also to the right of the centre line. The cycloid will therefore be dropping at the start.

(5) Plot the points as before.

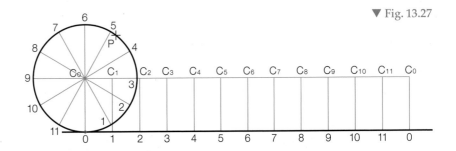

▼ Fig. 13.27

(6) The starting point and the end point must be at the same level.

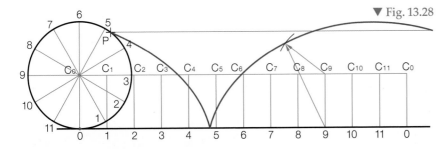

▼ Fig. 13.28

Epicycloid

If a circle rolls without slipping round the outside of a fixed circle then a point P on the circumference of the rolling circle will produce an epicycloid.

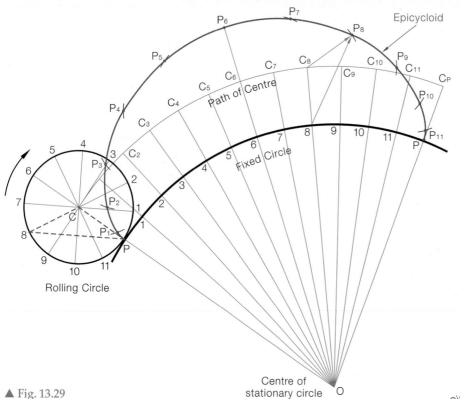

▲ Fig. 13.29

(1) Join the centre of the rolling circle and the centre of the fixed circle.

(2) Divide the circle into twelve using this line as one of the division lines.

(3) Step-off the twelve steps along the outside of the fixed circle and index.

(4) With O as centre, swing an arc from C. This will be the path of the centre as the circle rolls.

(5) Using radians from O through points 1, 2, 3 etc. On the circumference of the fixed circle locate the centres C_1, C_2, C_3 etc.

(6) Plot the locus as before.

See worksheet 13.1

Hypocycloid

If a circle rolls without slipping round the inside of a fixed circle, then a point P on the circumference of the rolling circle will produce a hypocycloid.

(1) Join the centres O and C and extend.

(2) Divide the rolling circle into twelve equal parts relative to this line.

(3) Step-off the twelve steps along the circumference of the fixed circle and index.

(4) With O as centre swing an arc from C giving the path of the centre as the circle rolls.

(5) Locate the centres C_1, C_2, C_3 etc. by using radians from O to points 1, 2, 3 etc. on the circumference of the fixed circle.

(6) Plot the locus as before.

Note: Point P need not be on one of the twelve divisions.

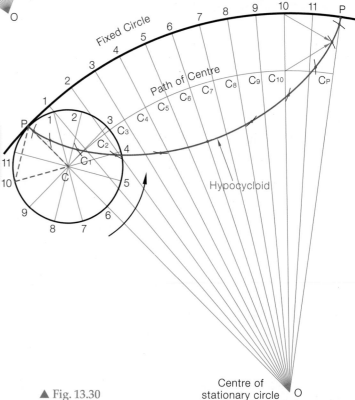

▲ Fig. 13.30

See worksheet 13.2

Inferior Trochoid

When a circle rolls, without slipping, along a straight line, then a point P inside the circle will follow the path of an inferior trochoid.

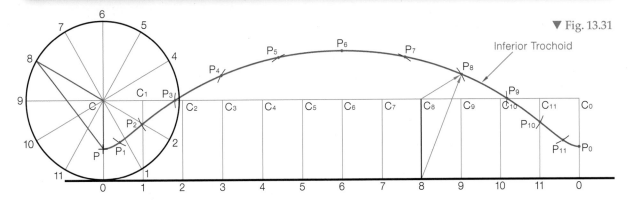

▼ Fig. 13.31

Inferior Trochoid

The construction is similar to the cycloid.

(1) Divide the circle into twelve equal parts and index.

(2) Step-off the twelve steps along the straight line to find the length of the circumference.

(3) Find the path of the centre line and locate C1, C2, C3 etc., as shown in Fig. 13.31.

(4) The points along the locus are located as previously described for the cycloid, measuring to point P inside the circle each time.

(5) Join the points to give a smooth curve.

Superior Trochoid

When a circle rolls, without slipping, along a straight line, then a point P outside the circle will follow the path of a superior trochoid.

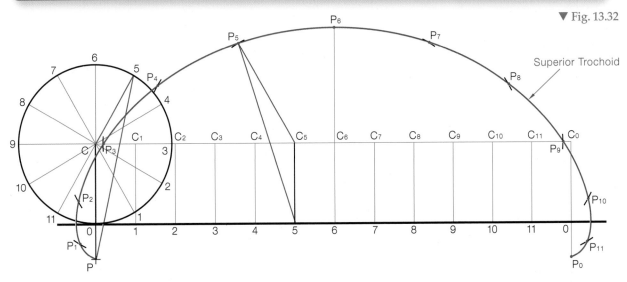

▼ Fig. 13.32

Superior Trochoid

(1) Divide the circle into twelve equal parts and index.

(2) Step-off the twelve steps along the straight line to find the length of the circumference.

(3) Locate C_1, C_2, C_3 etc.

(4) Locate P1 to P0 as shown previously.

(5) Draw the locus.

See worksheet 13.3

Inferior Epitrochoid

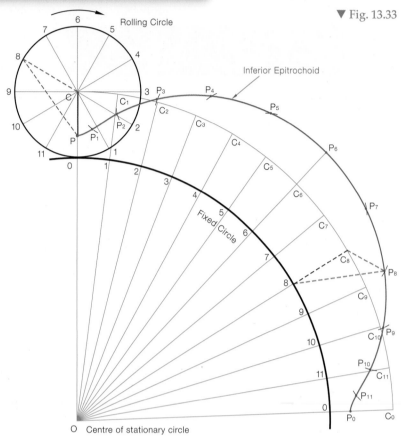

▼ Fig. 13.33

When a circle rolls, without slipping, around the outside of a fixed circle, then a point P inside the circle will follow the path of an inferior epitrochoid.

(1) Divide the circle into twelve equal parts.
(2) Set circumference off on the fixed circle.
(3) Rotate C about O and locate the twelve centres.
(4) Locate the points on the locus as before.

See worksheet 13.4

Superior Epitrochoid

When a circle rolls, without slipping, around the outside of a fixed circle, then a point P outside the circle will follow the path of a superior epitrochoid.

The construction of the locus follows the same method as before.

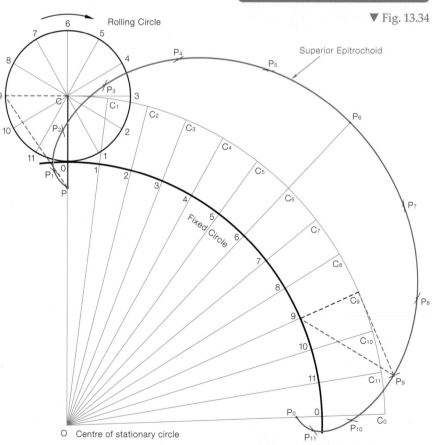

▼ Fig. 13.34

See worksheet 13.5

Inferior Hypotrochoid

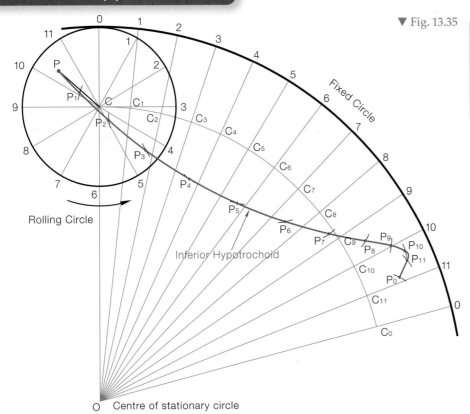

▼ Fig. 13.35

When a circle rolls, without slipping, around the inside of a fixed circle, then a point P inside the circle will follow the path of an inferior hypotrochoid.

Construction as before. Note the position of point P. The position of point P does not affect the method of construction.

See worksheet 13.6

Superior Hypotrochoid

When a circle rolls, without slipping, around the inside of a fixed circle, then a point P outside the circle will follow the path of a superior hypotrochoid.

Construction as before.

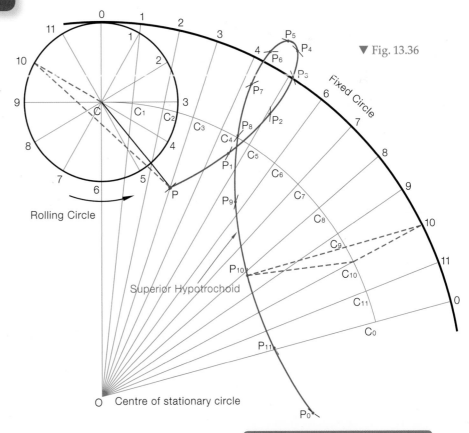

▼ Fig. 13.36

See worksheet 13.7

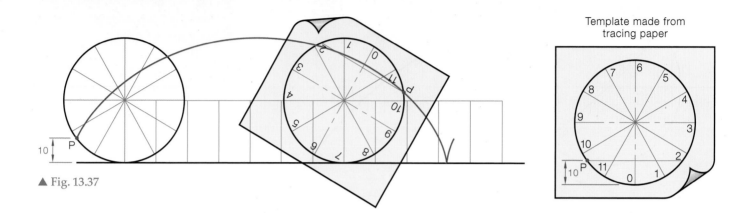

Use of Templates to Solve Problems on Cycloids, etc.

Template made from tracing paper

▲ Fig. 13.37

Most of these loci problems can be solved using a template. The template is moved into position and point P is plotted with a pencil or compass point, see Figures 13.37 and 13.38.

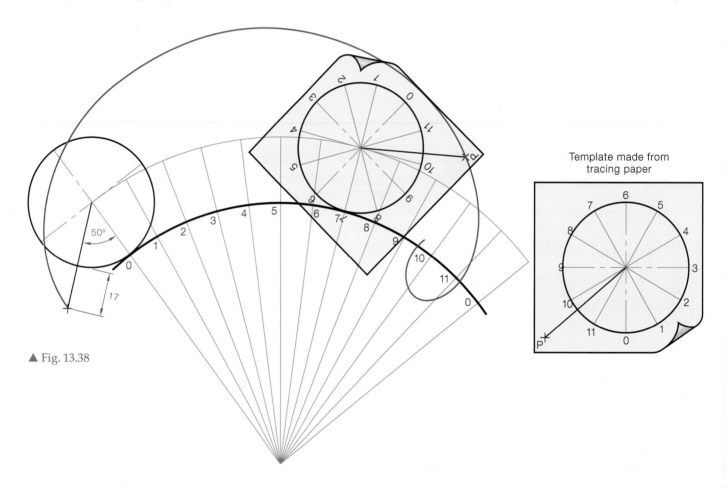

▲ Fig. 13.38

Template made from tracing paper

Tangent to an Involute, Archimedean Spiral, Cycloid, Epicycloid and Hypocycloid

Tangent to an Involute.

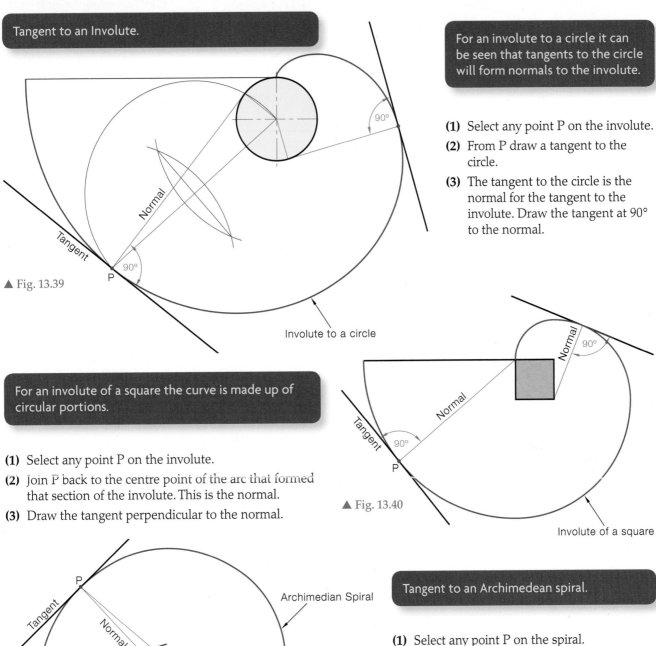

▲ Fig. 13.39

Involute to a circle

For an involute to a circle it can be seen that tangents to the circle will form normals to the involute.

(1) Select any point P on the involute.
(2) From P draw a tangent to the circle.
(3) The tangent to the circle is the normal for the tangent to the involute. Draw the tangent at 90° to the normal.

For an involute of a square the curve is made up of circular portions.

(1) Select any point P on the involute.
(2) Join P back to the centre point of the arc that formed that section of the involute. This is the normal.
(3) Draw the tangent perpendicular to the normal.

▲ Fig. 13.40

Involute of a square

Tangent to an Archimedean spiral.

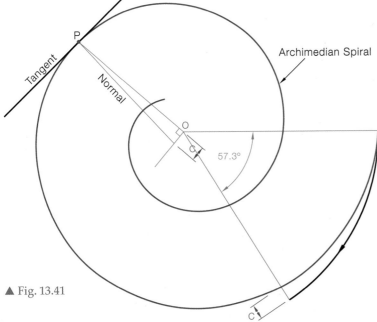

Archimedian Spiral

▲ Fig. 13.41

(1) Select any point P on the spiral.
(2) Join P to the pole, point O.
(3) Draw a perpendicular to PO at O.
(4) Measure out the constant C and draw the normal.
(5) The tangent is perpendicular to the normal. The constant c is the distance the spiral has moved closer to the pole over an angular distance of one radian. A radian equals approximately 57.3°, see Fig. 13.41.

Tangent to a Cycloid.

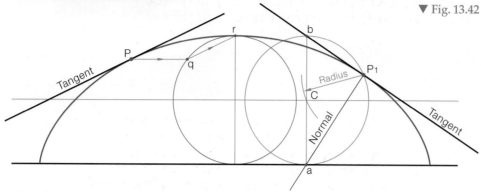

▼ Fig. 13.42   **Method 1**

(1) Choose any point P on the cycloid.
(2) Draw the circle at the cycloid's highest point.
(3) Project P horizontally to q.
(4) Join q to r.
(5) The tangent will be parallel to qr.

Method 2

(1) Choose any point P_1 on the cycloid.
(2) Using the radius of the circle, strike an arc from P_1 to locate c on the centre line.
(3) Draw the circle.
(4) The circle touches the base line at a. A line drawn from a through c will locate point b.
(5) P_1b is the tangent and P_1a is the normal.

Tangent to an epicycloid.

The construction is the same as for a cycloid.

(1) Choose point P anywhere.
(2) Locate and draw the circle.
(3) From O (the centre of the fixed circle) through c will locate points a and b.
(4) Pb is the tangent and Pa is the normal.

▼ Fig. 13.44

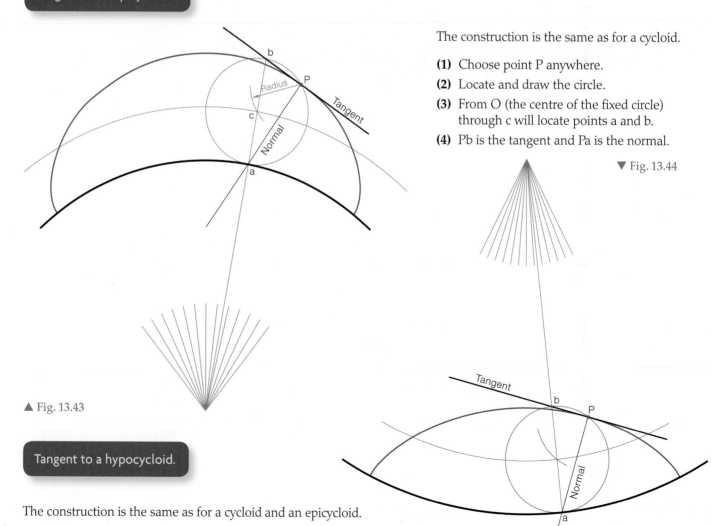

▲ Fig. 13.43

Tangent to a hypocycloid.

The construction is the same as for a cycloid and an epicycloid.

Worked Examples on Loci

In Fig. 13.45 the circle rolls clockwise for one revolution along the line AB. At the same time point P is moving to point C. Draw the path of point P for the combined movement.

(1) There are two movements occurring simultaneously. We will deal with one movement and then combine it with the other.

(2) Since we usually divide the rolling circle into twelve equal portions, it is easiest to break all the movements into twelve equal steps. We divide PC into twelve equal steps and index them. This is one movement. By the time the circle has travelled for half a revolution, point P will have moved to P_6.

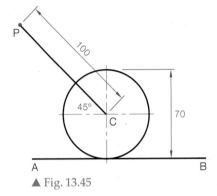

▲ Fig. 13.45

(3) Divide the circle and index.

(4) Step out the twelve steps and index.

(5) Locate the twelve centres, see Fig. 13.46.

(6) The points on the locus are located as before using arcs. We are not measuring to P at the end of the line, we are measuring to P_1, then P_2, then P_3 etc. For example: Take from 4 on the circumference of the circle to P_4 as radius. Place the compass on 4 on the base line and draw an arc. Take from the centre C of the circle to P_4 as radius. Place the compass on C_4 and draw an arc. Where the two arcs cross locates the fourth point on the locus, see Fig. 13.47.

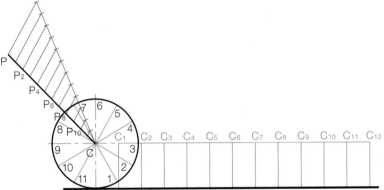

▲ Fig. 13.46

▲ Fig. 13.47

Fig. 13.48 shows a large circle B which rolls for half a revolution clockwise along the base line. At the same time the small circle A rolls for half a revolution around the circumference of the circle B, in a clockwise direction. Meanwhile point P moves to point D. Plot the locus of point P for the combined movements.

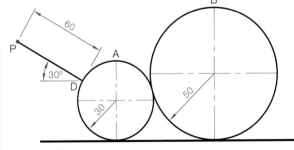

▲ Fig. 13.48

There are three movements occurring simultaneously in this problem. Complete one movement, combine it with the second and finally combine the first two with the third to give the full answer.

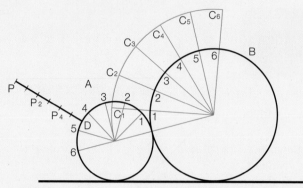

▲ Fig. 13.49

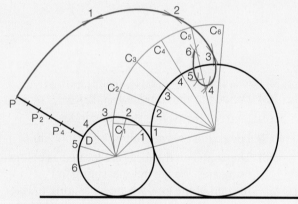

▲ Fig. 13.50

(1) Join the centres of the two circles.

(2) The small circle does a half turn. We divide half of it into six equal parts relative to the line joining the centres. Index these points.

(3) Step these steps off around the large circle.

(4) Locate the centres C_1 to C_6 by radiating from the centre of circle B.

(5) The line PD is now divided. It is divided into six equal parts because the next movement is in six steps.

(6) Plot the path of these two movements combined. Take the radius from 1 on the small circle to P_1. Scribe an arc from 1 on the large circle. Take a second radius from the centre of the small circle to P_1. Scribe an arc, to cross the first arc, from C_1, Fig. 13.50.

(7) We must combine these movements with the movement of the large circle. The large circle rotates for half a turn. Divide the half-circle into six equal parts.

(8) Step these off along the base line.

(9) Locate the six centres.

(10) The points on the locus are located by measuring to the first locus. Take from 1 on the large circle to point 1 on the locus as radius. Scribe an arc from point 1 on the base line. Take from the centre of the large circle to point 1 on the locus as radius. Scribe an arc from C_1 to cross the first arc etc., Fig. 13.51.

(11) Join the points with a smooth curve.

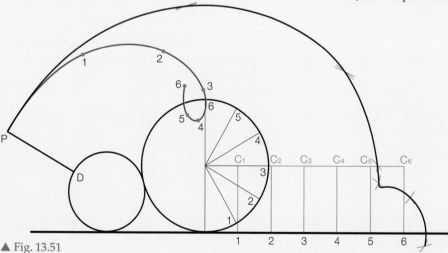

▲ Fig. 13.51

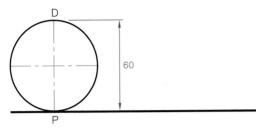

▲ Fig. 13.52

Fig. 13.52 shows a circle which rolls clockwise for one revolution on the given line. During the rolling of the circle an involute is unwound from P to D. Draw the locus of P for the combined movement.

There are two movements involved, the involute and the rolling circle. We start with the involute.

(1) Divide the half-circle into six equal portions. Construct a tangent at the end of each division.

(2) The string is unwinding from P to D, so at D it will be six units long. It shortens by one unit for each tangent moving toward point P.

(3) Divide the circle into twelve.

(4) Step the divisions out on the line.

(5) Index every second point as this will give us six steps, as we have in the involute.

(6) Locate C_1 to C_6.

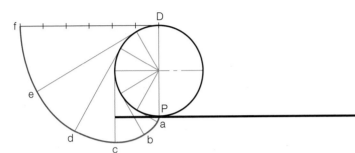

▲ Fig. 13.53

(7) Plot the points on the combined locus. Take from 1 on the circle to the first point on the involute, point a, as radius. Scribe an arc from 1 on the base line. Take from the centre of the circle to point a on the involute as radius. Scribe an arc from C_1 to cross the first arc, etc.

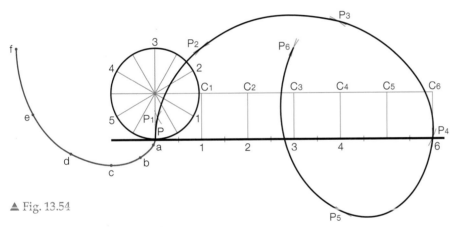

▲ Fig. 13.54

Activities

Q1. Draw an involute to the given shapes, figures 13.55 and 13.56. The involute should start at point P and unwind in a clockwise direction.

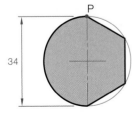

▲ Fig. 13.55

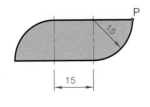

▲ Fig. 13.56

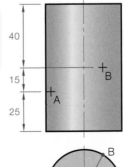

▲ Fig. 13.57

Q2. Given the plan and elevation of a cylinder with two points A and B on its surface. Draw a helix to go from the bottom to the top of the cylinder and to pass through points A and B.

Q3. Draw a single start, right-hand square screw thread given the inside diameter of 50 mm, outside diameter of 80 mm and the lead of 72 mm.

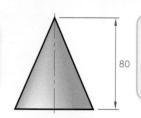

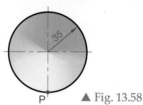

▲ Fig. 13.58

Q4. Draw a conical spiral to start at the base of the given cone at point P and to reach the apex in one revolution.

Q5. Draw an Archimedean spiral having its longest radius vector of 50 mm, its shortest radius vector of 14 mm and completing one convolution.

Q6. Draw an Archimedean spiral having 1½ convolutions. The spiral is to have a longest radius vector of 56 mm and a shortest radius vector of 20 mm.

Q7. Construct 1¼ convolutions of an Archimedean spiral given the longest vector as 60 mm and a decrease of 5 mm every 45°.

Q8. Construct ¾ of a convolution of an Archimedean spiral given the shortest radius vector of 15 mm and an increase every 15° of 3 mm.

Cycloids, epicycloids, etc.

Q9. The circle rolls clockwise along the given line without slipping. Plot the locus of point P for this movement.

HONOURS
Draw a tangent to the cycloid at the 6th point on the locus.

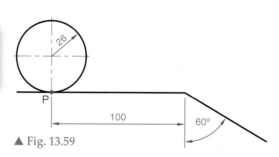

▲ Fig. 13.59

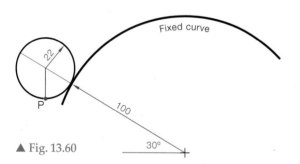

Fixed curve

▲ Fig. 13.60

Q10. In Fig. 13.60 the circle rolls clockwise along the fixed curve for one revolution. Plot the locus of point P for this movement.

HONOURS
Draw a tangent to the epicycloids from a point 30 mm from the fixed curve.

Q11. In Fig. 13.61 the small circle rolls round the
inside of the larger circle for one revolution. Plot
the locus of point P for this movement

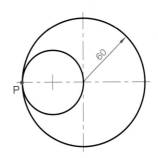

▲ Fig. 13.61

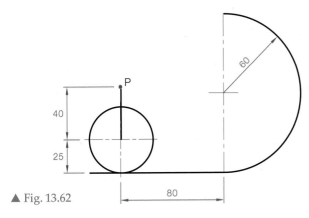

▲ Fig. 13.62

Q12. Plot the locus of point P as the circle rolls
clockwise for one complete revolution.

Q13. In Fig. 13.63 the large circle rolls round the small
circle for one revolution. Plot the locus of point P
for this movement.

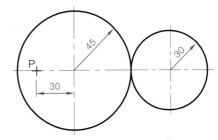

▲ Fig. 13.63

Dynamic Mechanisms 2

- Linkages   • Cams   • Gears

Types of Link Mechanism

Sliding link.

End A of the link slides along a set line forcing end B to slide along its set path.

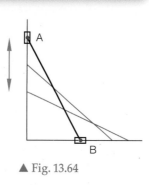

▲ Fig. 13.64

Swinging and sliding link.

As the rod swings about point A, the link C is sliding down.

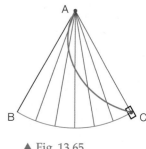

▲ Fig. 13.65

Crank and sliding link.

The rod AB rotates about point A. This is a crank. Rotating the crank causes link C to slide over and back.

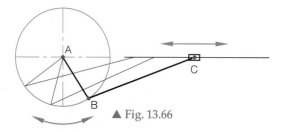

▲ Fig. 13.66

Double crank.

This mechanism only works if the length of BC equals that between the centres of A and D. Crank AB rotates. The link between B and C forces C to rotate about D.

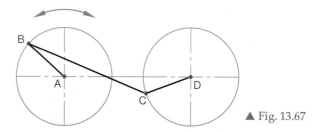

▲ Fig. 13.67

Crank and rocker.

As crank AB rotates, rocker arm CD moves forwards and backwards.

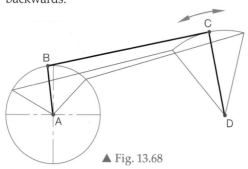

▲ Fig. 13.68

Crank and fixed through link.

C is fixed in position but allows BC to slide through it.

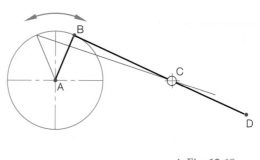

▲ Fig. 13.69

A ladder AB is leaning against a wall, with one end against the wall and the other on the floor. Plot the locus of the midpoint of the ladder as it slides to the floor.

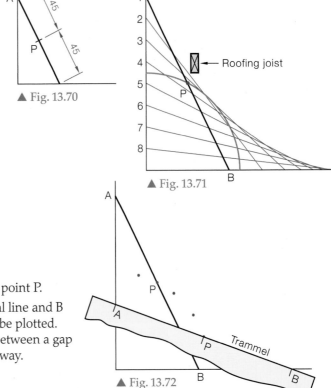

▲ Fig. 13.70

▲ Fig. 13.71

(1) Draw the problem, placing the ladder at a steep angle.

(2) Divide the distance from A to the corner into a number of parts.

(3) Draw the ladder in each position and locate point P in each case.

(4) Join all the plotted points to form the locus. This locus is called a glisette.

Alternative method

Many of these loci problems can be solved using a trammel.

(1) Mark off the length of the ladder AB and the position of point P.

(2) By moving the trammel so that A slides along the vertical line and B slides along the horizontal line, the locus of point P can be plotted. This construction may be used to see if a ladder will fit between a gap in roofing joists or if a long object will fit through a doorway.

▲ Fig. 13.72

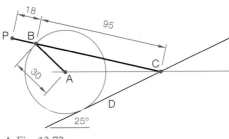

▲ Fig. 13.73

Fig. 13.73 shows a crank AB which revolves in a clockwise direction around pivot A. Link PC is pin-jointed at B. End C slides on line DE. Plot the locus of point P for one revolution of the crank.

(1) Set up the problem.

(2) Divide the circle into twelve equal parts.

(3) For each division draw in the link BC ensuring that C is always on the line DE and 95 mm long.

(4) Point P can be found for each position of the crank arm. The first six steps are shown.

(5) This problem can more easily be solved with a trammel as shown in Fig. 13.75.

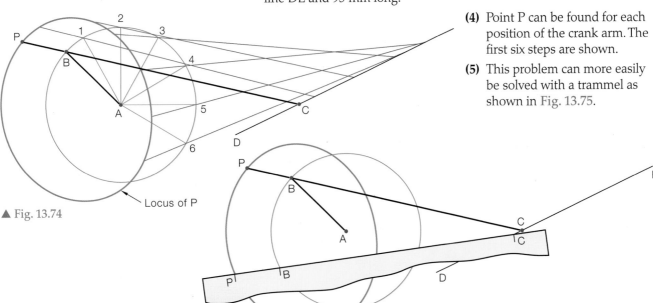

▲ Fig. 13.74

▲ Fig. 13.75

Fig. 13.76 represents an up-and-over garage door in a partly open position. Pivot C slides along line AF while A and B can pivot. Draw the locus of both E and D as the door opens and closes.

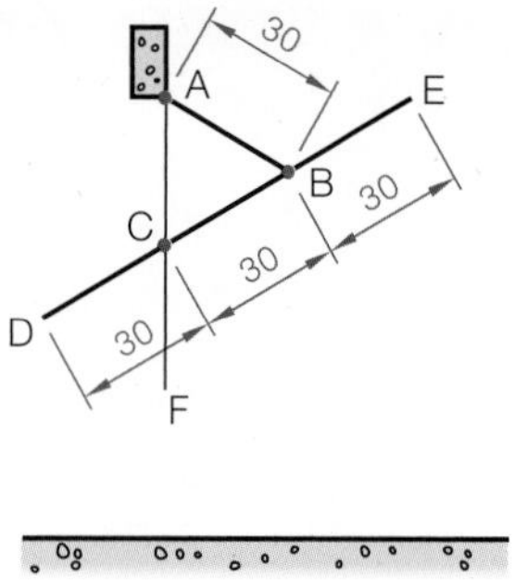

(1) Set up the problem as given.

(2) Cut a suitable trammel and on it mark the door length D to E. Mark the pivot points B and C.

(3) Pivot C follows the line AF and pivot B will follow a circular path with A as centre.

(4) Use the trammel to plot all the points.

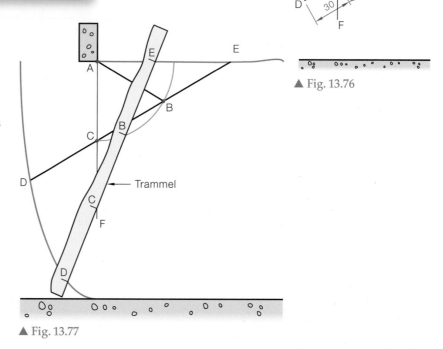

▲ Fig. 13.76

▲ Fig. 13.77

Fig. 13.78 shows a crank AB which rotates about point A. Link BP can slide through the pivot C. Plot the locus of P for one revolution of the crank.

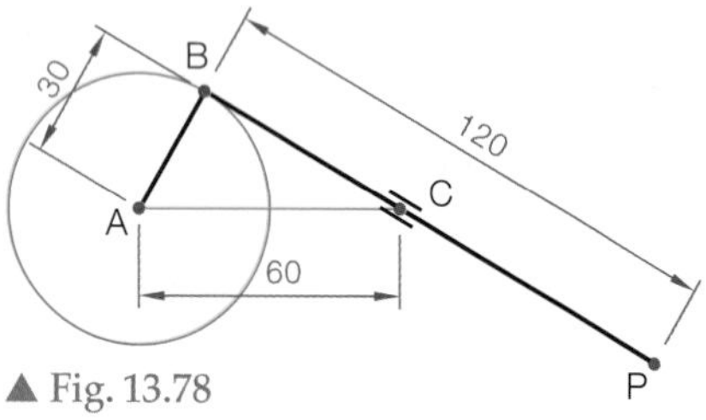

(1) Set up the problem.

(2) Cut a trammel and on it mark B and P.

(3) Use the trammel to plot the points by keeping B on the circle and the line BP passing through C.

▲ Fig. 13.78

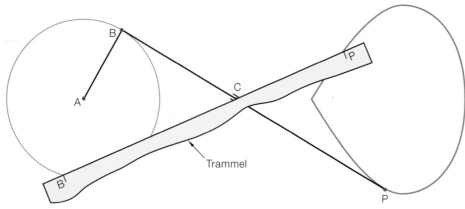

▲ Fig. 13.79

See worksheets 13.8 and 13.9

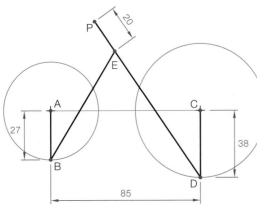

BE = 70 mm   BE = 85 mm

▲ Fig. 13.80

Fig. 13.80 shows a crank AB which rotates anti-clockwise about pivot C. Another crank CD rotates clockwise about pivot C. Link BE pivots at B and E. Link DEP pivots at D and E. Plot the locus of point P for one revolution of the cranks. (Both cranks rotate at the same rate.)

It should be noted that this mechanism has a number of moving parts and is not easily solved using a trammel.

(1) Divide both crank circles into twelve equal parts and index, remembering that AB rotates anticlockwise and CD rotates clockwise.

(2) At each position on the circles the full mechanism is constructed finding a point on the locus (construction for P_0, P_3 and P_7 shown).

(3) Join the twelve points on the path with a smooth curve.

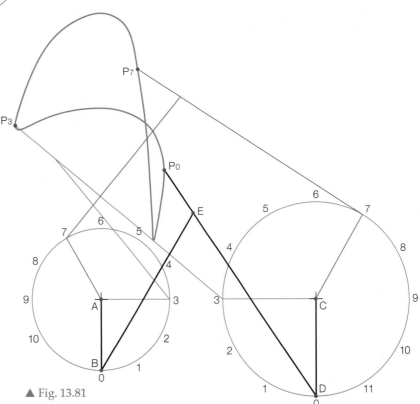

▲ Fig. 13.81

See worksheet 13.10

Displacement Diagram

Fig. 13.82 shows a crank AB which pivots about A. A rocker arm DC pivots about D. B and C are pivots and P is a sliding link. Plot the displacement diagram for point P for one complete clockwise revolution of the crank.

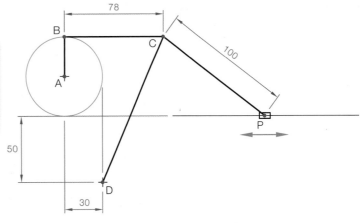

▲ Fig. 13.82

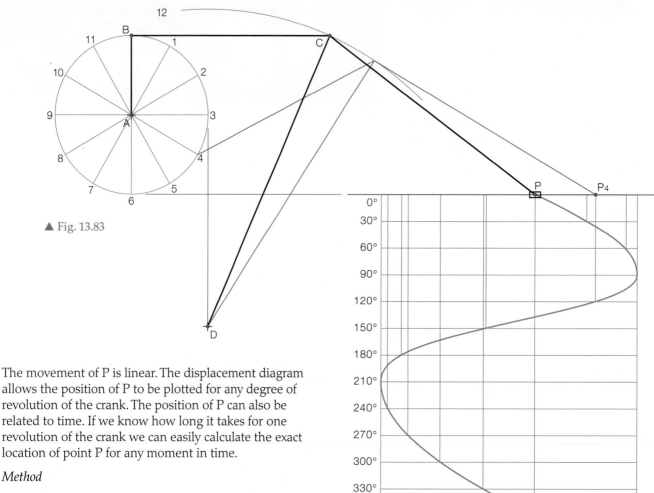

▲ Fig. 13.83

The movement of P is linear. The displacement diagram allows the position of P to be plotted for any degree of revolution of the crank. The position of P can also be related to time. If we know how long it takes for one revolution of the crank we can easily calculate the exact location of point P for any moment in time.

Method

(1) Plot all twelve positions of point P as the crank rotates. This will establish the maximum and minimum positions of point P.

(2) Set out a graph as shown in Fig. 13.83. The height of the graph does not matter as long as it is divided into twelve equal parts. The graph is divided into twelve because the rotation of the crank was broken into twelve equal steps.

(3) The position of point P is plotted for each 30° rotation. This point is plotted on the graph (P4 shown.)

(4) Repeat for each of the twelve steps of the crank's rotation.

Activities

Q1. Fig. 13.84 shows a crank AB which rotates for one complete revolution. Link BC is pin-jointed at B and end C is restricted to the path shown. Plot the locus of P for the movement.

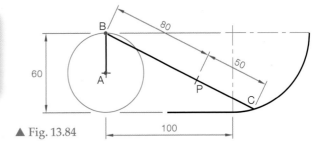

▲ Fig. 13.84

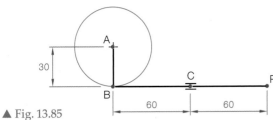

▲ Fig. 13.85

Q2. Crank AB rotates about point A. Link BP is pin-jointed at point B. Point C is a fixed-through pivot. Plot the locus of point P for one full revolution of the crank.

Q3. Crank AB rotates about A. Rocker arm DC rotates about D. Link BCP is pin-jointed at B and C. Plot the locus of point P for one complete revolution of the crank.

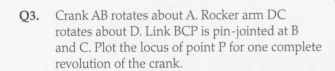

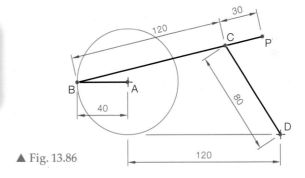

▲ Fig. 13.86

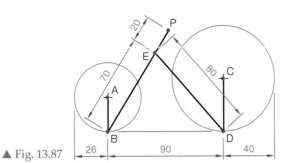

▲ Fig. 13.87

Q4. Fig. 13.87 shows a crank AB which rotates about A. Another crank CD rotates about C. Both cranks rotate at the same rate and in the same direction. Links DE and BEP are pivot-jointed at B, D and E. Plot the locus of point P for one complete revolution of the cranks.

Q5. Fig. 13.88 shows two cranks, AB and CD. AB rotates clockwise and rotates twice for every one revolution of CD, which rotates anticlockwise. B, D and E are pivot joints and P is a sliding link. Plot the locus of E for one revolution of CD (two revolutions of AB). Draw a displacement diagram for P for the full movement.

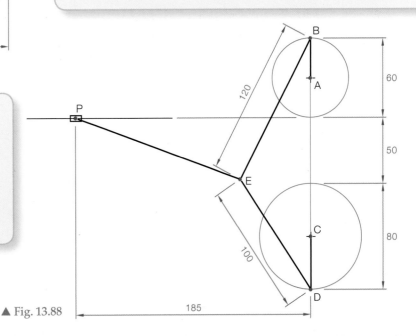

▲ Fig. 13.88

Cams

A cam is a shaped component generally used to change rotary movement into linear movement. Cams are used regularly in engine parts and mechanisms. The most usual types are **radial plate cams**. A shaft rotating at uniform speed carries a disc, usually of irregular shape, called the cam. A follower presses against the curved surface of the cam, Fig. 13.89. Rotation of the cam causes the follower to move according to the shape of the cam profile. The follower is kept in constant contact with the cam by gravity, or by using a spring. The follower shown in the diagram is a **knife-edge follower**. There are other types of follower which we will look at later on in the chapter. A knife-edge follower can follow very complicated cam shapes but wears rapidly.

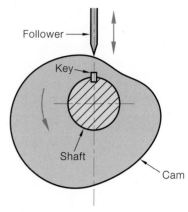

▲ Fig. 13.89

Displacement Diagrams

The movement of the follower is an important consideration in cam design. Its rate of movement and position varies hugely according to the cam profile. A displacement diagram is a means of planning this follower movement before the cam is constructed. It is a graph plotting the movement of the follower for one full revolution of the cam.

Uniform Velocity

The follower rises or falls at a constant speed. The movement will plot as a straight line on a graph.

Uniform velocity gives constant follower speed but produces abrupt changes which may cause the follower to jump. It should be noted that those portions of the cam that give uniform rise or fall to the follower will be portions of Archimedean spirals. When the follower dwells, the cam profile will be a portion of a circle having the same centre as the cam.

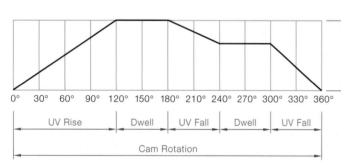

▲ Fig. 13.90

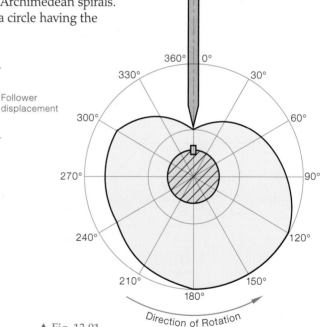

▲ Fig. 13.91

Simple Harmonic Motion (SHM)

Simple harmonic motion produces a very gentle transition from one movement to the next. The speed of the follower is not constant. The construction is based on a circle and produces a sine curve on the follower displacement diagram.

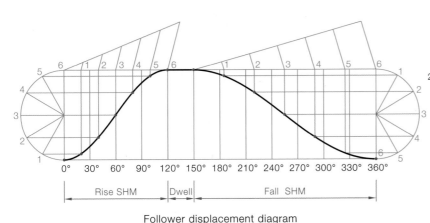

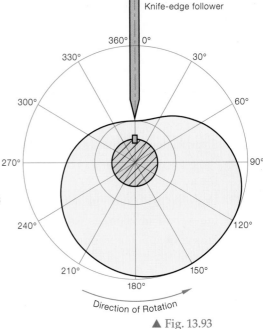

▲ Fig. 13.92

▲ Fig. 13.93

Method

(1) Draw a semicircle to match the rise that is required for the follower. This semicircle is usually placed at the end of the follower displacement diagram.

(2) Divide the semicircle into equal segments, usually six.

(3) Divide the length of rotation it takes for the full movement into the same number of equal parts.

(4) Plot the points as shown in Fig. 13.92.

Uniform Acceleration and Retardation (UAR)

As the name suggests, the follower accelerates smoothly and decelerates smoothly at the start and the end of this movement.

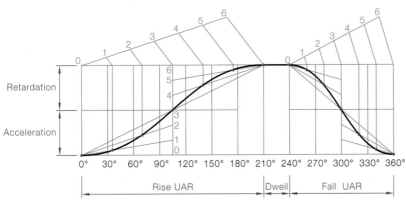

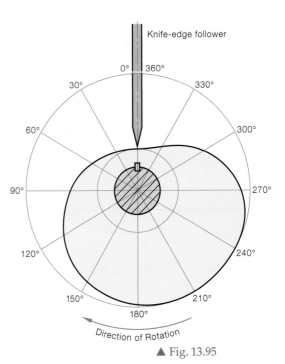

▲ Fig. 13.94

▲ Fig. 13.95

Method

The construction is based on two half parabolas. We use the rectangle method as shown in Fig. 13.94.

> Draw the profile of a clockwise cam to give the following displacement to an in-line knife-edge follower:
> 0° to 120° a UV rise of 36 mm,
> 120° to 330° a SHM fall of 36 mm,
> 330° to 360° dwell.
> The centre of the cam is 18 mm below the nearest approach of the follower.

(1) Start by drawing the follower displacement diagram. The height of the graph will be 36 mm. The length of the diagram does not matter but should be easily divisible by twelve.

(2) Project across the top and bottom of the follower displacement diagram. The centre of the cam will be 18 mm below the minimum line.

(3) Draw the maximum and minimum circles and divide them into twelve equal segments.

(4) Index these divisions. Since the cam rotates clockwise the divisions on the circles will be indexed anticlockwise.

(5) Project each point on a degree line on the follower displacement diagram across to the vertical axis of the cam.

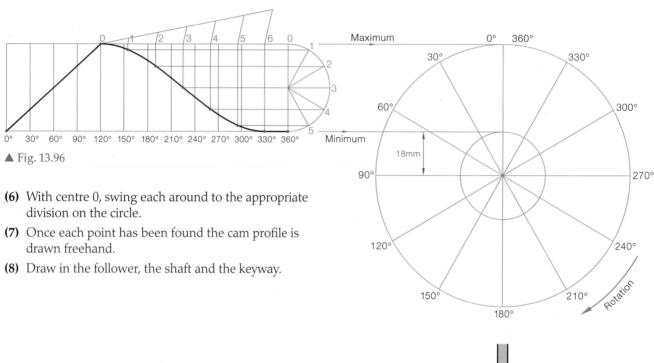

▲ Fig. 13.96

(6) With centre 0, swing each around to the appropriate division on the circle.

(7) Once each point has been found the cam profile is drawn freehand.

(8) Draw in the follower, the shaft and the keyway.

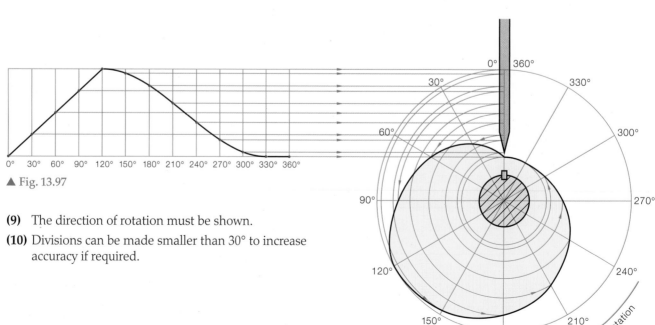

▲ Fig. 13.97

(9) The direction of rotation must be shown.

(10) Divisions can be made smaller than 30° to increase accuracy if required.

Draw the profile of an anti-clockwise cam to give the following displacement to an in-line knife-edge follower:
0° to 120° simple harmonic rise of 30 mm,
120° to 180° uniform velocity rise of 10 mm,
180° to 330° uniform acceleration and retardation fall of 40 mm,
330° to 360° dwell.
Cam centre 16 mm below nearest approach of the follower.

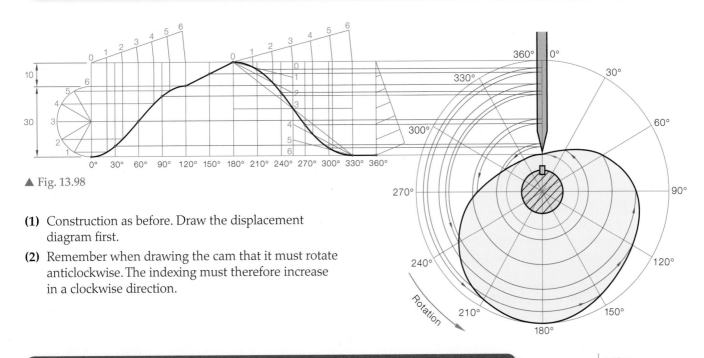

▲ Fig. 13.98

(1) Construction as before. Draw the displacement diagram first.

(2) Remember when drawing the cam that it must rotate anticlockwise. The indexing must therefore increase in a clockwise direction.

Plot the follower displacement diagram for an in-line knife-edge follower in contact with the cam profile shown in Fig. 13.99.

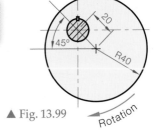

▲ Fig. 13.99

(1) Draw the cam.
(2) With centre C draw the maximum and minimum displacement circles.
(3) Divide the cam into segments and index.

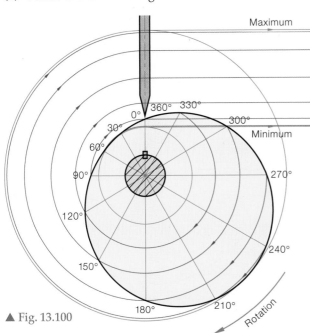

Follower Displacement Diagram

▲ Fig. 13.100

(4) Project the maximum and minimum heights of the follower from the centre line to give the top and bottom lines of the follower displacement diagram.

(5) With C as centre rotate the points on the division lines on the cam around onto the follower centre line.

(6) Project these points across to their corresponding positions on the follower displacement diagram.

(7) Complete the follower displacement diagram by drawing a smooth curve through the points.

Other follower types

Roller Follower

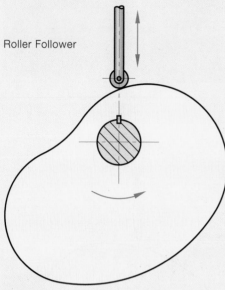

▲ Fig. 13.101

Flat Follower

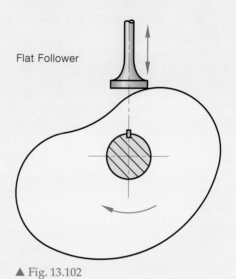

▲ Fig. 13.102

Given the follower displacement data:
0° to 120° uniform acceleration and retardation rise of 36 mm,
120° to 180° uniform velocity rise of 12 mm,
180° to 240° dwell,
240° to 360° simple harmonic motion fall of 48 mm.
The roller follower is in-line and 12 mm in diameter. Rotation of cam is clockwise. The nearest approach of the roller centre to the cam centre is 20 mm.

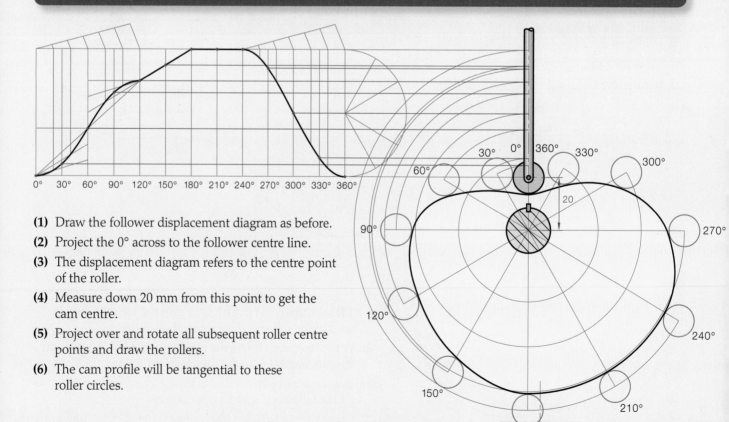

(1) Draw the follower displacement diagram as before.
(2) Project the 0° across to the follower centre line.
(3) The displacement diagram refers to the centre point of the roller.
(4) Measure down 20 mm from this point to get the cam centre.
(5) Project over and rotate all subsequent roller centre points and draw the rollers.
(6) The cam profile will be tangential to these roller circles.

▲ Fig. 13.103

HIGHER LEVEL

Given the follower displacement data:
0° to 60° dwell,
60° to 180° SHM rise of 30 mm,
180° to 240° UV rise of 18 mm,
240° to 360° UAR fall of 48 mm.
The follower is in-line and flat and extends 6 mm to either side of the centre line. The centre of the cam is 16 mm below the nearest approach of the follower. The cam rotates anti-clockwise.

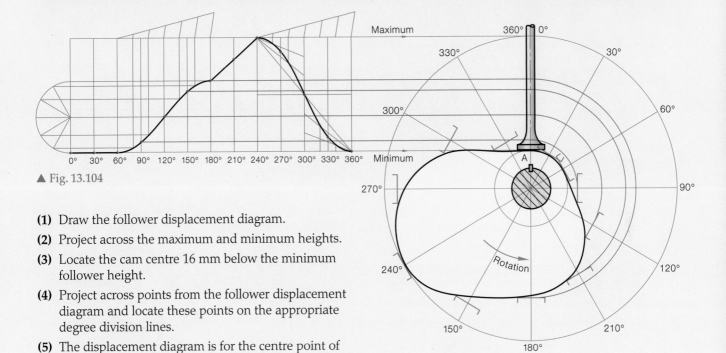

▲ Fig. 13.104

(1) Draw the follower displacement diagram.
(2) Project across the maximum and minimum heights.
(3) Locate the cam centre 16 mm below the minimum follower height.
(4) Project across points from the follower displacement diagram and locate these points on the appropriate degree division lines.
(5) The displacement diagram is for the centre point of the base of the follower, point A. At each point located around the circle draw the follower base as shown.
(6) Draw the cam profile so that the follower touches it at each location.

See worksheets 13.12, 13.13 and 13.14

HIGHER LEVEL

Terms Used in Gearing

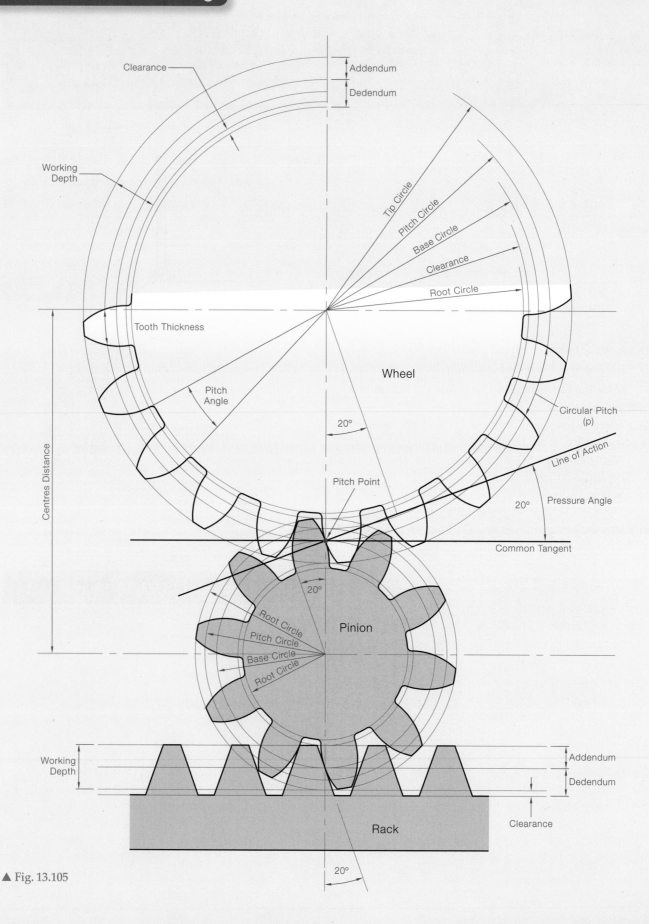

Clearance

Addendum

Dedendum

Working Depth

Tip Circle

Pitch Circle

Base Circle

Clearance

Root Circle

Tooth Thickness

Wheel

Pitch Angle

Centres Distance

Circular Pitch (p)

Line of Action

20°

20°

Pressure Angle

Pitch Point

Common Tangent

20°

Root Circle

Pitch Circle

Base Circle

Root Circle

Pinion

Working Depth

Addendum

Dedendum

Clearance

Rack

20°

HIGHER LEVEL

▲ Fig. 13.105

Addendum (a)	The part of the tooth that extends outside the pitch circle or pitchline. The addendum will always equal the module. **a = m**
Base Circle	An imaginary circle from which the tooth shape is generated. The base circle diameter = the pitch circle diameter × cos (pressure angle) BCD = PCD × cos (pressure angle)
Circular Pitch (p)	Circular pitch is the distance from a point on one tooth to the corresponding point on the next tooth, measured round the pitch circle. **p = πm**
Circular Tooth Thickness	The thickness of a tooth measured along the pitch circle. **Circular tooth thickness** $\dfrac{p}{2} = \dfrac{\pi m}{s}$
Clearance (c)	Clearance equals one quarter of the addendum. The clearance is the space underneath the tooth when it is in mesh. **c = d – a = 0.25a = 0.25 m**
Dedendum (d)	The part of the tooth which is inside the pitch circle or pitch line. The dedendum equals 1.25 × addendum. **d = 1.25 × a**
Line of Action	Contact between the teeth of meshing gears takes place along a line tangential to the two base circles. This line passes through the pitch point.
Module (m)	The module is the pitch circle diameter divided by the number of teeth. $$m = \frac{PCD}{t} = \frac{\text{Pitch circle diameter}}{\text{No. of teeth}}$$ For example, a gear having a PCD of 200 and 20 teeth will have a module of 10.
PCD	Pitch circle diameter.
Pinion	When two gears are in mesh the smaller gear is called the pinion.
Pitch Angle	360° divided by the number of teeth.
Pitch Circle (PC)	This is the circle representing the original cylinder which transmitted motion by friction.
Pitch Point	When two gears are in mesh their pitch circles will be tangential to each other. The pitch point is the point of contact between these two circles.
Pressure Angle	The angle between the line of action and the common tangent to the pitch circles at the pitch point. The pressure angle is normally **20°** but may be **14.5°**.
Tip Circle	A circle through the tips of the teeth.
Wheel	When two gears are in mesh the larger one is called the wheel.
Whole Depth	This is the depth of a tooth from tip to root. The whole depth equals the addendum and dedendum.
Working Depth	The whole depth minus the clearance.

HIGHER LEVEL

Gear Basics

We will start by considering the theoretically perfect gears – two toothless discs. These gears touch at a single point. The rotation of one gear is perfectly transmitted to the other. There is no friction between the gears and there is no friction or wear on the bearings. Unfortunately, if these gears are not held tightly together they will slip. Furthermore, when they are held tightly together we will have friction and wear on the gears themselves and on the bearings and there will be a considerable loss of power.

To overcome this difficulty we cut teeth into the discs, so that they will engage each other without slipping and without unduly increasing the friction. **The diameters of these perfect toothless gears are the Pitch Circle diameters of the gears**.

Gear teeth

The aim when designing teeth shape is that the faces of the teeth will roll across each other, minimising the sliding friction. There are two types of curve commonly used: epicycloidal (the curve generated by tracing a point on a circle as it rolls around another circle); and involute (the curve generated by unwinding a line from a circle).

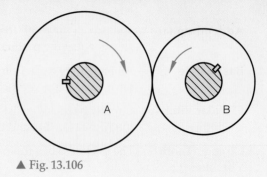

▲ Fig. 13.106

Gear ratio

The relative speed of rotation of the two discs is proportional to their radii. Since the circumferences of the circles are in contact a point on the circumference of disc A will move the same distance as a point on the circumference of disc B as they both rotate.

Circumference of large disc A $2\pi R$: Circumference of smaller disc B $2\pi r$

$$\cancel{2\pi}R : \cancel{2\pi}r$$

$$R \quad : \quad r$$

The ratio of the rotational speeds is called the gear ratio. If the wheel has a PCD of 100 mm and the pinion has a PCD of 50 mm then the gear ratio will be 2:1. The pinion rotates twice as fast as the wheel. This, of course, will only apply if both **gears have the same pressure angle and module**.

Gear tooth design

As mentioned previously the ideal for all gearing is to have only rolling contact between the tooth surfaces of mating gear teeth, thus reducing both wear and friction. When two teeth interact as a pair of gears rotate, the mating curves must satisfy certain conditions to obtain this rolling action. Given almost any reasonable curve for one tooth, a mating tooth can be derived that will give this rolling action. Such a pair of curves are said to be **conjugate**. It is especially neat if the two conjugate curves are based on the same construction. Involute gears satisfy this requirement.

Involute Gears

A piece of string is wrapped tightly around a disc. Unwind the free end, keeping the string tight at all times. The free end as it unravels will trace out an involute curve, Fig. 13.107. By using the same construction for another disc, another involute is formed which is conjugate to the first. Use these two curves, or parts of them, as the sides of gear teeth and the teeth will roll together as they mesh. Modern machinery uses involute gearing predominantly.

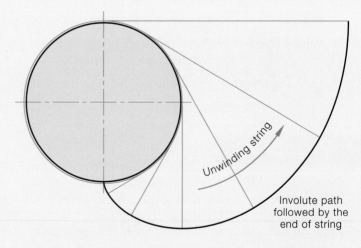

Unwinding string

Involute path followed by the end of string

▲ Fig. 13.107

Epicycloidal Gears

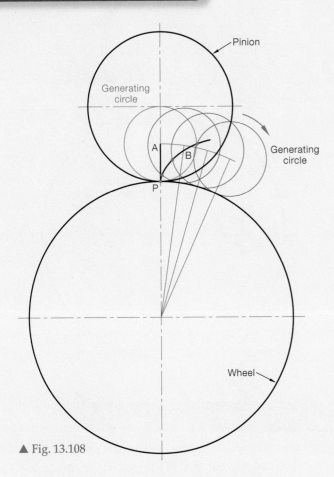

▲ Fig. 13.108

Cycloidal gearing requires two different curves to obtain conjugate action. Fig. 13.108 shows two discs, the wheel and the pinion. A third disc is introduced which is used to generate the tooth profile. If we plot the path of point P on the generating circle as it rolls around the outside of the wheel circle it generates curve B, which is an epicycloid. Using the same generating circle to roll on the inside of the pinion circle a conjugate curve is formed which is a hypocycloid. When the generating circle has a diameter equal to the radius of the pinion circle, the hypocycloid formed is a straight line, A, as shown. The addendum of the wheel is an epicycloid curve B and the dedendum of the pinion is a hypocycloid, straight line, A in this example.

In the same way a generating circle in the wheel generates the flank C of the tooth on the lower gear and the addendum D of the pinion, Fig. 13.109. Between them the two generating circles have generated the tooth shape for each of the two gears. Of particular interest here is that if the sizes of the generating circles are chosen carefully the dedendum of the teeth will be radial straight lines. Fig. 13.110 shows the proof that a hypocycloid generated by a circle rolling inside a circle of twice its radius will be a straight line.

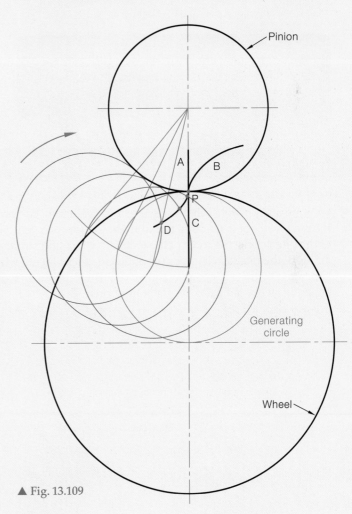

▲ Fig. 13.109

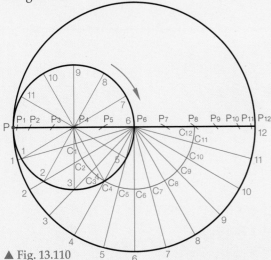

▲ Fig. 13.110

Law of Gearing

Gears are arranged to have sliding contact between pairs of surfaces formed by the teeth of the gears, the rotation of the gears bringing successive pairs into contact. The teeth surfaces in sliding contact have a common tangent and the pressure being exerted between these two teeth will be normal to this tangent. This normal forms the line of action for the gears shown in Fig. 13.111. The line of action and the common tangent between the pitch circles form an angle, the pressure angle. For involute gears this pressure angle is a constant and is usually 20° or 14.5°. For cycloidal gear teeth the pressure angle is variable, becoming zero for contact at the pitch point.

In order that gear motion is smooth, quiet and free from vibration, the Law of Gearing must be satisfied.

> **Law of Gearing**
> The normal to the common tangent between two gear teeth surfaces must pass through the pitch point of the gears.

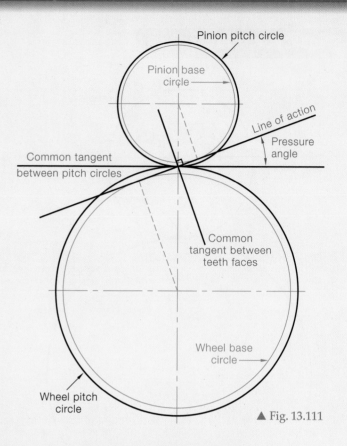

▲ Fig. 13.111

Some Things to Note about the Size of the Generating Circle

We have already noted that using a pair of generating circles having radii equal to half that of the pitch circles produces the neat result of generating **radial dedenda** for each gear tooth. If the generating circle is **smaller** than half the radius of the pitch circle, the roots of the teeth are wider and stronger but not radial. A generating circle **larger** than half the radius of the pitch circle produces undercut, necked teeth which may be weak. The teeth of a cycloidal rack are cycloids generated by the rolling generating circle. They are not straight, like they are in an involute rack, and their shape depends on the radius of the generating circle.

Worked Examples

(1) Draw the pitch circle, tip circle and root circle. We are given the pitch circle diameter of 160 mm or radius 80 mm. The addendum equals the module. Therefore the addendum equals 10 mm. The tip circle radius will be equal to the radius of the pitch circle plus the addendum, 80 mm + 10 mm = 90 mm. The root circle radius will be equal to the radius of the pitch circle minus the dedendum. The dedendum will be 12.5 mm, therefore the root circle radius will be 67.5 mm (dedendum = 1.25 module).

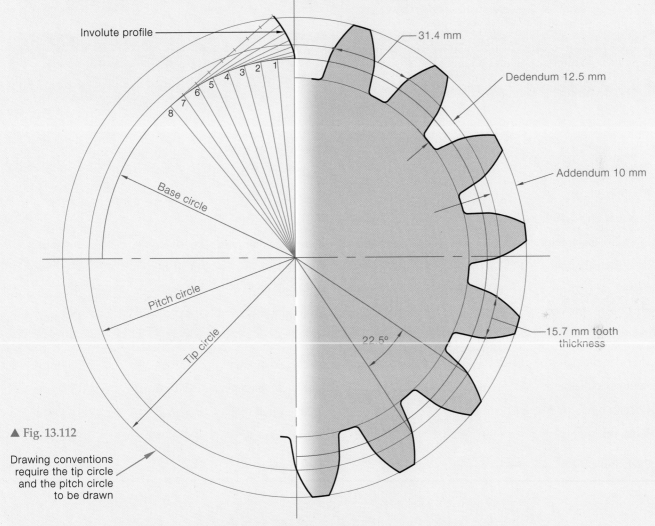

Involute profile

31.4 mm

Dedendum 12.5 mm

Base circle

Addendum 10 mm

Pitch circle

Tip circle

22.5°

15.7 mm tooth thickness

▲ Fig. 13.112

Drawing conventions require the tip circle and the pitch circle to be drawn

HIGHER LEVEL

(2) Calculate the radius of the base circle, the circle from which the tooth profile is generated.

Base circle diameter = Pitch circle diameter × cos (pressure angle)

$$BCD = 160 \text{ mm} \times \cos 20°$$
$$BCD = 150.4 \text{ mm}$$

Draw the base circle.

(3) Calculate the number of teeth.

$$PCD = \text{module (m)} \times \text{number of teeth (t)}$$
$$\Rightarrow \quad \frac{PCD}{m} = t$$
$$\frac{160}{10} = 16 \text{ teeth}$$

See worksheet 13.15

HIGHER LEVEL

(4) Calculate the circular pitch, the distance from one point on a tooth to a similar point on the next.

$$p = \pi m$$

$$p = 31.4 \text{ mm}$$

The tooth thickness measured on the pitch circle equals half of this, 15.7 mm.

The angular pitch equals $\dfrac{360°}{t} = \dfrac{360°}{16} = 22.5°$

(5) Set out the teeth spacing on the pitch circle either by angular measurement or by measurement along the circumference.

(6) Generate one involute from the base circle which is used to draw all the teeth profiles. The construction of an involute has been covered earlier and is shown on Fig. 13.113. The involute is unwound until the tip circle is reached.

(7) The portion of the dedendum inside the base circle usually radiates toward the centre or can curve slightly.

(8) For the other half only the pitch circle and the tip circle are drawn.

Draw two involute spur gears showing the gears in mesh. Show five teeth on each gear. The gear ratio is 5:4. Driver gear details: module 10, 20 teeth, pressure angle 20°. Tabulate all necessary data for the two gears.

Driver Gear				Driven Gear			
Module (m)		10		Module (m)			10
No. of teeth (t)		20		No. of teeth (t)	5:4 = 20:16		16
Pressure angle (θ)		20°		Pressure angle (θ)			20°
Pitch circle diameter	m × t	200 mm		Pitch circle diameter	m × t		160 mm
Base circle diameter	PCD × cos θ	188 mm		Base circle diameter	PCD × cos θ		150.4 mm
Addendum (a)	a = m	10 mm		Addendum (a)	a = m		10 mm
Dedendum (d)	1.25 × a	12.5 mm		Dedendum (d)	1.25 × a		12.5 mm
Clearance	0.25 × m	2.5 mm		Clearance	0.25 × m		2.5 mm
Tip circle diameter	PCD + a + a	220 mm		Tip circle diameter	PCD + a + a		180 mm
Root circle diameter	PCD – d – d	175 mm		Root circle diameter	PCD – d – d		135 mm
Circular pitch (p)	π × m 31.4 mm			Circular pitch (p)	π × m		31.4 mm
Tooth thickness	$\frac{p}{2}$	215.7 mm		Tooth thickness	$\frac{p}{2}$		15.7 mm
Pitch angle	$\frac{360°}{t}$	18°		Pitch angle	$\frac{360°}{t}$		22.5°

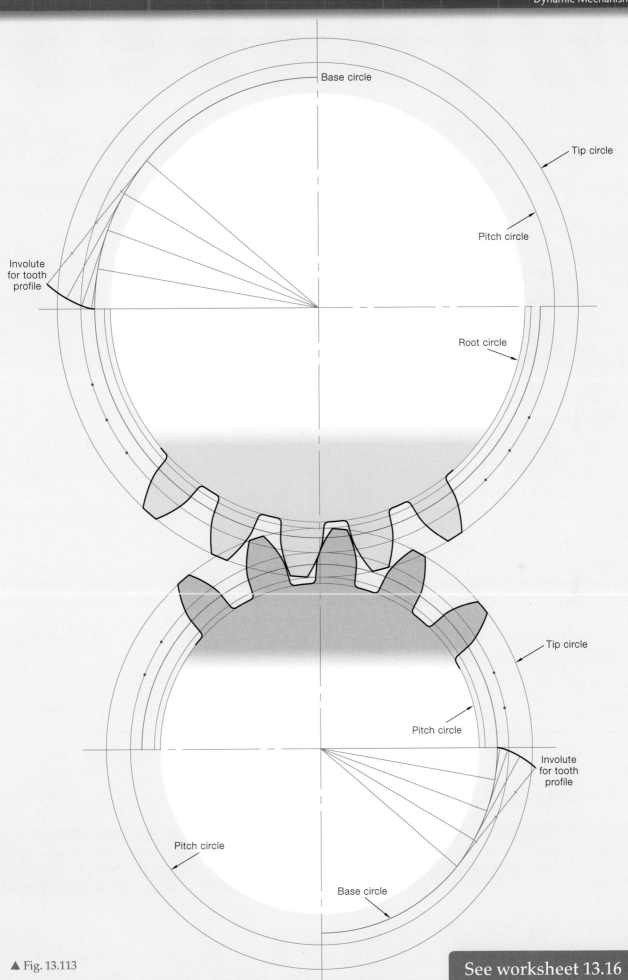

▲ Fig. 13.113

See worksheet 13.16

Fig. 13.114 shows a spur gear train. Draw the following table. Complete it by inserting the missing gear train information.

Gear	Teeth	Module	PCD	Rotation	Speed rpm
A	36	6		Clockwise	300
B	24				
C	12				

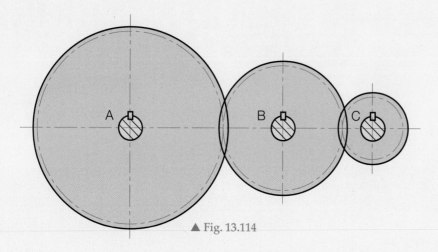

▲ Fig. 13.114

Solution

(1) The module for meshing gears in a train should be the same for all the gears or they will vibrate and wear badly.

(2) The PCD, pitch circle diameter = number of teeth × module.

(3) The rotation of gears in a train alternates between clockwise and anticlockwise.

(4) The speed of the rotating gears is related to the number of teeth. For every complete turn of gear A, gear B must rotate 1.5 times. An rpm of 300 for gear A will give an rpm of 450 for gear B. Gear C rotates twice for every complete turn of gear B. The smallest gear must therefore rotate at 900 rpm.

Gear	Teeth	Module	PCD	Rotation	Speed rpm
A	36	6	216	Clockwise	300
B	24	6	144	Anti-clockwise	450
C	12	6	72	Clockwise	900

An involute gear wheel with 24 teeth, 20° pressure angle and module 10 is in mesh with a rack. Draw, full size, the gear and rack in mesh, showing five teeth on the gear and five teeth on the rack. Tabulate all relevant information and calculations.

Gear Wheel

Module (m)		10
No. of teeth (t)		24
Pressure angle (θ)		20°
Pitch circle diameter	m × t	240 mm
Base circle diameter	PCD × cos θ	225.5 mm
Addendum (a)	a = m	10 mm
Dedendum (d)	1.25 × a	12.5 mm
Clearance	d × a	2.5 mm
Tip circle diameter	PCD + 2a 2	60 mm
Root circle diameter	PCD − 2d	215 mm
Circular pitch (p)	π × m	31.4 mm
Tooth thickness	$\frac{p}{2}$	15.7 mm
Pitch angle	$\frac{360°}{t}$	22.5°

Rack

Module	10
Pressure angle	20°
Addendum	10 mm
Dedendum	12.5 mm
Clearance	2.5 mm
Pitch	31.4 mm
Tooth thickness	15.7 mm

(1) Draw the pitch circle, tip circle and root circle.

(2) The base circle can be found by calculation or by finding the circle that is tangential to the line of action.

(3) Draw the pitch line, tip line and root line for the rack. The pitch line and pitch circle are tangential at point P.

(4) Construct the involute tooth profile from the base circle and using tracing paper reproduce this curve to pass through point P.

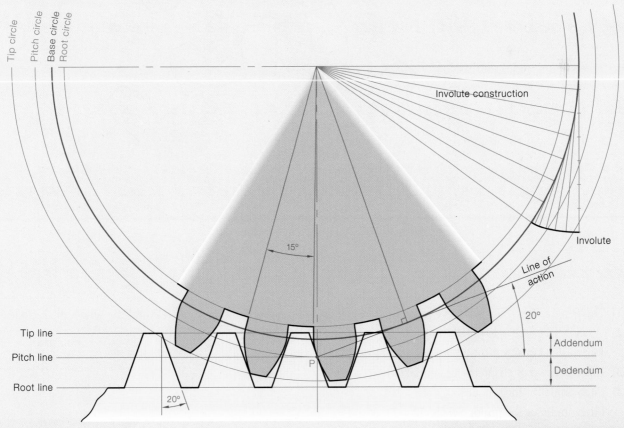

▲ Fig. 13.115

See worksheet 13.17

(5) The circular pitch, measured along the pitch circle, is 31.4 mm or 15°. Construct five teeth using these spacings.

(6) The rack should be considered to be a gear of infinite radius. The tooth thickness is measured along the pitch line and the tooth angle is 20° as shown in Fig. 13.115.

> A cycloidal gear wheel with 18 teeth and a module of 10 is in mesh with a cycloidal pinion gear with 12 teeth and module of 10. Draw, full size, the gears in mesh showing five teeth on each gear. The generating circles used are to produce radial dedenda on each gear.

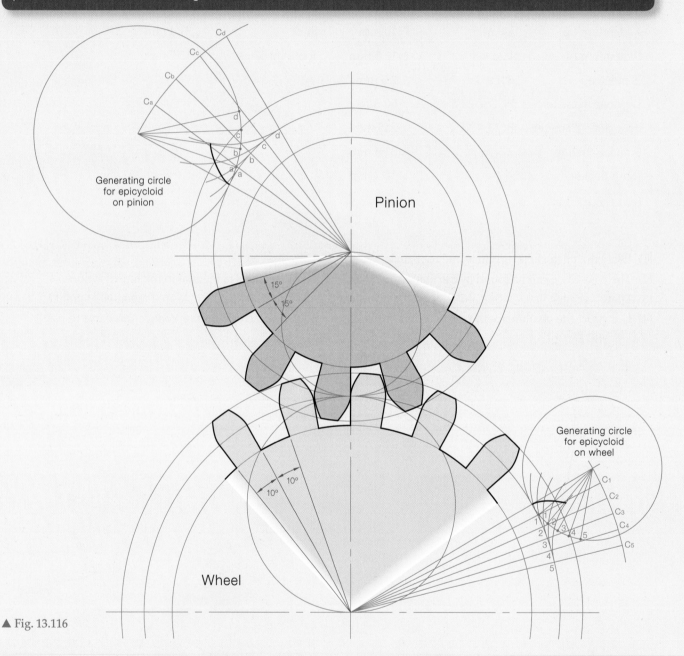

▲ Fig. 13.116

(1) The generating circles will have radii equal to half the radii of the pinion pitch circle and the wheel pitch circle.

(2) Wheel PCD = 18 × 10 = 180 mm.
Pinion PCD = 12 × 10 = 120 mm.

(3) Draw the two pitch circles tangential to each other.

(4) Pitch angle for the wheel 360° ÷ 18 = 20°
Pitch angle for the pinion 360° ÷ 12 = 30°

(5) Draw the tip circle and the root circle for each gear and draw in the dedendum line for each tooth based on the pitch angle and the fact that they will be radial lines.

See worksheet 13.18

(6) Use the generating circle rolling along the pitch circle to produce the epicycloidal curve for the gear tooth.

(7) Use tracing paper to duplicate the curves.

> A cycloidal pinion with 20 teeth and a module of 10 is in mesh with a rack. Draw, full size, the rack and pinion in mesh showing five teeth on the pinion and six teeth on the rack. The pinion is to have radial dedenda.

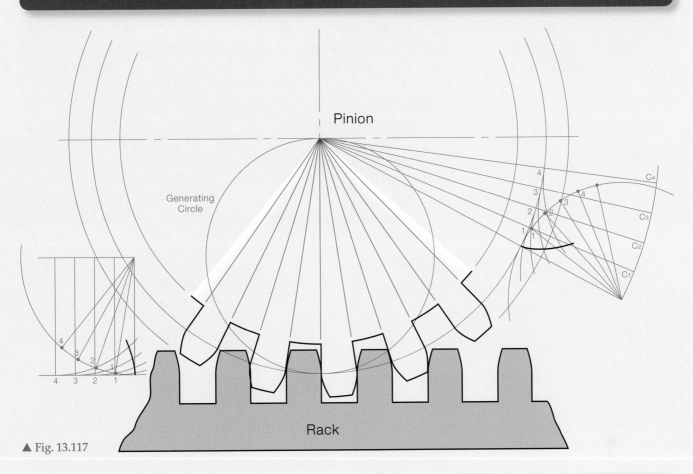

▲ Fig. 13.117

Pinion Details

Module (m)		10
No. of teeth (t)		20
Pressure angle (θ)		20°
Pitch circle diameter	m × t	200 mm
Base circle diameter	PCD × cos θ	225.5 mm
Addendum (a)	a = m	10 mm
Dedendum (d)	1.25 × a	12.5 mm
Clearance	d × a	2.5 mm
Tip circle diameter	PCD + 2a	220 mm
Root circle diameter	PCD − 2d	175 mm
Circular pitch (p)	π × m	31.4 mm
Tooth thickness	$\frac{p}{2}$	15.7 mm
Pitch angle	$\frac{360°}{t}$	18°

Rack Details

Module	10
Addendum	10 mm
Dedendum	12.5 mm
Clearance	2.5 mm
Tooth thickness	15.7 mm

> The construction of the solution is similar to the previous example. Note that the same sized generating circle is used for the pinion and rack. The teeth of the rack have parallel-sided dedenda and cycloidal addenda.

See worksheet 13.19

Activities

Cams

Q1. A plate cam rotating clockwise is to give an in-line knife-edge follower the following motion.

0–120°	lift 32 mm with uniform velocity
120–180°	dwell
180–360°	fall 32 mm with simple harmonic motion

  (i) Draw the cam profile if the minimum cam radius is 38 mm and the camshaft diameter is 24 mm.

  (ii) Draw the displacement diagram for the follower.

Q2.

  (i) Draw a radial cam with minimum radius of 36 mm and clockwise rotation to give the following motion to a knife-edge follower.

0–120°	rise 30 mm with simple harmonic motion
120–210°	rise of 22 mm with uniform velocity
210–360°	fall of 52 mm with uniform acceleration and retardation

  (ii) Draw the displacement diagram for the follower.

Q3. Draw a radial cam with a minimum radius of 30 mm and anticlockwise rotation to give the following motion to an in-line knife-edge follower.

0–90°	rise 30 mm with uniform velocity
90–120°	dwell
120–210°	rise 20 mm with simple harmonic motion
210–360°	fall to initial position with uniform acceleration and retardation

Q4. Draw a radial cam with minimum radius of 30 mm and clockwise rotation to give the followingmotion to an in-line knife-edge follower.

0–90°	rise 30 mm with simple harmonic motion
90–240°	rise 24 mm with uniform acceleration and retardation
240–360°	fall 54 mm with uniform velocity

Q5. Fig. 13.118 shows the profile of a radial cam, which operates a knife-edge follower.

  (i) Draw the cam.

  (ii) Draw the displacement diagram for this cam showing displacement per second. The cam rotates at 6 revolutions per minute.

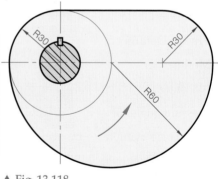

▲ Fig. 13.118

Q6. Fig. 13.119 shows the profile of a radial cam, which operates a knife-edge follower.

  (i) Draw the cam.

  (ii) Draw the follower displacement diagram showing displacement per second. The cam turns once every 18 seconds.

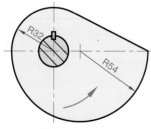

▲ Fig. 13.119

Q7. Draw the profile and displacement diagram for a cam rotating in an anticlockwise direction.

The cam has a minimum radius of 40 mm. The follower is a 24 mm diameter roller and has the following motion:

0–90°	rise of 30 mm with uniform velocity
90–180°	dwell
180–270°	rise of 20 mm with simple harmonic motion
270–300°	fall of 15 mm with simple harmonic motion
300–360°	fall of 35 mm with uniform velocity

Q8. Construct a cam profile to give an in-line flat-ended follower the following motion. Follower base extends 8 mm each side of the centre line.

0–60°	dwell
60–180°	rise of 40 mm with uniform acceleration and retardation
180–210°	dwell
210–360°	fall of 40 mm with simple harmonic motion

The cam rotates clockwise and its minimum radius is 30 mm.

Gears: involute teeth

Q9. Draw full-size, five teeth of an involute gear. The gear is to have 32 teeth of module 6 and a pressure angle of 20°.

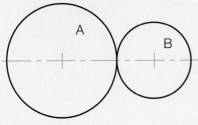

▲ Fig. 13.120

Q10. Gear A has 24 teeth and a module of 8. Gear B has 16 teeth and a module of 8. Show 4 teeth in mesh on each gear and use conventions for the rest of the gears.

Q11. A pinion with 16 teeth is to mesh with a rack whose teeth have a pressure angle of 20° and an addendum of 12 mm. The travel of the rack is to be 250 mm.

Draw all the teeth on the rack and five teeth in mesh on the pinion. Tabulate all necessary data. The teeth of the pinion are of involute form.

Q12. A cycloidal gear wheel with 20 teeth and module of 12 is in mesh with a cycloidal gear pinion. The gear ratio is 5:3. Both gears have radial dedenda.

(i) Calculate all relevant information and show it in tabular form.

(ii) Draw the profile of the gear wheels in mesh, showing five teeth on each gear.

Q13. A pinion with 15 teeth is to mesh with a rack. The pinion has cycloidal teeth form and a module of 12. Its dedenda are to be radial.

(i) Calculate all relevant data and show it in tabular form.

(ii) Draw the profile of the rack and pinion in mesh showing five teeth on each.

14 Structural Forms

Syllabus Outline

Areas to be studied:

- Structural forms, natural and manufactured.
- Singly and doubly ruled surfaces.
- The hyperbolic paraboloid as a ruled surface.
- *The hyperbolic paraboloid as a surface of translation.*
- *Plane directors.*
- The hyperboloid of revolution, projections and sections.
- Sections through singly and doubly ruled surfaces.
- *The geodesic dome of not more than four points of frequency.*

Learning Outcomes

Students should be able to:

Higher and Ordinary levels

- Investigate the development of structural forms in a historical context.
- Identify the key structural forms including arches, domes, vaults, frames and surface structures.
- Produce line drawings of the basic structural forms.
- Produce two-dimensional drawings of arches, domes, vaults and surface structures.
- Construct a hyperbolic paraboloid as a ruled surface.
- Determine the true shape of sections through curved surfaces.
- Project views and sections of a hyperboloid of revolution.

Higher Level only

- *Relate the key properties of structural forms to their design and construction.*
- *Produce three-dimensional drawings of arches, domes, vaults and surface structures.*
- *Determine plane directors for ruled surfaces, and construct ruled surfaces given plane directors and directrices.*
- *Project views of a hyperbolic paraboloid defined as a surface of translation.*
- *Construct geodesic domes of not more than four points of frequency.*
- *Investigate and represent structural forms as they occur in the environment.*

In this chapter we will be looking at the historical development of some common structural forms including the arch, the dome and the vault. We will then move on to look at some structural forms of special interest, the hyperbolic parabaloid and the hyperboloid of revolution.

 ## Column and Beam

Using columns and beams is the simplest way to make an opening in a wall. The column or post is the vertical member and the beam is the horizontal member. The beam supports the weight (load) above it and its own weight. This weight is then transferred to the columns and from these to the lower structure. This type of construction was used in prehistoric times and is still used in modern-day structures.

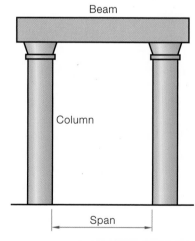

▲ Fig. 14.1

The range of materials available to ancient Romans, Egyptians and Greeks was quite limited (timber and stone) and therefore the spans that could be crossed with beams were relatively short. Stone, in particular, is weak in bending. The longer the beam is, the more likely it is to bend. Long stone beams would be susceptible to failure. Furthermore, since a beam is a single member, it was difficult to obtain in long lengths. Modern materials such as steel and concrete allow longer spans, particularly when used together. A bending beam is under compression at the top and under tension at the bottom. Concrete is very strong in compression and is good at the top of the beam. Steel is strong in tension and is good at the bottom of the beam. Steel and concrete together make a strong beam. The construction of columns presented fewer problems in ancient times for two reasons. First, columns are fundamentally members under compression and the main building material, stone, is excellent under compression. Second, columns could be made up from small segments stacked on top of each other. The load when applied actually compresses the joint, making it stronger.

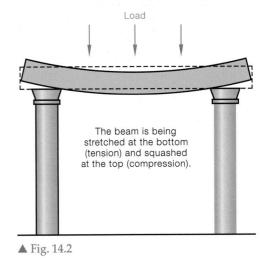

Load

The beam is being stretched at the bottom (tension) and squashed at the top (compression).

▲ Fig. 14.2

The Arch

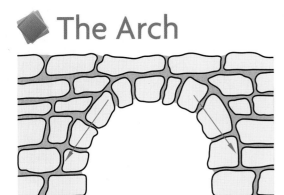

Thrust downwards and outwards

▲ Fig. 14.3

The arch was developed as a means of crossing larger spans than was practical/possible with monolithic stone beams. The arch spans an opening without using any beams at all, just a lot of small stones or bricks. These smaller building elements support each other.

The invention of the arch is credited to the Etruscans, before the Roman Empire was established. The Etruscans used the arch for gates, bridges and drains. When the Roman Empire conquered the Etruscans, they adopted the arch into their architecture and used it widely when building bridges, aqueducts, gates, entrances, etc.

The forces exerted by an arch, because of its bend upwards, tend to be both downwards and outwards. The walls to the side of an arch must be of sufficient mass to counteract this diagonal thrust. A single arch therefore will not be stable on two columns unless the columns are heavy enough to buttress against these forces. A series of arches will buttress each other and may be supported on light columns.

Arch Terminology

Centre – the centre(s) from which the curve(s) of the arch is drawn.

Extrado – the top or outer surface of a voussoir.

Intrado – the bottom or inner surface of a voissoir.

Rise – the vertical distance from the spring line to the highest point on the inner curve of the arch

Span – the inner width of the arch.

Spring Line – the line from which the curve of the arch starts.

Springer – the first voussoir on the left and the right of the arch.

Voussoirs – the individual elements that make up the arch. Usually tapered.

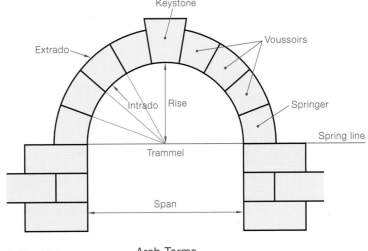

▲ Fig. 14.4   Arch Terms

The Vault

The logical progression from the arch is the vault. When the arch is deepened enough to form a part of a cylinder or barrel we have a vault.

The Egyptians were one of the first civilisations to make widespread use of the vault. They used the vault in tombs, storage rooms and drains. The Romans later adopted the vault into their architecture and developed it further to form the groined vault.

A groined vault is made up of two barrel vaults of the same size and height joining each other at right angles. It will cover a square area. The lines of intersection are called the groins. For a groined vault the whole roof area is supported on four corner piers. This opened up the floor area and was used to great advantage in the construction of large buildings. Many medieval cathedrals have great examples of both barrel and groined vaults.

The construction of a vault consisted of building an arch at the ends. Between the arches a long tunnel was formed from concrete. Centerings or temporary supports were introduced to support the concrete while the vault was being constructed. Buttresses were often used to give the heavy vaults support.

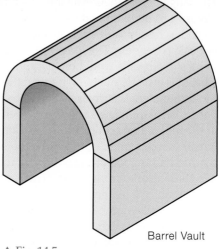
Barrel Vault

▲ Fig. 14.5

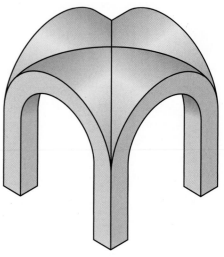

▲ Fig. 14.6

Domes

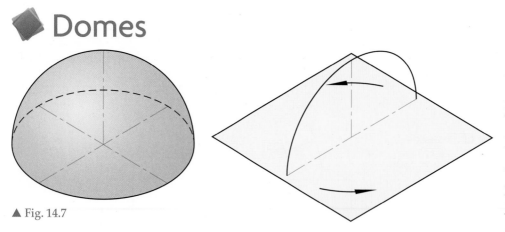

▲ Fig. 14.7

Domes, like the vault, evolved from the arch. A dome is an arch which has been rotated about its centre line. The masonry dome was first constructed around 100 AD by the Romans. The forces exerted by a dome are equal all around its perimeter. Because of the limited variety of building materials available at that time (stone and cement), the domes that were constructed were heavy, requiring extensive buttressing.

The availability of steel to architects and builders in the nineteenth century made dome construction less difficult. Steel has a high strength-to-weight ratio compared to stone and it can also be made into continuous forms. For awkward shapes like domes, this is a great advantage.

The geodesic dome, which is a skeletal frame of a spherical dome, was developed by Buckminster Fuller in the 1940s. It is a lightweight construction and generally sits at ground level.

Most domes are created by rotating a semicircle or similar curve about a centre line.

A parabola, hyperbola, semi-ellipse or similar but non-regular curve will produce a dome. However, the curve must be convex as opposed to concave. In other words, it must bulge outwards.

The geodesic dome is a dome created with triangles. It is structurally very stable and can be built to a very large scale. Its construction is not based on rotation of a curve about an axis but rather on the platonic solids. More on the geodesic dome later.

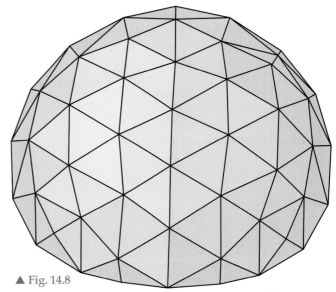

▲ Fig. 14.8

 # Frames

There are many examples in modern architecture where frames of one type or another are used to speed up and expand the limits of the construction process. The prefabricated frame can be made in ideal conditions, with exact accuracy and to a uniform standard.

Lattice Girder

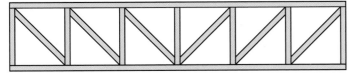

▲ Fig. 14.9

It is only common sense that the wider the span that a beam has to cross, the larger that beam must be in cross-section. As the span widens it will eventually become uneconomical to span across it with solid section beams because of the amount of material used. The lattice girder (Fig. 14.9) provides a strong, light alternative. The lattice girder will be deeper and wider than the solid beam, yet uses less actual material and is stronger if constructed properly.

The lattice girder is broken into triangles. The triangle is the most stable geometric shape and will not be distorted in shape unless one of its sides is lengthened or shortened. Pin-jointing at the ends of each member produces a well-braced, stable frame.

Truss

The triangular truss also bases its strength on triangulation. The larger triangle is often broken into smaller triangles using struts (members under compression) and ties (members under tension). The resulting frame has very high strength in relation to the amount of material used. The truss, when in place, produces a vertical downward force on the walls. This type of frame is well suited to the light wall construction of the modern day.

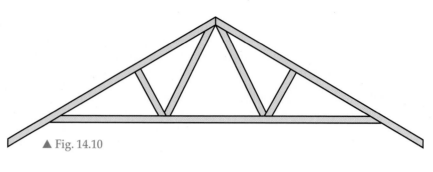

▲ Fig. 14.10

Roof trusses may be constructed from timber or steel and vary hugely in shape and size.

Portal Frames

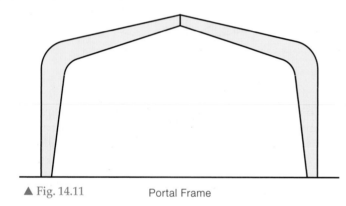

▲ Fig. 14.11   Portal Frame

Portal frames may be constructed of reinforced concrete, steel and often laminated wood. The frame is thickened at the corners to help transfer the load from the top section to the vertical section. This type of frame is widely used in factory and warehouse construction because it forms walls and roof frame in the same unit. The portal frame is a relatively modern form of construction. Roof trusses may be constructed from timber or steel and vary hugely in shape and size.

Surface Structures

A surface structure is one whose surface both encloses a space and provides support. The material used is usually reinforced concrete because of its strength and because of the versatility it offers in shape.

Slab

The simplest form of surface structure is the horizontal slab or the vertical panel. A slab combined with columns or vertical panels will quickly create a structure which is self-supporting.

By folding or corrugating thin materials their stiffness can be increased enormously. This property has been applied to the simple slab to produce many varied types of surface structure called shell structures.

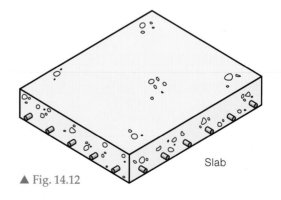

Slab

▲ Fig. 14.12

Shell Structures

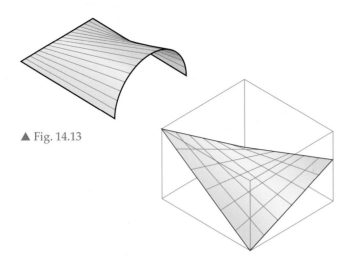

▲ Fig. 14.13

These generate their strength from their shape rather than the thickness of material used. They are generally made from thin concrete with a mesh of steel reinforcement. Shell structures, as a building form, were first used in the twentieth century and were a result of improvements in cement and concrete production. The shapes produced by single shells or combinations of shells can be aesthetically pleasing and produce free-flowing designs.

The shell of a bird's egg is both thin and brittle yet can withstand very large, evenly distributed loads. The curved shape helps distribute the load. Many shell structures used in modern architecture have a curved shape and yet can be made up from straight-line elements. This is helpful when constructing a reinforced concrete shell as the reinforcing bars do not need to be bent.

Surface Structures

A surface may be considered to be generated by the motion of a line, the generatrix. Surfaces are divided into two groups:

(1) Those that are generated by a moving straight line are called **ruled surfaces**.
(2) These that are generated by a moving curved line are called **double curved surfaces**.

Any position of the generatrix, be it a straight line or a curve, is called an element of the curve.

Ruled Surface

There are three types of ruled surface:

(1) the plane,
(2) the single curved surface,
(3) the warped surface.

1. The Plane

The plane is generated by a straight line moving so as to touch two other parallel, straight lines, Fig. 14.14.

It can also be seen as a straight line moving so as to touch two intersecting straight lines, Fig. 14.15.

Alternatively, it can be seen as a straight line moving so as to touch a plane figure at two places at all times, Fig. 14.16.

By definition a plane is a surface such that when any two points are taken on it, the straight line joining them will lie completely on the surface.

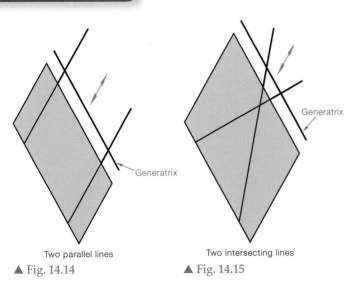

Two parallel lines
▲ Fig. 14.14

Two intersecting lines
▲ Fig. 14.15

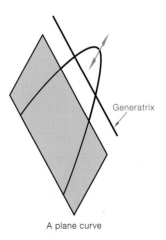

A plane curve
▲ Fig. 14.16

2. The Single Curved Surface

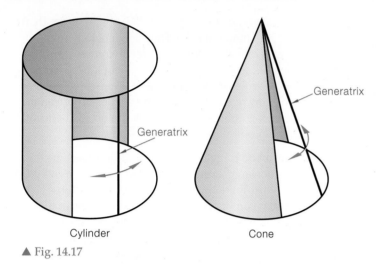

This is a developable ruled surface. The surface can be unrolled to lie on a plane. The straight line elements are parallel or intersecting. Examples of single curved surfaces are the cylinder and the cone. This category would also include oblique cylinders and cones and surfaces generated by moving the generatrix around elliptical curves as well as circles.

Cylinder   Cone

▲ Fig. 14.17

3. The Warped Surface

A warped surface is a ruled surface that is not developable. No two consecutive elements are parallel or intersecting. No two adjacent positions of the generatrix lie in the same plane. There is a huge variety of warped surfaces. Common examples are the conoid, cylindroid, hyperboloid of revolution and the hyperbolic paraboloid.

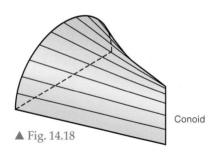

Conoid

▲ Fig. 14.18

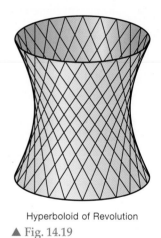

Hyperboloid of Revolution

▲ Fig. 14.19

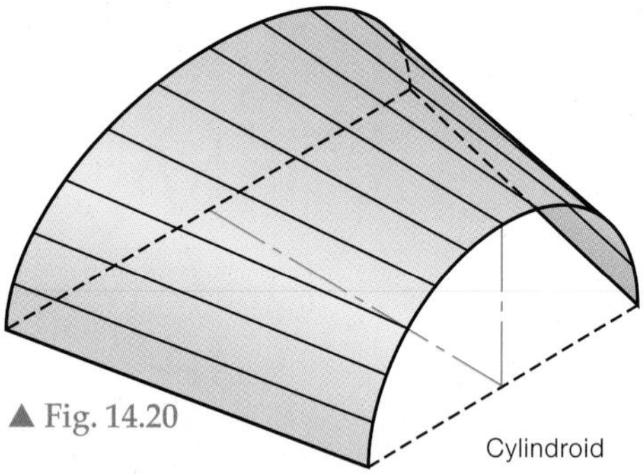

▲ Fig. 14.20

Cylindroid

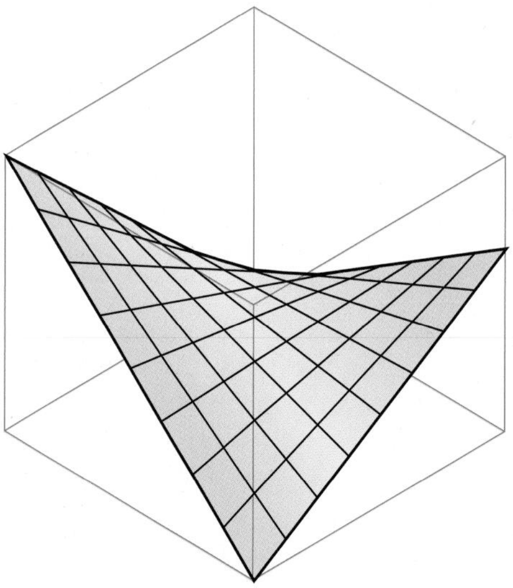

Hyperbolic Paraboloid

▲ Fig. 14.21

Double-curved Surfaces

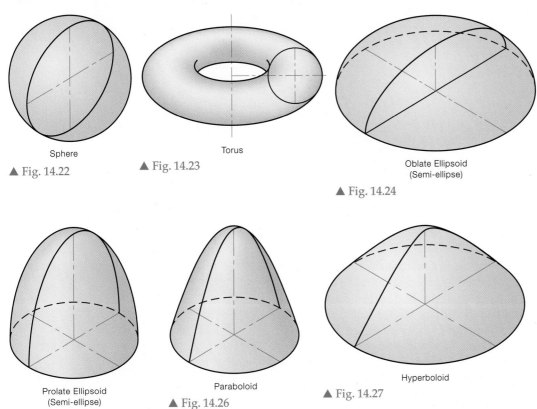

Sphere
▲ Fig. 14.22

▲ Fig. 14.23
Torus

Oblate Ellipsoid
(Semi-ellipse)
▲ Fig. 14.24

Prolate Ellipsoid
(Semi-ellipse)
▲ Fig. 14.25

Paraboloid
▲ Fig. 14.26

Hyperboloid
▲ Fig. 14.27

Double-curved surfaces are generated by a curved line moving according to a certain law. The most common double-curved surfaces are formed by revolving a curve about an axis in the same plane. Examples of these would be the sphere, torus, oblate ellipsoid, prolate ellipsoid, paraboloid and hyperboloid.

Hyperboloid of Revolution

The hyperboloid of revolution is a ruled surface. It is generated by revolving a straight line about another non-parallel, non-intersecting line as its axis. Figures 14.28 and 14.29 show this arrangement. It is clear from the diagram that any section of a hyperboloid of revolution which is perpendicular to the axis will produce a circle.

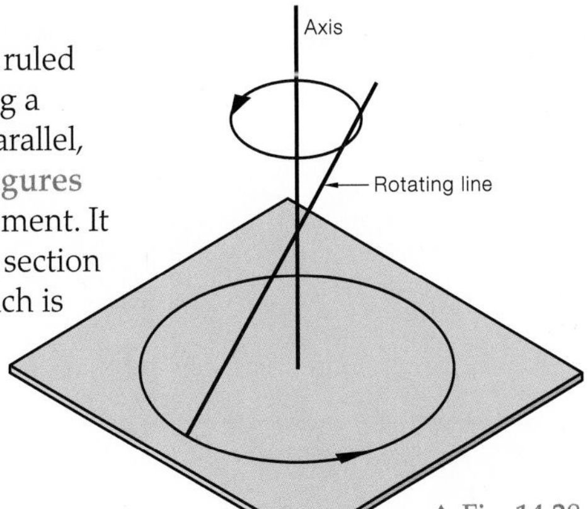

Axis

Rotating line

▲ Fig. 14.28

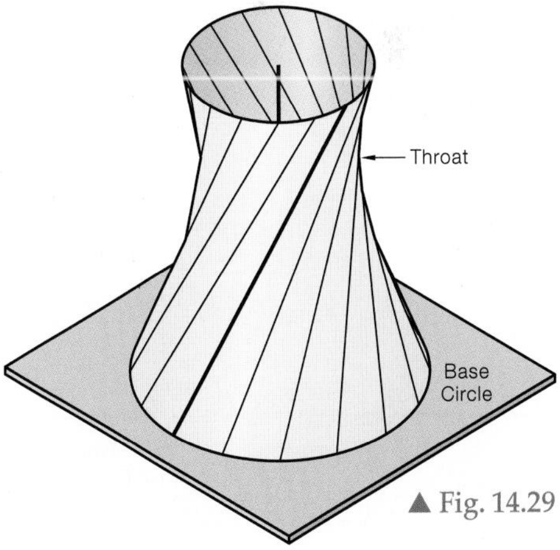

Throat

Base
Circle

▲ Fig. 14.29

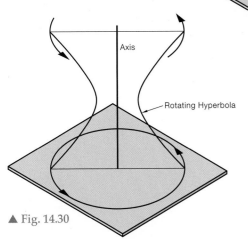

Axis

Rotating Hyperbola

▲ Fig. 14.30

The curves produced at the sides are hyperbolas. The narrowest part of the hyperboloid of revolution is called the throat or the throat circle. The extreme limits of this shell structure are the cylinder and cone. As the throat circle and the base circle became closer to each other in size the hyperboloid of revolution becomes more cylindrical. As the throat circle decreases in size and nears a radius of zero the hyperboloid becomes more cone-like.

A hyperboloid of revolution can also be constructed by rotating one arm or both arms of a double hyperbola about the conjugate axis. Figures 14.30 and 14.31 show such a double hyperbola.

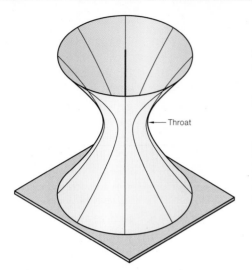

▲ Fig. 14.31

As mentioned already, the hyperboloid is a ruled surface. A ruled surface is a surface that for every point on it, there is a straight line passing through it, which lies on that surface for its entire length. When a point on the surface has two such lines passing through it, it is called a doubly ruled surface. The hyperboloid of revolution is such a surface as is evident from Fig. 14.32 on the next page. There are only three doubly ruled surfaces: the hyperboloid of revolution, the hyperbolic paraboloid and the plane.

Construction of a Hyperboloid of Revolution

Method 1
Given the base circle, throat circle and height of a hyperboloid of revolution. Construct the shape using elements.

(1) Draw the plan as given and the elevation. The narrowest part of the structure is the throat.

A hyperboloid of revolution can be made up of straight-line elements. Each element will form a tangent to the throat circle in plan.

(2) In plan draw an element which starts on the base circle, is tangential to the throat circle and continues to hit the base circle again, e.g. element 1.

(3) In this example the larger circle in plan represents both the base circle and the top circle of the structure. Project point 1 to the base of the elevation and point 'a' to the top of the elevation. Join these points.

(4) At suitable spacing around the circle draw more elements in plan and project to elevation.

(5) The shape forms as the elements are plotted.

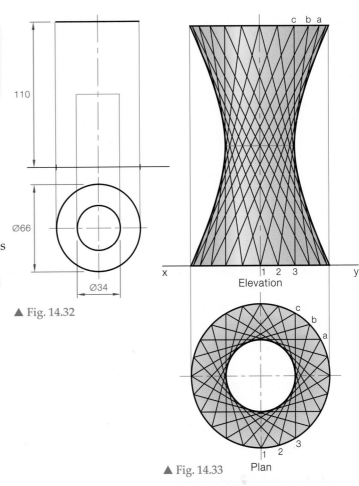

▲ Fig. 14.32

▲ Fig. 14.33　Plan

See worksheet 14.1

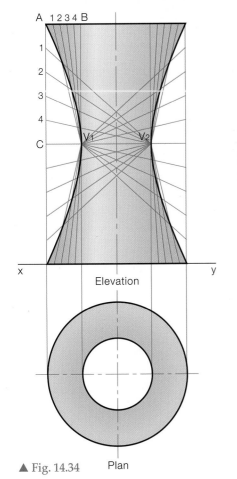

▲ Fig. 14.34　Plan

Method 2
Given the same information as in the previous example, construct a hyperboloid of revolution using the rectangle method.

This method is based on the construction of a double hyperbola using the rectangle method.

(1) Draw the given plan and mark off the heights in elevation.

(2) Project up the outer extremities of the circles from the plan thus creating the rectangles into which the curves will fit.

(3) Mark V_1 and V_2 the vertices of the curves.

(4) In rectangle $ABCV_1$ we divide edge AB into a number of equal parts and edge AC into the same number of equal parts.

(5) Join the divisions on AB to vertex V_1.

(6) Join the divisions on AC to vertex V_2.

(7) Where line $V_1 1$ and line $V_2 1$ cross gives a point on the hyperbola. Similarly for lines $V_1 2$ and $V_2 2$ etc.

(8) Repeat construction for other sections of the curves.

Method 3
Given the same information as in Method 1 construct a hyperboloid of revolution using the asymptote method.

The asymptotes to the curves are elements which are seen as true lengths in elevation.

The hyperbola will get closer to the asymptote as it extends but will never touch it.

The asymptotes will always cross at throat level.

(1) Draw the given plan and set off the heights in elevation.

(2) Since the asymptotes are true lengths in elevation they must be horizontal in plan. Draw the horizontal line AB in plan tangential to the throat circle.

(3) Projecting A and B from plan to the top and bottom of the elevation will find the asymptotes AB.

(4) Pick any number of points on the asymptote in plan, e.g. points 1 to 4.

(5) Project these points onto the asymptote in elevation.

(6) Rotate point 3 for instance, in plan, onto the central axis.

(7) Project the rotated point to elevation and across from point 3 on the asymptote in elevation. This locates a point on the curve.

(8) Repeat for the other points.

(9) The shape is completed by using symmetry.

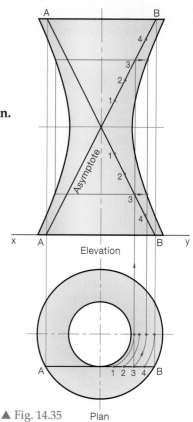

▲ Fig. 14.35   Plan

Important things to remember about the Hyperboloid of Revolution

See worksheet 14.2

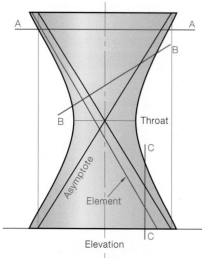

▲ Fig. 14.36   Plan

(1) Sections cut perpendicular to the axis will be circles.

(2) A straight line on the surface is an element and will be a tangent to the throat circle in the plan.

(3) The asymptotes are elements which are seen as true lengths in elevation.

(4) The asymptotes cross each other where the axis and the throat meet.

Hyperbolas of revolutions are used in cooling towers and in gear profiles.

Section A–A is a circle

Section B–B is an ellipse

Section C–C is a hyperbola

Worked Examples

Fig. 14.37 shows the outline plan and elevation of a cooling tower. It is in the form of a hyperboloid of revolution.

(i) Draw the given plan and elevation.

(ii) Determine the true shape of the section S–S.

Scale 1:500

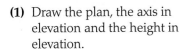

▲ Fig. 14.37

(1) Draw the plan, the axis in elevation and the height in elevation.

(2) Construct the hyperboloid of revolution as described earlier.

Section S–S:

(1) Select a number of points on the section line, e.g. a, b and c.

(2) Take horizontal sections through each of these points. These horizontal sections will produce circles in plan. The radii of these sections are r_1, r_2 and r_3.

(3) Project points a, b and c from elevation onto the appropriate circles in plan.

(4) The section can now be drawn by projecting perpendicular to the section line. Widths W_1, W_2 and W_3 are taken from plan. The section is an ellipse.

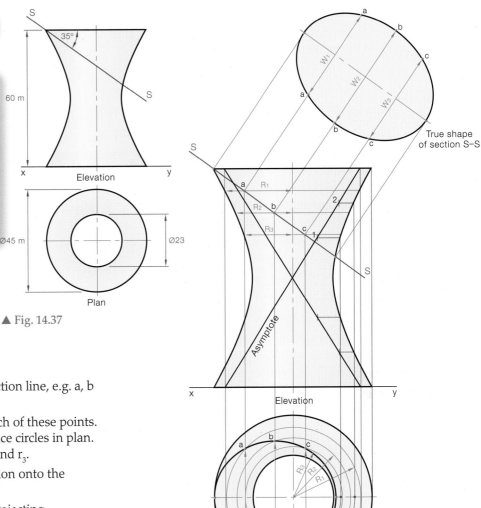

▲ Fig. 14.38

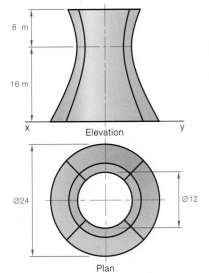

▲ Fig. 14.39

Fig. 14.39 shows the outline plan and elevation of a building. It is in the form of a hyperboloid of revolution. The joint lines on the surface are shown in plan and elevation. Draw the given views.

Scale 1:200

(1) In plan, draw the base circle and the throat circle as given. The medium-sized circle cannot be drawn yet as we do not know its radius.

(2) Draw the xy line, throat line, top line and axis in elevation.

(3) Draw the asymptotes in plan. These are seen as a horizontal line in plan tangential to the throat circle.

(4) Where the asymptote line in plan hits the base circle at P will give the starting points of the asymptotes in elevation on the xy line at P_1.

(5) The asymptotes always cross at the centre of the throat line in elevation. Draw the asymptotes.

(6) Construct the outer curves of the elevation as explained before.

(7) Where the asymptote meets the top surface at 2 is projected down to point 2 on the asymptote in plan. This is a point on the medium-sized circle. Draw the circle.

Joint lines

(1) Rotate points 1, 2 and 3 on the asymptote in plan onto the joint line, giving 5, 6 and 7. These points on the joint line, because they are on the same horizontal section, can be projected to elevation as shown.

(2) Points 4 and 8 are on the throat circle and base circle respectively and can be projected to elevation. The right joint line is a symmetrical image of the left.

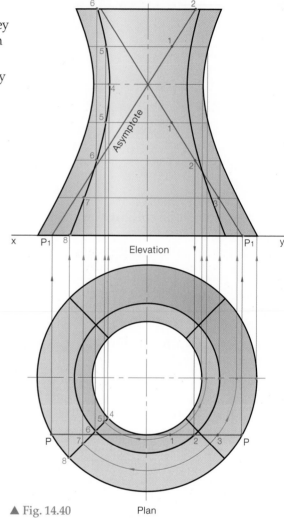

▲ Fig. 14.40

Hyperbolic Paraboloid

A hyperbolic paraboloid surface is obtained by translating a parabola with a downward curvature (ABC) along a parabola with an upward curvature (RST). The vertex of parabola ABC stays in contact with the parabola RST and the parabola hangs vertically at all times.

> Horizontal sections produce a double hyperbola while vertical sections produce a portion of the parabola ABC.

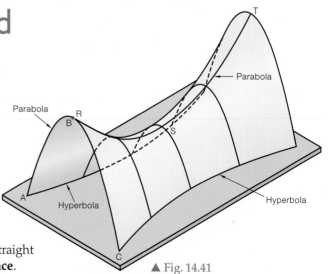

▲ Fig. 14.41

The hyperbolic paraboloid surface can also be generated by straight lines as shown in Fig. 14.42. It is called a **doubly ruled surface**.

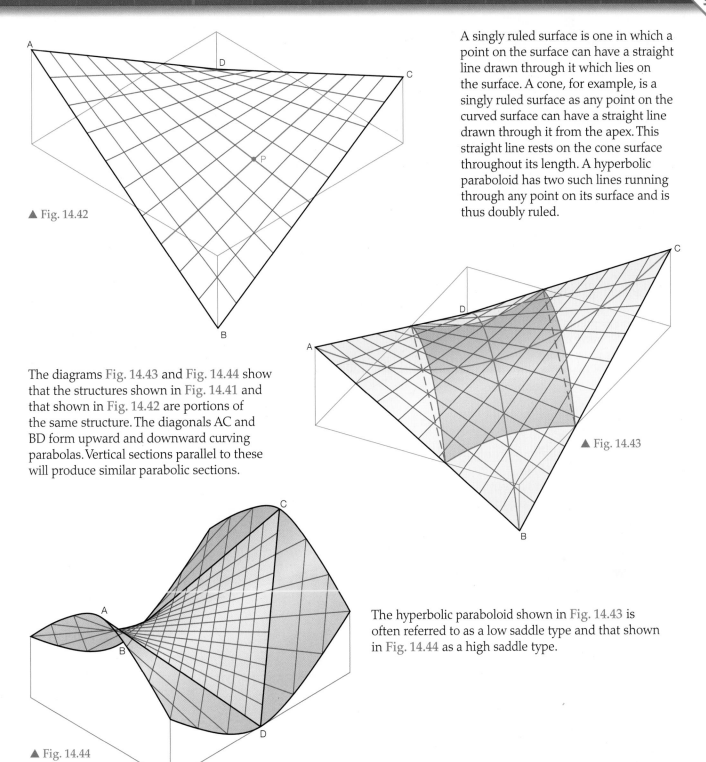

A singly ruled surface is one in which a point on the surface can have a straight line drawn through it which lies on the surface. A cone, for example, is a singly ruled surface as any point on the curved surface can have a straight line drawn through it from the apex. This straight line rests on the cone surface throughout its length. A hyperbolic paraboloid has two such lines running through any point on its surface and is thus doubly ruled.

▲ Fig. 14.42

The diagrams Fig. 14.43 and Fig. 14.44 show that the structures shown in Fig. 14.41 and that shown in Fig. 14.42 are portions of the same structure. The diagonals AC and BD form upward and downward curving parabolas. Vertical sections parallel to these will produce similar parabolic sections.

▲ Fig. 14.43

The hyperbolic paraboloid shown in Fig. 14.43 is often referred to as a low saddle type and that shown in Fig. 14.44 as a high saddle type.

▲ Fig. 14.44

Fig. 14.45 shows the outline plan of a hyperbolic paraboloid roof surface ABCD. The corners A and C are at ground level. Corner B is 12 m above ground level and corner D is 20 m above ground level.

(i)   Draw the given plan and project an elevation.

(ii) Draw an end view of the roof.

(iii) Show the curvature of the roof along a line joining A to C.

Scale 1:200

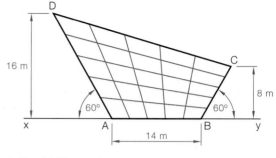

▲ Fig. 14.45

(1) Draw the outline of the plan as given.

(2) Each of the sides must be divided into five equal spaces as shown. This can be done by measuring or by division of lines as described before.

(3) Join the elements as shown. It is worth noting here that these structures must have four sides. The division marks on one edge must be joined to division marks on an opposite side, e.g. AB divisions join to CD divisions, and BC divisions join to AD divisions.

(4) Project the elevation of the corners using the heights given in the question. A joins to B to C to D back to A.

(5) The sides in the elevation can be divided by projecting the divisions up from the plan or by measuring.

(6) By indexing the first in a set of elements in plan the corresponding element in elevation can easily be found.

(7) Complete the elevation.

(8) The end view is found in the same way with the division points being found by projection from the front elevation, from the plan or by measuring.

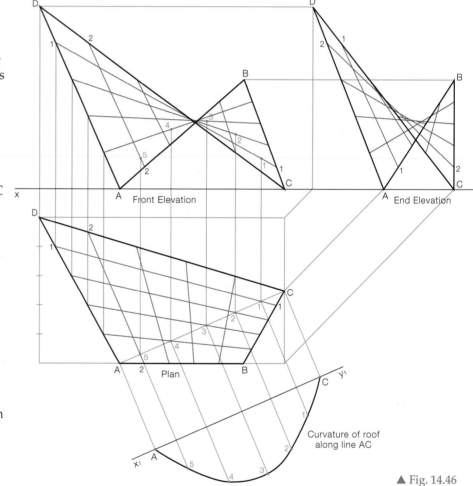

▲ Fig. 14.46

Curvature

(1) Join A to C in plan and identify points 1 to 5 where the section lines cross the elements. The more horizontal elements in plan are most suitable.

(2) Draw an x_1y_1 line parallel to the AC line.

(3) Project points AC and 1 to 5 out onto the sectional view. The projection lines must be perpendicular to the AC line and the x_1y_1 line.

(4) The heights of each point must be found from the elevation. Point 1 in plan on element 1 must be projected to elevation onto element 1. The height of this point is taken from elevation and transferred to the sectional view.

(5) Repeat for the other points and join to give the curve.

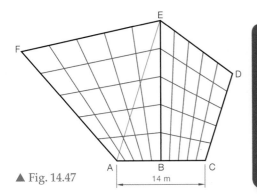

▲ Fig. 14.47

Two adjoining hyperbolic paraboloid roof surfaces ABEF and BCDE are shown in plan. BCDE makes up half a pentagon and AEF is an equilateral triangle. The corners A, C and E are at ground level. Corners D and F are 16 m above ground level and corner B is 20 m above ground level.

(i)   Draw the plan and project an elevation.

(ii) Project an end elevation.

(iii) Show the curvature of the roof along the line AE.

Scale 1:200

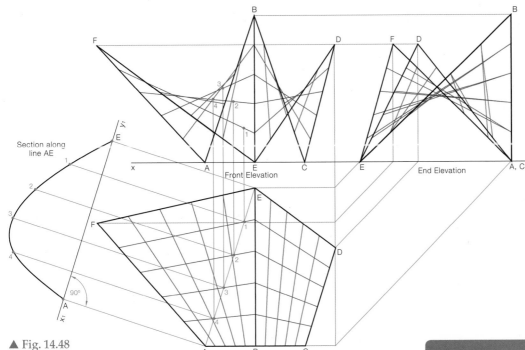

▲ Fig. 14.48

The construction is very similar to that for the previous example. It is worth noting that in solving these problems we do not concern ourselves with finding hidden lines. The whole framework is considered during drawing as a wire frame and hence has no hidden lines.

See worksheets 14.3 and 14.4

Hyperboloid of Revolution (contd)

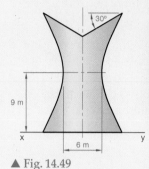

▲ Fig. 14.49

Fig. 14.49 shows the elevation of a hyperboloid of revolution which has been cut at the top. The true length of all full elements on the surface of this structure is 21 m.

(i)   Draw the plan and elevation of the building.

(ii) Project an end view.

(iii) Find the true shape of one side of the cut section.

Scale 1:100

HIGHER LEVEL

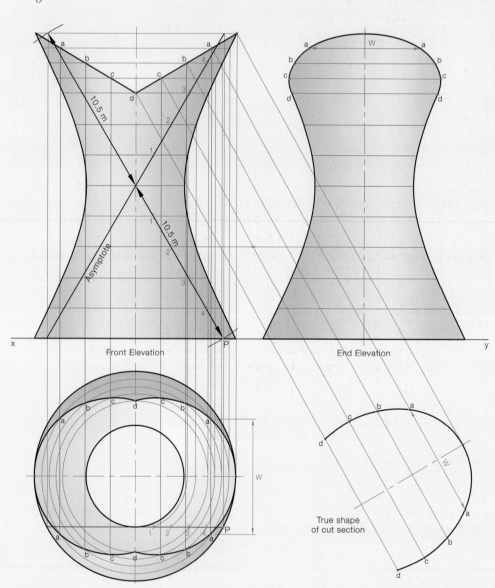

▲ Fig. 14.50

(1) Set up the xy line, axis, throat line and overall height in elevation.

(2) Draw the throat circle in plan.

(3) The true length of all full straight line elements is 21 m. The asymptotes are elements and are seen as true lengths in elevation. The asymptotes always cross in the middle of the throat. Set the compass to half the length of the asymptote, place it at the centre of the throat and draw an arc to hit the xy line at P. Draw a horizontal line tangential to the throat circle in plan. Project P onto this line. Point P is on the base circle.

(4) Draw the hyperboloid as explained earlier.

(5) To find the points on the section in plan we take horizontal sections which produce circles in plan onto which the appropriate points are projected.

(6) The end view and auxiliary are found by taking widths from the front elevation and plan.

See worksheets 14.5 and 14.6

The elevation of a piece of sculpture is shown in Fig. 14.51. It is in the form of two solid semi-hyperboloids of revolution. Any straight line element on the full hyperboloid of revolution would measure 17 m.

(i)   Draw the front elevation, end elevation and plan of the sculpture.

(ii) Determine the true shape of section S–S.

Scale 1:100

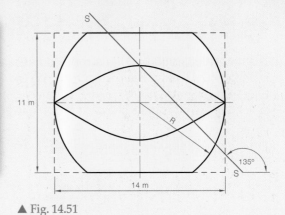

▲ Fig. 14.51

(1) The asymptotes will be 17 m long. Since they are only semi-hyperbolic paraboloids we only use half of this distance. Swing an arc from P to cut the side at Q. Point P is projected to the end view and the asymptote is drawn vertically. The throat circle is tangential to the asymptote in end view.

(2) The hyperboloid is constructed in the usual way.

(3) The shaped ends are found in end view and plan by taking sections perpendicular to the axes which appear as circles in end view.

(4) The section S–S is also found by using sections (construction not shown).

Section S–S

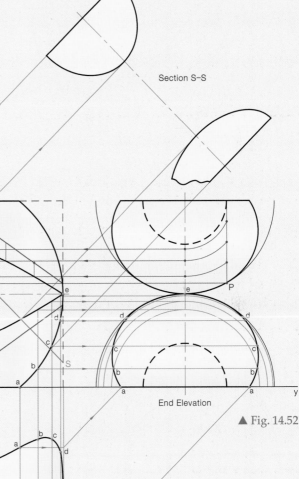

Front Elevation

End Elevation

▲ Fig. 14.52

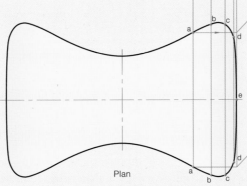

Plan

Hyperbolic Paraboloid (contd.)

The hyperbolic paraboloid is a warped surface and therefore cannot be developed. It can also be referred to as a warped quadrilateral. We have seen earlier that it can be considered to be a surface generated by a straight line. The straight line is called a generatrix. This straight line moves along two non-parallel, non-intersecting lines (skew lines) called linear directrices. All this can be clearly seen from the previous work on this surface. What perhaps is not so clear is that the generatrix, as it slides along the linear directrices, must always stay parallel to a plane, called the plane director. In fact, because the hyperbolic paraboloid is a doubly ruled surface, it has two sets of generatrices, two sets of linear directrices and two sets of plane directors.

Fig. 14.54 shows the plan and elevation of a hyperbolic paraboloid having two linear directrices ad and bc. The vertical plane is the plane director. Since the xy line in plan represents the edge view of the vertical plane, all the generatrices will be parallel to the xy line in plan.

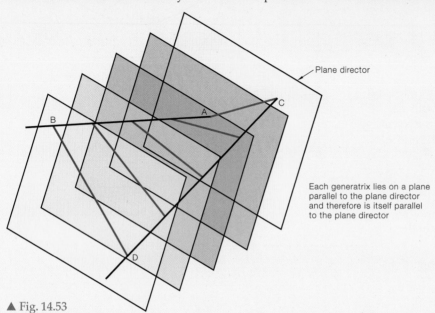

Plane director

Each generatrix lies on a plane parallel to the plane director and therefore is itself parallel to the plane director

▲ Fig. 14.53

No matter what hyperbolic paraboloid we have, we can get an edge view of its plane director by getting auxiliary views which will show its generatrices as parallel.

The plane director need not be one of the reference planes. In Fig. 14.55 the plane director is a vertical plane that is simply inclined. In plan we see the edge view of the plane director and all the elements appear parallel to it.

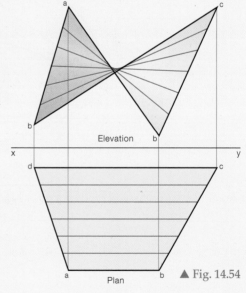

▲ Fig. 14.54

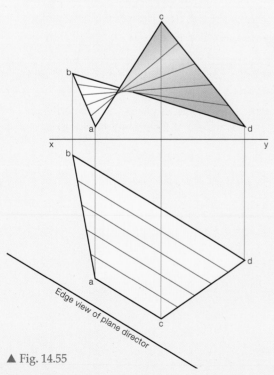

▲ Fig. 14.55

In both Figures 14.54 and Fig. 14.55 the elements of the structure appear parallel either in plan or elevation. If the plane director is an oblique plane, the elements will not appear parallel in either of these views and the use of an auxiliary view is required.

Fig. 14.56 shows an example of such a hyperbolic paraboloid. In order to find the plane director we must find a view of the structure that will show the generatrices as appearing parallel. The extreme elements ab and cd are used in Fig. 14.55 to find this view. The construction used is exactly that used in skew lines problems to show the two lines as parallel.

(1) Draw a level line from c and from d draw a line parallel to ab to intersect at x.

(2) Project x down to plan. In the plan draw a line from d parallel to ab in plan to intersect at x in plan.

(3) Join c to x and view in this direction to project a view of the structure showing all elements as parallel.

(4) The plane director can be drawn in the auxiliary. It is seen as an edge view and will be parallel to the generatrices.

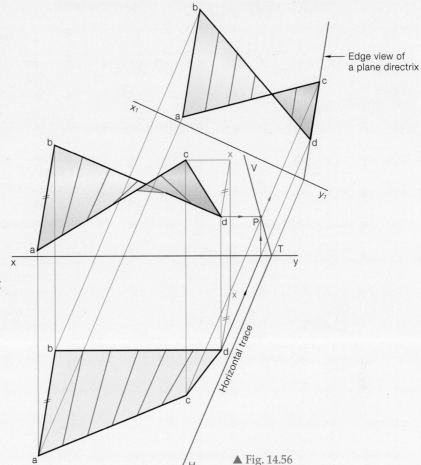

▲ Fig. 14.56

(5) In Fig. 14.56 the plane director is containing element cd. Extend the edge view of the plane director to hit the x_1y_1. This point is a point view of the horizontal trace. Project the horizontal trace back to plan.

(6) The vertical trace is found by using a point on the plane director, e.g. point c or point d. We have point d in plan and elevation, we have the horizontal trace and we require the vertical trace.

(7) Project d in plan, to the xy line, parallel to the horizontal trace to give point o.

(8) Project vertically and from d in the elevation project horizontally to give point p. Point p is a point on the vertical trace.

There is an infinite number of plane directors for any hyperbolic paraboloid surface. They will all be parallel to each other but their position can vary.

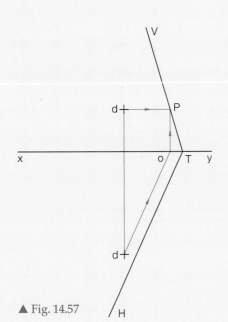

▲ Fig. 14.57

Given two skew line directrices ab and cd and the traces of the plane director of a hyperbolic paraboloid. To determine the elements of the surface.

a = 30, 10, 68

b = 75, 21, 40

c = 18, 45, 10

d = 82, 9, 27

(1) Find the edge view of the plane director by projecting an auxiliary view in the direction of the horizontal trace.

(2) Draw the directrices ab and cd in this auxiliary.

(3) The elements can now be drawn in the auxiliary, parallel to the edge view of the plane director. The most extreme elements are found first and further elements spaced out evenly between these.

(4) Project the elements back to plan and project to elevation.

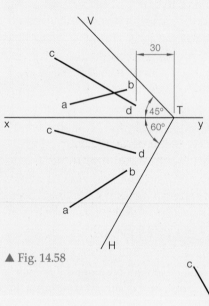

▲ Fig. 14.58

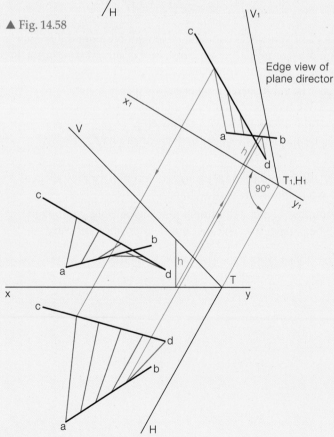

▲ Fig. 14.59

See worksheet 14.7

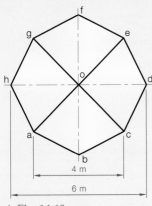

▲ Fig. 14.60

Fig. 14.60 shows the outline plan of a rain shelter. The structure is in the form of four hyperbolic paraboloid surfaces, abco, cdeo, efgo and ghao. Points b, d, f and h are at ground level. Points a, c, e and g are 5 m above ground level and point o is 6 m above ground level.

(i) Draw the plan and elevation of the surfaces ghao, abco and cdeo.

(ii) Find the curvature of the roof along the line joining b to e.

(iii) Find the traces of the plane director for the edges ab and co and having its horizontal trace containing point b.

Scale 1:50

(1) Draw the plan and project the elevation. Decide on how many elements to draw on each surface. In this example, the side of each structure was divided into five equal parts.

(2) Join in the elements. Remember that points on one edge must be joined to points on its opposite side. For example, points on ab join to points on oc.

(3) The section is found as explained before.

(4) The plane director is found by finding an auxiliary view that shows the edges ab and co as parallel. This is a skew lines problem and the construction is as explained earlier.

(5) Where the plane director meets the x_1y_1 gives the horizontal trace which is projected back to plan.

(6) Point 'a' which is also on the plane director is used to find the vertical trace.

HIGHER LEVEL

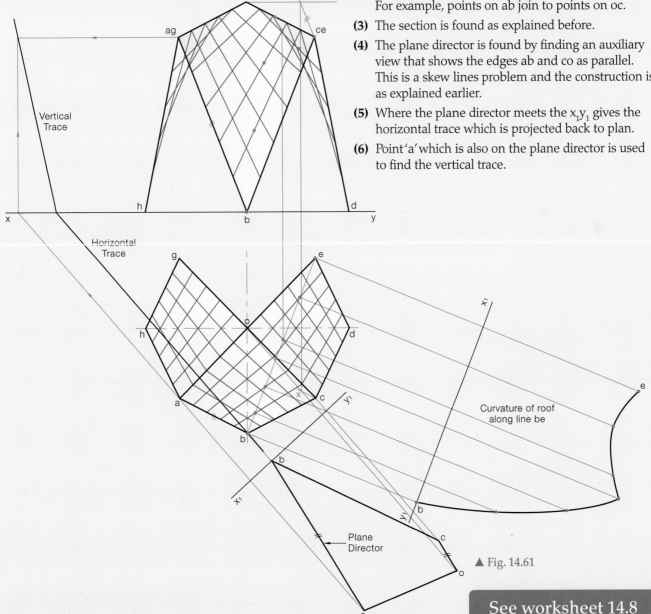

▲ Fig. 14.61

See worksheet 14.8

Fig. 14.62 shows the plan of a shell structure in the form of a hyperbolic paraboloid. Curve DBA is semi-elliptical in plan. Curves DE and BF are found by extending the surface ABCD until it meets ground level.

(i) Draw the plan and elevation of the structure.

(ii) Project the end view.

Scale 1:200

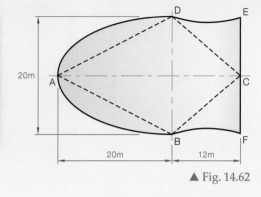

▲ Fig. 14.62

(1) Set up ABCD in plan and elevation.

(2) Draw the semi-ellipse in plan using the trammel or similar method.

(3) Divide the sides of the hyperbolic paraboloid into a suitable number of equal spaces, both in plan and elevation.

(4) The curve DAB is found in elevation by extending the elements in plan to reach the semi-ellipse at 1, 2, 3 and 4. These points are projected to elevation to meet the elements extended.

(5) The curves DE and BF are found by extending the elements in elevation to meet the xy line at p and q.

(6) p and q are projected to plan to intersect the elements extended.

(7) The end view is found by projection from the other two views.

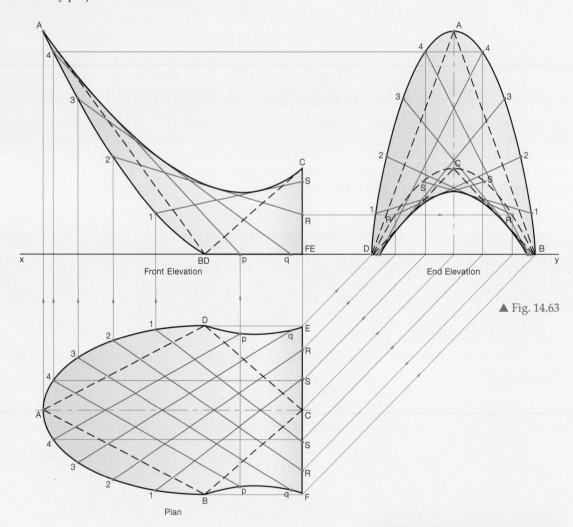

▲ Fig. 14.63

See worksheet 14.9

Hyperbolic Paraboloid as a Surface of Translation

As has been explained earlier at the introduction to this topic, the hyperbolic paraboloid can be seen as a structure made up of straight line elements obeying certain rules or as a parabolic curve sliding on its vertex along an inverted parabolic curve. We will now look at some problems based on this type of model.

Fig. 14.64 shows a pictorial view of a shell structure. The surface of the structure is generated by translating the parabola ABC in a vertical position along the parabola BE whose vertex is at E. Draw the plan and elevation of the structure.

Scale 1:200

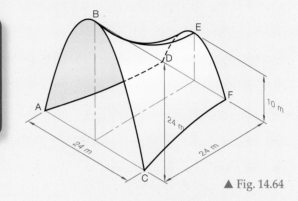

▲ Fig. 14.64

(1) Draw the parabola ABC.

(2) In front elevation draw point B and E.

(3) Construct the parabola BE ensuring that the vertex is at E.

(4) All vertical sections will produce parabolas which are part of the ABC parabola. The end curve DEF is part of the ABC parabola. The width w is found in plan by stepping height h down from the top of parabola ABC giving width w.

(5) Curves AD and CF are hyperbolas and are constructed as explained earlier.

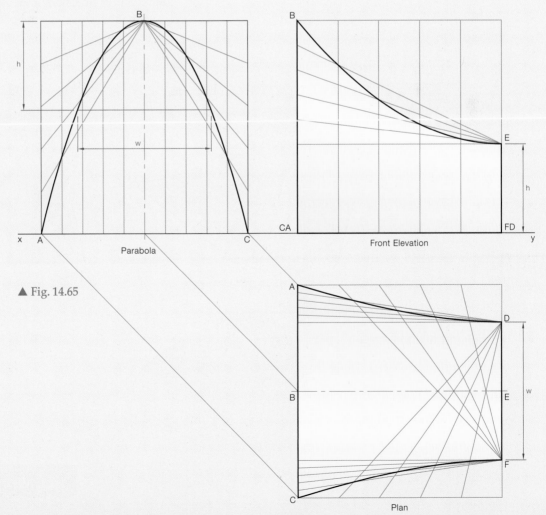

▲ Fig. 14.65

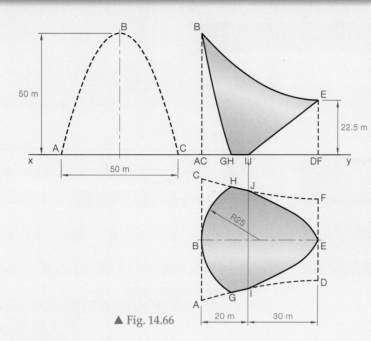

▲ Fig. 14.66

Fig. 14.66 shows the plan and elevation of a shell structure which is in the form of a hyperbolic paraboloid. It is formed by sliding parabola ABC in a vertical position along the parabola BE whose vertex is at E. The shell has been cut as shown.

(i) Draw the plan and elevation of the unit.

(ii) Project an end view of the unit.

Scale 1:500

(1) Draw the parabola ABC.

(2) Construct the parabola BE in elevation having its vertex at E.

(3) In the plan, the width of the end DEF is not given and must be found. Take the height of E in elevation and step it **down** from the top of parabola ABC. This gives the **width** of DF in plan.

(4) The left side of the plan can be completed and the right side of the elevation.

(5) w_1 and w_2 are taken from plan, stepped out from the axis of parabola ABC to find h_1 and h_2 which are stepped down from BE.

(6) h_3 and h_4 are taken from elevation, stepped down from the vertex of parabola ABC to find w_3 and w_4 which find points in the plan.

(7) The end view is projected from front elevation and plan.

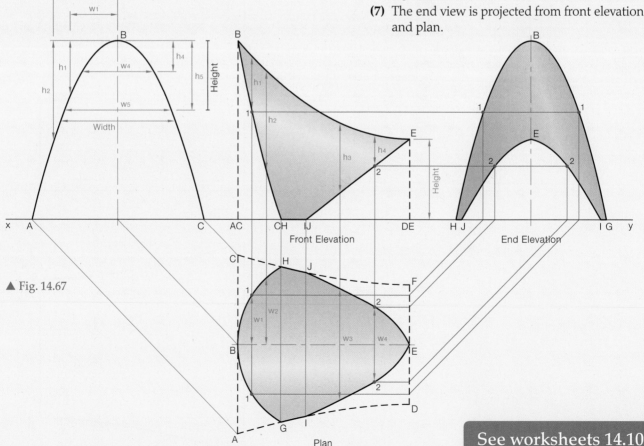

▲ Fig. 14.67

See worksheets 14.10

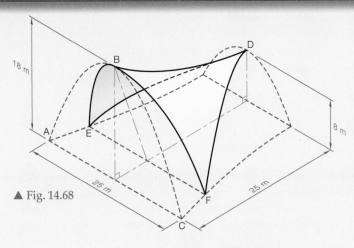

▲ Fig. 14.68

Fig. 14.68 shows a pictorial view of a shell structure. Six of these units are combined to form a total roof surface as shown in plan in Fig. 14.69. The surface of the unit is generated by translating the parabola ABC in a vertical position along the parabola BC whose vertex is at D.

(i)   Draw the plan and elevation of the unit.

(ii) Project an end view of the unit.

(iii) Find the true shape of curve DF.

Scale 1:200

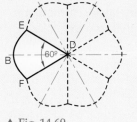

▲ Fig. 14.69

(1) Draw parabola ABC.

(2) Draw the rectangle that contains the front elevation and construct the half parabola BD.

(3) Draw the plan of the uncut shell structure by taking heights from parabola BD to the xy line (e.g. H_1) and step these heights **down** from the top of parabola ABC to give widths (e.g. W_1) which are used in the plan.

(4) Cut the shell structure in plan to form an inclusive angle of 60° thus finding E and F.

(5) Project E and F to the xy line and join to B. The left of the front elevation is completed and the right of the plan is completed.

(6) Take heights in elevation from parabola BD to straight line BFE (e.g. H_2).

(7) Step these heights **down** from the top of parabola ABC to find widths which are used in the plan (e.g. W_2).

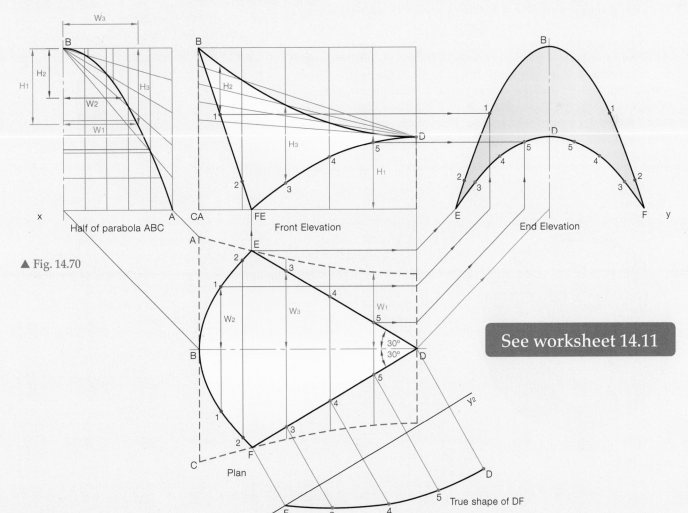

▲ Fig. 14.70

Half of parabola ABC   Front Elevation   End Elevation

See worksheet 14.11

Plan

True shape of DF

(8) Widths are now taken in plan from the axis to line DE (e.g. W_3).

(9) Use these widths on the parabola ABC to find heights from the top of the parabola down to the curve (e.g. H_3).

(10) The end view is projected in the normal way.

(11) The true shape of curve DF is found by projecting an auxiliary elevation with $x_1 y_1$ parallel to line DF in plan.

Geodesic Domes

A geodesic dome is a type of structure shaped like a piece of a sphere. This structure is made up of a complex network of triangles that form a roughly spherical surface. The more triangles, the more closely the dome approximates the shape of a true sphere. The geodesic dome was invented by Buckminster Fuller in the late 1940s. He hoped to use such domes to improve the housing of humanity and envisaged that giant domes would cover whole cities.

Geodesic domes are light structures yet very rigid and inherently strong. They have no need for internal supports, as they are self-supporting and therefore leave the internal floor area completely open and unobstructed. They are attractive aesthetically and philosophically because you are getting more internal area using less building materials. There are, unfortunately, some severe practical difficulties in constructing these 'perfect buildings', which has limited their use to public spaces, exhibition halls and enthusiast projects. With so many edges and joints it is difficult and expensive to waterproof these domes. Rain seems to find a way in, no matter what precautions are taken. Furthermore, the fact that the internal surfaces are curved can lead to its own problems in a man-made world that favours rectangular, more modular furniture.

Spherical Geometry

The term 'geodesic' comes from the Greek geo, earth, and daiesthai, to divide. We have earth-dividing domes. For a sphere, the shortest distance between two points A and B on the surface, travelling along the sphere's surface, is called a **geodesic**. A geodesic is always part of the circumference of a circle which has its centre at the centre of the sphere. Such a circle is called a **great circle**. An unlimited number of great circles can be drawn on the sphere's surface. Other smaller circles can be drawn on the surface but their centres will not coincide with the sphere's centre. These lesser circles play little or no part in dome theory.

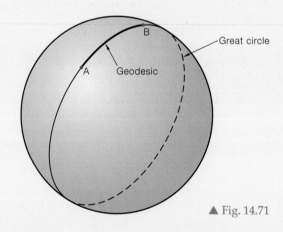

▲ Fig. 14.71

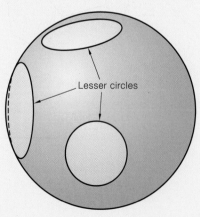

Lesser circles

▲ Fig. 14.72

The two points on a sphere that the geodesic line connects can also be connected by a chord that cuts through the sphere. Geodesic domes use these chords as struts. The struts form triangles and it is from these triangles that the dome forms its strength. Before looking at the make-up of the triangles in a geodesic dome we must first look at much more simple shapes, on which the more complex geodesic shapes are based, **the platonic solids**.

HIGHER LEVEL

The Five Regular Polyhedra

There are only five regular polyhedra: the tetrahedron, cube, octahedron, dodecahedron and icosahedron. For each of these solids all the faces are similar regular polygons, all the edges are equal in length and the same number of faces meet at every vertex.

Why only five regular polyhedra?

> In any convex polyhedron the sum of the face angles at a vertex is always less than 360º.

In order to form a three-dimensional solid there must be a minimum of three faces meeting at any one vertex. By looking at the interior angles of regular polygons which can act as faces, it is evident that only three polygons may be used.

(1) Equilateral triangle with interior angles of 60°.

(2) Square with interior angles of 90°.

(3) Regular pentagon with interior angles of 108°.

A regular hexagon which is the next polygon in line has an interior angle of 120°. Three hexagonal faces meeting at a vertex will have interior angles adding up to exactly 360°, not less than 360° and therefore do not obey the rule.

By using equilateral triangles to form a regular polyhedron, there can be three, four or five of them meeting at a vertex, any more and the rule will be broken. From this we get the tetrahedron, octahedron and isosahedron. By using squares, there can only be three at each vertex, thus forming a cube. Finally, by using pentagons, again only three can meet at each vertex, thus forming a dodecahedron.

▼ Fig. 14.73

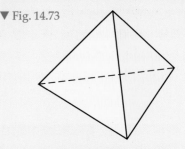

Tetrahedron
4 faces, 4 vertices, 6 edges

▼ Fig. 14.74

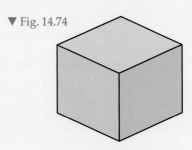

Cube
6 faces, 8 vertices, 12 edges

▼ Fig. 14.75

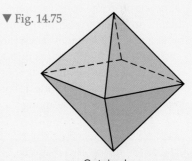

Octahedron
8 faces, 6 vertices, 12 edges

▼ Fig. 14.76

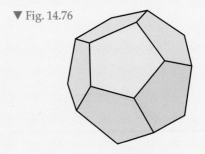

Dodecahedron
12 faces, 20 vertices, 30 edges

▼ Fig. 14.77

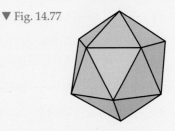

Icosahedron
20 faces, 12 vertices, 30 edges

HIGHER LEVEL

Faces, Vertices and Edges

There is obviously a relationship between the number of faces, vertices and edges for each of these regular polyhedra. This relationship was discovered by Leonhard Euler (1707–83).

> Faces + Vertices – Edges = 2
> F + V – E = 2

This relationship stands true for the five regular polyhedra mentioned earlier, but also for any polyhedra, regular or not, which can be enclosed in a sphere having each vertex touching the sphere surface. This formula is useful when working on domes because it can help to count vertices.

Platonic Solids and the Sphere

Each of the platonic solids can be circumscribed by a sphere, such that each vertex of the solid rests on the sphere surface and each edge of the surface forms a chord joining two such points. As such these five solids form the basis of geodesic dome construction. They are, however, poor approximations to a sphere. Of the five the tetrahedron, octahedron and icosahedron offer better stability because of their triangular make-up. If we look at the icosahedron, which has 20 triangular faces, the vertices are all equidistant from the centre so they determine a sphere. If we subdivide each of the triangular faces into smaller triangles, then some of the vertices of the smaller triangles lie inside the sphere rather than on it. By pushing these points radially outwards from the icosahedron until they meet the sphere, we arrive at the vertices of our geodesic sphere. Obviously by pushing the corners of the smaller triangles out to the sphere surface we are both changing the lengths of the triangle sides and their angles.

Frequency of a Geodesic Dome

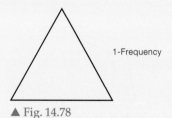

1-Frequency

▲ Fig. 14.78

The frequency of a geodesic dome is the measure of the number of triangles into which each face is subdivided. A 1-frequency dome or sphere is just an icosahedron (for example) or part of an icosahedron whose faces have not been subdivided. For a 2-frequency dome, the sides of each icosahedral face are divided into two so that each face is divided into four smaller triangles. For a 3-frequency dome the sides are divided in three, so that the faces become nine smaller triangles and so on.

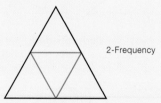

2-Frequency

▲ Fig. 14.79

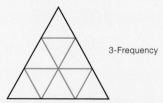

3-Frequency

▲ Fig. 14.80

HIGHER LEVEL

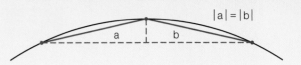

$|a| = |b|$

▲ Fig. 14.81

The roundness of the dome is improved by dividing the edges into shorter lengths and raising more points to the surface of the sphere. Raising the midpoint of an edge to the sphere creates two shorter edges, both equal, which give a better approximation to the curvature of the sphere. Increasing the subdivisions to 3-frequency or 4-frequency produces better approximations and struts of varying lengths. The lengths of these struts may be calculated or can be found from tables.

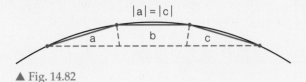
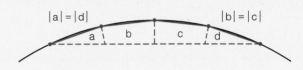

$|a| = |c|$ $|a| = |d|$ $|b| = |c|$

▲ Fig. 14.82

 # How to Draw a Geodesic Dome

As has been mentioned earlier, all geodesic domes are derived from one or other of the platonic solids. Of these five solids, the three that are made up with triangles are most favoured:

the tetrahedron – 4 faces,

the octahedron – 8 faces,

the icosahedron – 20 faces.

The icosahedron produces domes that most closely match a sphere.

We first look at how to draw these three solids and how to find their circumscribing spheres.

Tetrahedron

(1) The plan of a tetrahedron resting on one of its faces is an equilateral triangle and its apex 0 is found by bisecting the angles.

(2) The end view can be used to find the tetrahedron's height as it shows edge 0,3 as a true length.

(3) Complete the front elevation.

(4) The centre of the circumscribing sphere lies on the axis of the solid and touches all vertices. In the end view, bisect true length 0,3 to intersect the axis through 0 to locate c. Draw the sphere in all views.

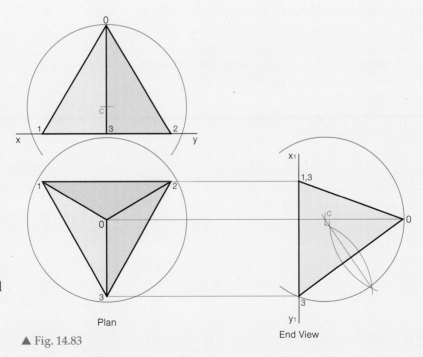

Plan

End View

▲ Fig. 14.83

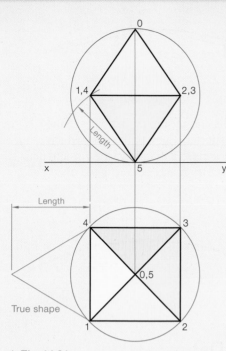

Octahedron

(1) The plan of the octahedron appears as a square with the diagonals joined.

(2) The height for the elevation is found by drawing the true shape of one of the faces and using its length as shown to locate points 1 and 4.

(3) The circumscribing sphere is drawn in elevation and then in plan.

▲ Fig. 14.84

Icosahedron

(1) The plan of the top five triangles of an icosahedron having its apex facing straight up will form a perfect pentagon.

The sides of the pentagon equal the true length of each edge of the icosahedron and the edges leading up to the apex appear as spokes of this pentagon leading into the centre.

(2) Construct the pentagon in plan.

(3) Draw lines from each of the vertices of the pentagon to its centre to form the spokes.

(4) Find a starting point for the lower pentagon by extending one of these spokes, e.g. 3,0 to intersect a circumscribing circle about the pentagon. The vertices for the second pentagon will lie on the same circle.

(5) Complete the plan.

(6) Two heights are needed to draw the elevation. Find the true shape of one of the faces. Consider this as a rebatment of the face.

(7) Draw auxiliary views to show face 0,1,2 as an edge view by viewing along true length 2,1. By using length L from the true shape height A can be found.

(8) Similarly, an edge view of surface 1,2,3 will find height B.

(9) Construct elevation.

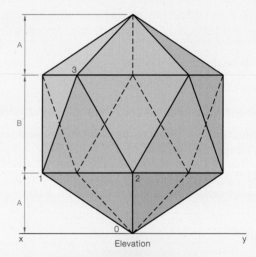

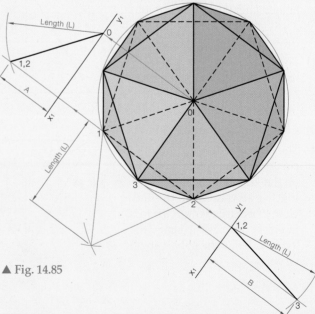

▲ Fig. 14.85

Circumscribing Sphere

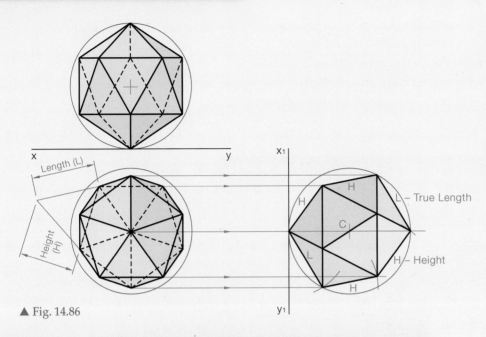

▲ Fig. 14.86

The circumscribing sphere can easily be found in elevation. If only a partial elevation is to be drawn, centre C can be found by projecting a view showing one face edge on and one edge as a true length.

By bisecting the true length and extending to cross the axis centre, C is located.

3-Frequency Geodesic Dome (Octahedral)

In this example the construction for one of the four faces is shown. The other three faces may be found subsequently by symmetry or rotation about point O.

(1) Draw a semi-octahedron in plan.

(2) Project the end view which shows two of the faces, edge views. Draw the circumscribing sphere.

(3) In the plan view, subdivide each edge of the face Oc_1c_4 into three equal spaces. Connect all the resultant points with straight lines as shown to form a triangular grid that should divide triangle Oc_1c_4 into nine smaller triangles.

(4) Index all the points as shown.

(5) Project points b_1, b_2 and b_3 to the end view.

(6) Point b_2, in plan, lies on line Ob_2 which is parallel to the x_1y_1. Radiate a line from c in end view, through b_2 to locate b_2, a point on the circumscribing sphere.

(7) Project back to plan.

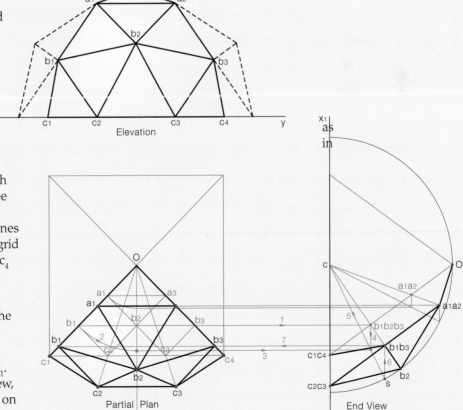

▲ Fig. 14.87

HIGHER LEVEL

(8) The radial projection lines from O to most points in the triangular grid of triangle Oc_1c_4 in the plan view, however, are not parallel to the x_1y_1 line. These must be rotated.

(9) A radial line is drawn from O through b_1 in plan, for example.

(10) Rotate Ob_1 about point O until it is parallel to x_1y_1.

(11) As Ob_1 rotates in plan point b_1 moves horizontally in end view.

(12) The rotated radial is extended to hit the circumscribed sphere at point s.

(13) By projecting point s back onto the original radial cb_1 extended we find point b_1 in end view.

(14) Points b_1 and b_3 can be projected from end view, back onto the radials in plan.

(15) Repeat this process for points a_1 and a_2.

3-Frequency Geodesic Dome (3/8 Icosahedral)

Only the top five equilateral triangles of the icosahedron are used to produce this dome.

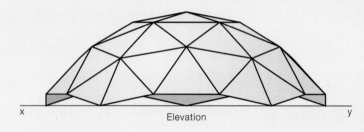

(1) Draw the plan of the top five equilateral triangles. They form a pentagon in plan.

(2) Project an auxiliary view or an end view that will show one face as an edge view OAB and one edge as a true length OD.

(3) Construct the circumscribing sphere.

(4) Subdivide each edge of OAB into three equal parts and join up to form a triangular grid.

(5) Each of the points is projected radially to the circumscribing sphere.

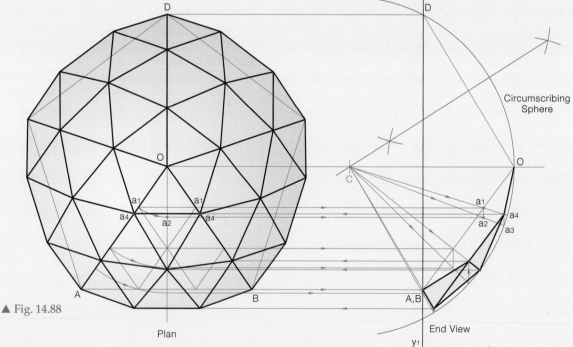

▲ Fig. 14.88

Method

Point a_1 on the grid in plan is projected to end view. Radial Oa_1 is rotated in plan to give Oa_2. Point a_2 is found in end view. Radiate a line from the centre of the circumscribing sphere C through a_2 in end view to intersect the sphere surface at a_3. This radial Ca_2a_3 is rotated back into position giving Ca_1a_4. Point a_4 is the new position of a_1 on the geodesic surface and is projected back to plan onto the radial Oa_1 extended.

Note: In elevation the bottom edges of the dome do not lie on the horizontal plane. In practice these irregularities at the bottom of the dome are easily accommodated by using dwarf walls.

Activities

Q1. Fig. **14.89** shows the outline plan and elevation of a cooling tower. It is in the form of a hyperboloid of revolution.

   (i) Draw the given views.

   (ii) Find the true shape of section S–S.

                     Scale 1:50

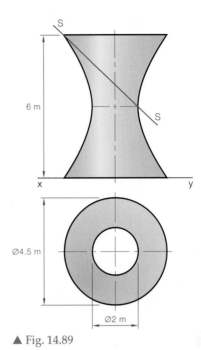

▲ Fig. 14.89

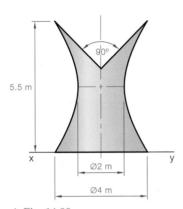

▲ Fig. 14.90

Q2. The diagram Fig. **14.90** shows a hyperboloid of revolution which has been shaped at the top.

   (i) Draw the plan and elevation of the hyperboloid.

   (ii) Project an end elevation.

                     Scale 1:50

Q3. A garden sculpture in the form of a cut hyperboloid of revolution is shown in **Fig. 14.91**. Draw the plan, elevation and end view of the sculpture.

                     Scale 1:10

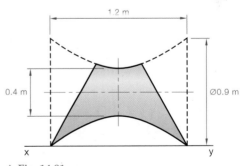

▲ Fig. 14.91

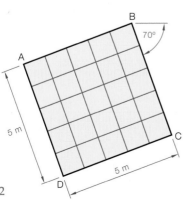

▲ Fig. 14.92

Q4. Fig. **14.92** shows the outline plan of a hyperbolic paraboloid roof **ABCD**. The corners **B** and **D** are at ground level. Corner **A** is 2 m above ground level and corner **C** is 6 m above ground level.

   (i) Draw the given plan and project an elevation.

   (ii) Project an end view of the roof.

   (iii) Find the curvature of the roof along the line joining A to C.

                     Scale 1:50

Q5. Fig. 14.93 shows the outline plan of a hyperbolic paraboloid roof made up of two surfaces, **abcd** and **bcef**. The corners **a**, **d**, **e** and **f** are at ground level, corner **c** is 1 m above the ground and corner **b** is 5 m above the ground.

(i)   Draw the given plan and project an elevation.

(ii)   Project an end view of the roof.

(iii) Find the curvature of the roof along a line joining d and f.

(iv)   Draw a new elevation of the roof which shows the true length of edge dc.

Scale 1:50

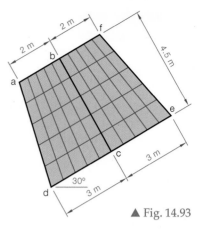

▲ Fig. 14.93

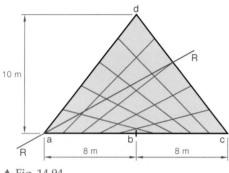

▲ Fig. 14.94

Q6. Fig. 14.94 shows the outline plan of a hyperbolic paraboloid roof **abcd**. The corners **a** and **c** are 1 m above ground level. Corner **b** is 4 m above ground level and corner **d** is 12 m above ground level.

(i)   Draw the given plan and project an elevation.

(ii)   Project an end view of the roof.

(iii) Show the true shape of section R–R through the roof.

Scale 1:100

Q7. Given two skew line directrices of a hyperbolic paraboloid ab and cd. Also, given the traces of the plane director, determine five elements on the surface of the hyperbolic paraboloid.

a = 40, 30, 40

b = 120, 10, 10

c = 60, 10, 50

d = 130, 60, 60

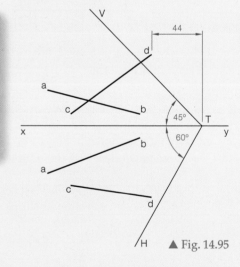

▲ Fig. 14.95

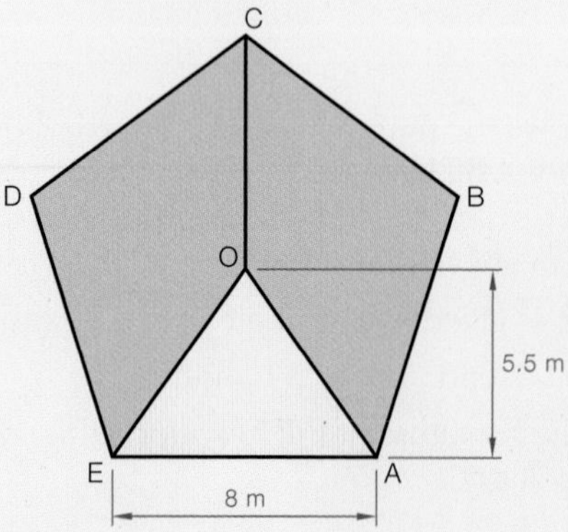

Q8. Fig. 14.96 shows the regular pentagonal plan of two adjoining hyperbolic paraboloid roof surfaces ABCO and EDCO. The surface AEO is a plane surface. Points A and E are at ground level, D and B are 3 m above ground level, C is 5 m above the ground level and O is 10 m above ground level.

(i)   Draw the given plan and project an elevation.

(ii)   Show the curvature of the roof along the line CE and DO.

(iii) Determine the plane director for the edges EO and DC on the surface DCOE. Show the traces of the plane director containing the element EO.

▲ Fig. 14.96

Scale 1:100

Q9. Fig. 14.97 shows the outline plan of four adjoining hyperbolic paraboloid roof surfaces **ABCO**, **CDEO**, **EFGO** and **GHAO**. The full roof perimeter is a square in plan. The four surfaces have been cut as shown, to form a circle in plan. The corners **A**, **C**, **E** and **G** are at ground level, corners **B**, **D**, **F** and **H** are 10 m above ground level and corner **O** is 22 m above ground level.

 (i) Draw the plan and project an elevation.

 (ii) Determine the traces of the plane director for the edges AB and OC of the hyperbolic paraboloid surface ABCO and having its horizontal trace passing through C.

 (iii) Find the curvature of the roof along a line joining F to C.

 Scale 1:200

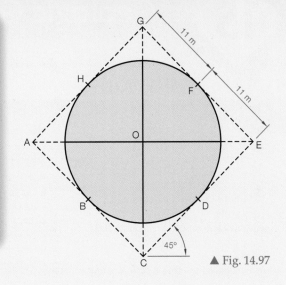

▲ Fig. 14.97

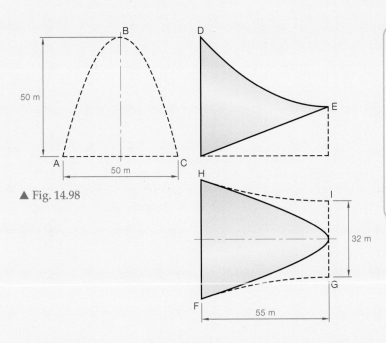

▲ Fig. 14.98

Q10. Fig. 14.98 shows the plan and elevation of a structure which is in the form of a hyperbolicparaboloid shell. The curve DE is a parabola whose vertex is at E. The surface of the unit is generated by translating the parabola ABC in a vertical position along the parabola DE.

 (i) Draw the given plan and elevation.

 (ii) Project an end view.

 Scale 1:500

Q11. Draw the plan, elevation and end view of an icosahedron of 60 mm side having one vertex resting on the horizontal plane and one vertical axis.

Q12. Explain the term 'frequency' in relation to geodesic structures.

Q13. Draw the plan and elevation of a 3-frequency geodesic dome based on an octahedron of 90 mm side.

HIGHER LEVEL

15 Geologic Geometry

Syllabus Outline

Areas to be studied:

- Appropriate symbols and notation.
- Interpolation and plotting of contours.
- Methods of showing slopes and gradients.
- Profiles determined from contours.
- *Use of skew boreholes in mining problems.*
- Determining the true dip of ore strata.
- *Determining the apparent dip of ore strata.*
- Strike and thickness of strata.
- Determination of outcrop.
- Cutting and embankment sections for level constructions.
- *Cutting and embankment sections for inclined constructions.*

Learning Outcomes

Students should be able to:

Higher and Ordinary levels

- Understand concepts such as bearings, grid layout, true north, etc.
- Interpolate and plot contours on a map for given data.
- Show profiles determined from contours.
- Determine cuttings and embankments for level roads and surfaces.
- Determine the true dip, strike and thickness of strata.
- Determine the outcrop profile for given strata.

Higher Level only

- *Determine cuttings and embankments for inclined roads and surfaces.*
- *Determine the apparent dip of strata.*
- *Solve mining problems through the use of skew boreholes.*

Our studies to date have concerned drawings of man-made objects, be they machine parts or houses. This chapter will investigate the natural geological features of the earth, mapping the earth's surface, mining, and finally the excavation works necessary for road building. Maps and map data are used throughout the course of the chapter. The accuracy of these maps and this data is extremely important in this type of work because of the scale of these earthworks projects.

Like all subjects, geologic geometry has its own subject-specific terminology. A good starting point is to define and explain some of these terms with notes and diagrams.

 # Contours

A contour is a line on a map to locate all points of equal elevation. This elevation/height can be relative to sea level or a chosen datum height. Contours may measure elevations above or below this datum level. On a single contour all points have the same elevation.

 # Contour Interval

This is the vertical distance between horizontal planes passing through successive contours. In Fig. 15.1 the contour interval is 10 m. On any given map the contour interval should not change.

Magnetic North

All maps should have the direction of north marked on them to allow for the correct orientation of the map. Magnetic north is found by using a compass. The direction of other lines or features on the map can be determined by reference to the north direction. On-site compass readings, however, are not to be taken as highly accurate indications of north. There are two reasons for this: (1) local magnetism may affect the position of the compass needle and (2) magnetic north and true north are not exactly the same.

Magnetic north can change due to the shifting of the earth's magnetic field.

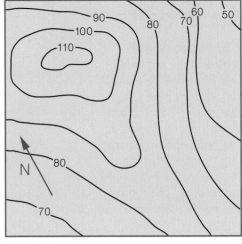
▲ Fig. 15.1

True North

For accurate orientation of lines on a map, the angle of a line relative to true north is often needed. Sightings on a star (usually Polaris, the North Star) or the sun can give accurate readings from which true north can be calculated. A map will often indicate by how much magnetic north varies from true north.

North 39° West

North 60° East

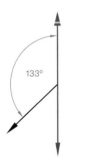 Bearing

The bearing of a line is the angle between the line and magnetic north. The bearing of a line may be established by using a directional compass. The correct method of recording bearings is by reference to the north or the south. Fig. 15.2 shows some examples. If a bearing is N 39° W, it could be also described as S 141° W. Similarly N 133° W could be described as S 47° W.

or North 133° West
    South 47° West

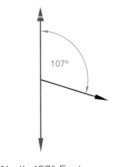

or North 107° East
    South 73° East

▲ Fig. 15.2

Profiles

A profile is a vertical section along a given line. It clearly shows the variation in slope along that line. Fig. 15.3 shows the process of plotting a profile; the points where the contours cross the line AB are projected onto an elevation. The profile will not be completely accurate as the profile path between the plotted points is only guessed.

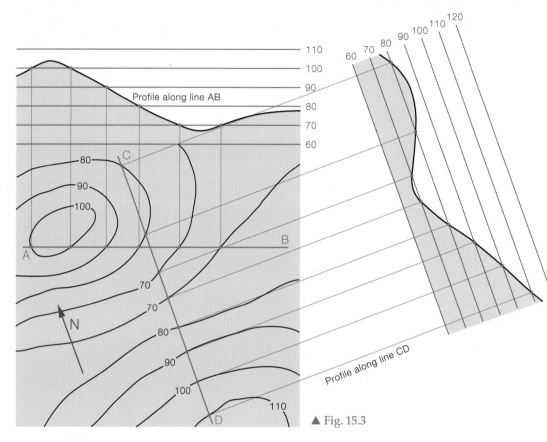

Profile along line AB

Profile along line CD

▲ Fig. 15.3

Gradient

The gradient is the slope of the ground at a particular place. By examining the contours on a map an approximate gradient can be given. When the contours are close together the gradient is very steep. As the gap between contours widens on the map the slope decreases. Very widely spaced contours indicate land that is almost flat and/or land that is actually flat in places. A more accurate measurement of gradient is found by drawing a profile. At any point on the profile a slope can be found. Gradient can be given as a ratio or represented by a proportional triangle.

Fig. 15.4 shows how the gradient can be found along line AB. Written as a ratio it compares the vertical gain by the horizontal travel. 20:24 = 10:12 = 1:1.2, 1 in 1.2 m. The triangle graphically represents the same ratio.

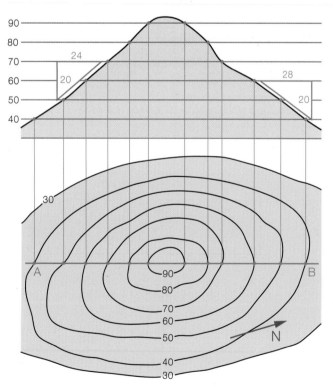

▲ Fig. 15.4

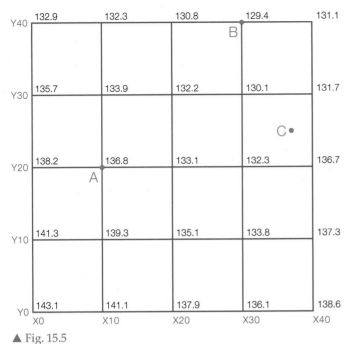

▲ Fig. 15.5

Grid Layout

When surveying a site to determine contours and gradients one of the most practical approaches is to use a grid layout. The size of the grid squares affects the accuracy of the survey. Elevations/levels are taken at the corners of the squares and the ground is assumed to slope uniformly between adjacent level points. It is now possible to find fairly accurate contours by using **interpolation**. Fig. 15.5 shows a portion of a grid layout using 10 m squares. By using xy coordinates each corner can easily be identified. For example, corner A is X10,Y20, corner B is X30,Y40 and point C, which is not on a corner, may also be specified X37,Y25.

 ## Interpolation of Contours

The interpolation of contours is the finding of contours from grid levels. In Fig. 15.6 the positions of 2 m contours are needed. Edge AB of the grid will contain a point on contour 142 m. The difference in levels between A and B is 1.8 m. Divide AB into 18 equal parts and thus locate level 142 m as shown. In a similar way a point on the 142 m contour can be located on edge AC of the grid. The difference in levels here is 2 m. Divide AC into 20 equal parts and locate the 142 m level. Further points can be found using this method. Interpolation can be very slow and tedious. Fig. 15.7 shows the grid levels converted into contours.

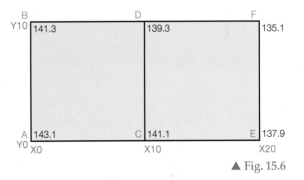

▲ Fig. 15.6

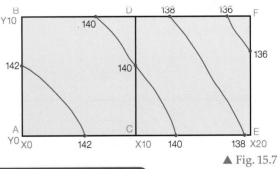

▲ Fig. 15.7

Using a Template to Help

Interpolation is based on the division of the sides of the grid boxes into different numbers of equal parts. A template to speed up the division process would help a great deal.

(1) On tracing paper draw a line AB of any length and at one end draw a perpendicular CD.

(2) Step a number of equal spaces up and down from B on the line CD.

(3) Join all these points back to A.

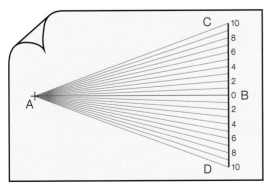

▲ Fig. 15.8

Once measurements are taken perpendicular to line AB, it will be seen that the spacing between the lines remains equal all the way from B to A. The line CD should be longer than the sides of the squares of the grid and the number of divisions should be enough to cope with the largest difference in levels between two adjacent corners of the grid.

There is a difference of 17.1 – 15.7 = 1.4 m between the two ends of the grid square in Fig. 15.9. Slide the template across the grid until the grid side is divided into 14 divisions. Use a pin to mark the contour positions. The line CD must be kept parallel to the grid sides.

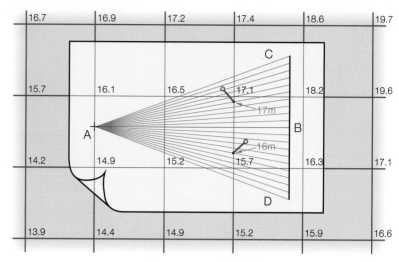

▲ Fig. 15.9

Worked Examples

A portion of a grid layout is shown in Fig. 15.10. A 10 m square grid has been used. To a scale of 1:200 draw out the grid and plot the contour lines at 1 m vertical intervals using interpolation.

(1) If using a template it should be constructed to have at least 26 spaces and the CD line should be longer than 50 mm.

(2) By proportional division of the sides of the grids the contours may also be found. Contour 22 is shown in Fig. 15.11.

21.4	21.0	21.2	20.6	20.1	19.6
23.2	22.7	22.2	21.7	21.1	20.4
25.4	24.8	24.3	23.9	22.4	21.1
26.9	26.6	25.8	25.3	24.2	23.7

▲ Fig. 15.10

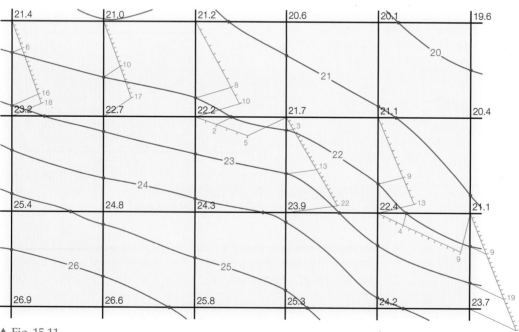

▲ Fig. 15.11

The map in Fig. 15.12 shows ground contours at 5 m intervals. An object stands vertically on the ground at A. Determine the minimum height of the object if it is to be visible from the ground at B.

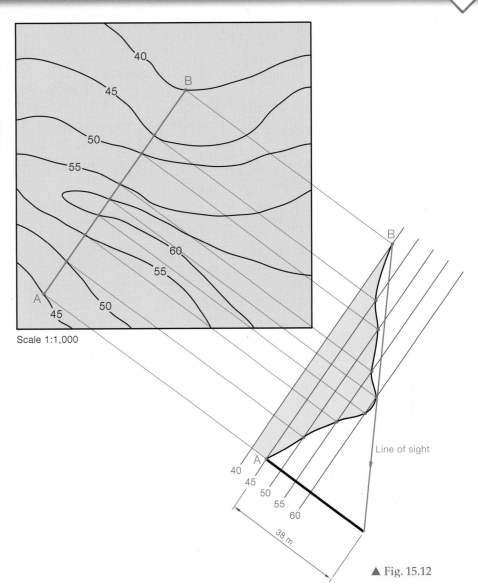

Scale 1:1,000

To solve this problem a profile is found along the line AB.

(1) Join A to B.

(2) The lowest point on the profile will be 40 m. Set up the profile lines parallel to line AB.

(3) The spacing between these profile lines will be the scaled equivalent of 5 m.

(4) Project the points where line AB crosses the contours onto the profile. The projection lines are perpendicular to AB.

(5) Draw the profile.

(6) Draw the lowest line of sight from B tangential to the profile (light travels in straight lines).

(7) Draw the vertical object at A to meet the line of sight. If the object is above 38 m tall it will be seen from the ground at point B.

▲ Fig. 15.12

 # The Geometry of Mining

Mining concerns the removal of useless material and useful material both on the surface (opencast mining) and beneath the surface. Mining companies like to minimise the mining of useless material and maximise the mining of useful material. To this end, surveying, testing and planning are involved.

In this chapter we deal with mineral deposits with definite limits and boundaries. These are known as veins or strata. The strata are made up of rock or ore and are assumed to be of uniform thickness and be planar on top and bottom surfaces. Obviously in real geographic situations the stratum may undulate and vary in thickness.

The stratum of ore may come to the surface as in Fig. 15.13. This is an outcrop point. Outcrop points may facilitate open mining and thus minimise expense. The vein, however, may not intersect the surface of the earth. In cases like this the vein's theoretical outcrop point may serve as a starting point for mining.

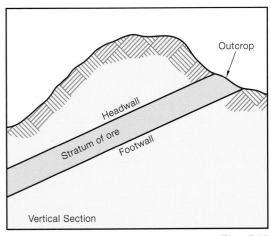

Vertical Section

▲ Fig. 15.13

Terminology

▼ Fig. 15.14

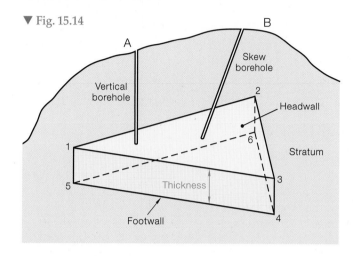

Stratum – A layer, seam or vein of ore, generally assumed to be an inclined plane of uniform thickness.

Headwall – The top surface of the stratum, 1, 2, 3, Fig. 15.14.

Footwall – The lower surface of the stratum, 4, 5, 6, Fig. 15.14.

Thickness – The perpendicular distance between the headwall and the footwall.

Outcrop – A point at which a section of the stratum comes to the earth's surface.

Dip – The angle a stratum makes with the horizontal plane (the slope of the stratum).

Strike – The bearing of a level line on the surface of the stratum. It is usually related to the compass north. It is shown in plan.

Borehole – Hole drilled from the surface of the earth through a stratum of ore in order to determine its position and thickness.

The map shown in Fig. 15.15 shows ground contours at 10 m vertical intervals. Also shown are points A, B and C which are outcrop points on a stratum of ore. Determine the strike of the stratum.

(1) Since A, B and C are outcrop points they are all on the stratum. Join the points giving a triangular plane of ore.

(2) Project an elevation of this plane using the heights of the contours.

(3) In elevation draw a level line across the plane ABC. Usually the starting point for this level line is the mid-height vertex. In this example the line is drawn from B to intersect edge AC at point 1.

(4) Find line B1 in plan by projecting point 1 down to edge AC in plan. Join point 1 to vertex B.

(5) The angle the line B1 makes with the given north is the strike. It is written as North 105° East.

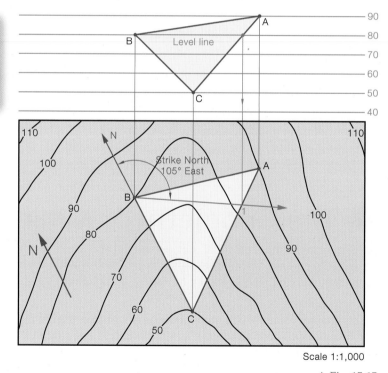

Scale 1:1,000

▲ Fig. 15.15

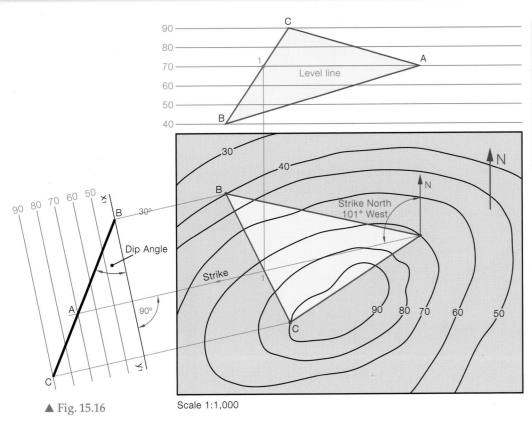

▲ Fig. 15.16   Scale 1:1,000

The map shown in Fig. 15.16 shows ground contours at 10 m intervals. Also shown are points A, B and C which are outcrop points on a stratum of ore. Determine the dip and strike of the stratum.

(1) Construct the plan and elevation of the stratum as explained in the previous example.

(2) A level line is drawn in elevation and is projected to plan. The angle line A1 makes with the given north is the strike.

(3) By projecting an auxiliary view of the stratum viewing in the direction of the strike an edge view of the stratum is found. Points A, B and C line up.

(4) The angle the edge view of the stratum makes with the horizontal is the dip.

See worksheets 15.1 and 15.2

Fig. 15.17 shows ground contours at 10 m vertical intervals on a map. A, B and C are outcrop points on a stratum of ore.

(i) Determine the dip and strike of the stratum.

(ii) Find the outline of the outcrop between points A and C, and between points C and B.

(1) Find the dip and strike as outlined previously.

(2) The outcrop line is where the stratum comes to the surface. In the auxiliary the stratum is seen as an edge view.

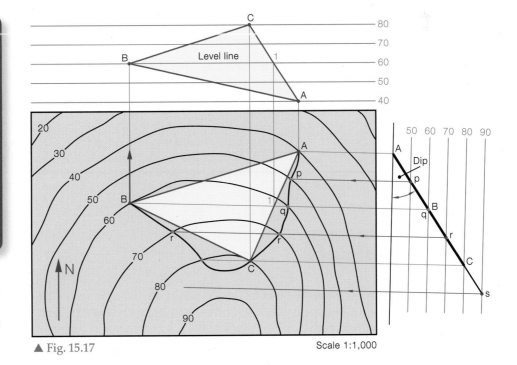

▲ Fig. 15.17   Scale 1:1,000

Where this edge view crosses the levels lines they are projected back to give points on the contours in plan. For example, the edge view crosses the 50 m level at point p. Point p is projected back to the map and is found on the 50 m contour line. Similarly for point q. Point r when projected back crosses the 70 m contour twice and thus gives two points on the outcrop.

(3) Join the points with a line, remembering to include points A, B and C.

(4) It should be noted that the 90 m contour definitely does not include outcrop points. This is proved by extending the edge view in the auxiliary to the 90 m level at point s. This point projected back does not intersect the 90 m contour in plan.

Up to now the examples given have all used outcrop points to locate the stratum. Boreholes may also be used to locate points on the stratum. Vertical boreholes or inclined boreholes may be used.

See worksheet 15.3

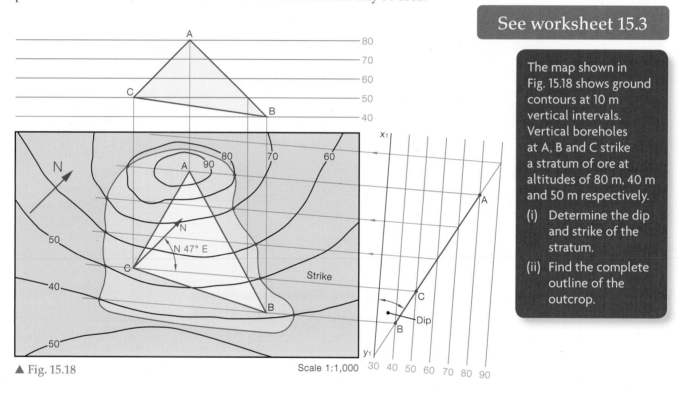

▲ Fig. 15.18   Scale 1:1,000   30 40 50 60 70 80 90

The map shown in Fig. 15.18 shows ground contours at 10 m vertical intervals. Vertical boreholes at A, B and C strike a stratum of ore at altitudes of 80 m, 40 m and 50 m respectively.
(i) Determine the dip and strike of the stratum.
(ii) Find the complete outline of the outcrop.

(1) Points A, B and C are found by using the altitudes from the question.

(2) Find the strike and dip of the stratum in the usual way.

(3) The outcrop is found as explained in the previous example. It should be noted that A, B and C are not part of the outcrop.

(4) There are two outcrop points on the 80 m contour and none on the 90 m contour. When drawing the outcrop line, care must be taken to join the two points without crossing a contour line. In a similar way there are two outcrop points on the 40 m contour. These points must be joined without crossing the 50 m contour line.

See worksheet 15.4

Stratum thickness

Up to this point we have ignored the fact that the stratum of ore has a thickness. The problems have dealt with the top surface of the stratum (the headwall) or the bottom surface of the stratum (the footwall). As has been mentioned earlier, in solving these problems, it is assumed that the stratum thickness remains constant throughout, i.e. that the headwall and footwall are parallel.

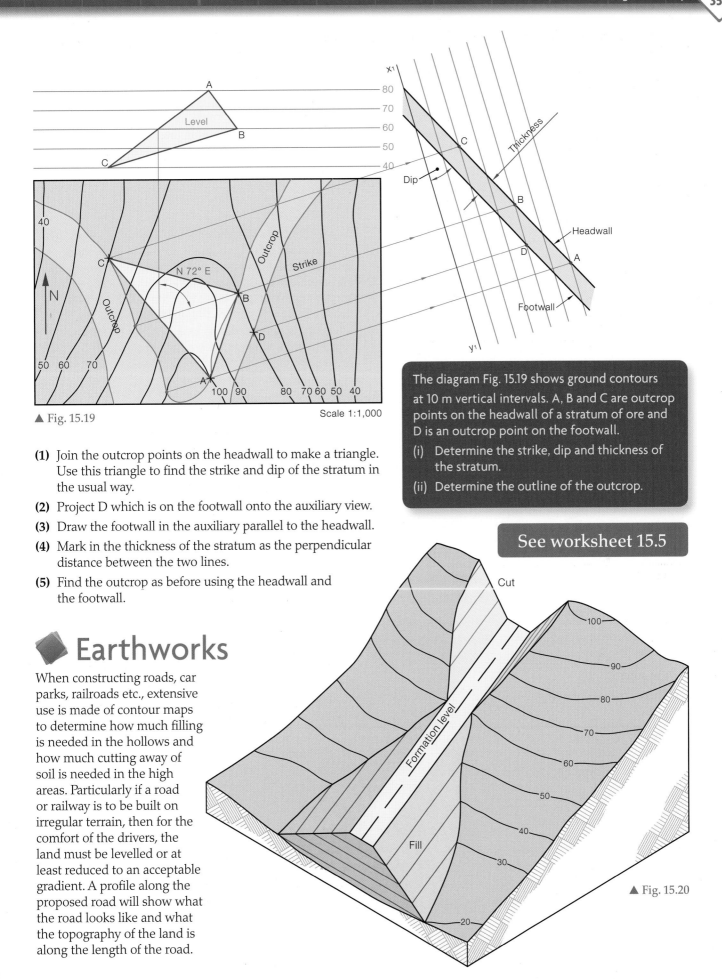

▲ Fig. 15.19

Scale 1:1,000

The diagram Fig. 15.19 shows ground contours at 10 m vertical intervals. A, B and C are outcrop points on the headwall of a stratum of ore and D is an outcrop point on the footwall.

(i) Determine the strike, dip and thickness of the stratum.

(ii) Determine the outline of the outcrop.

(1) Join the outcrop points on the headwall to make a triangle. Use this triangle to find the strike and dip of the stratum in the usual way.

(2) Project D which is on the footwall onto the auxiliary view.

(3) Draw the footwall in the auxiliary parallel to the headwall.

(4) Mark in the thickness of the stratum as the perpendicular distance between the two lines.

(5) Find the outcrop as before using the headwall and the footwall.

See worksheet 15.5

Earthworks

When constructing roads, car parks, railroads etc., extensive use is made of contour maps to determine how much filling is needed in the hollows and how much cutting away of soil is needed in the high areas. Particularly if a road or railway is to be built on irregular terrain, then for the comfort of the drivers, the land must be levelled or at least reduced to an acceptable gradient. A profile along the proposed road will show what the road looks like and what the topography of the land is along the length of the road.

▲ Fig. 15.20

The formation level refers to the level of the proposed road or car park. The cut is the amount of land that has to be cut away to bring the level of land down to the formation level. The fill is the amount of fill of material that needs to be put in a hollow to bring the level up to the formation level. In the construction of most roads there will be both cut and fill. The side slopes for the fill are kept the same for the whole road and similarly for the slope of the cutting. Fig. 15.20 shows a pictorial of a level road passing through a sloped terrain. The road is level and has a height of 60 m. It can be seen that when the road crosses the 60 m contour there is no cut or fill needed. As the ground rises above 60 m it must be cut away and as it drops below 60 m the area needs to be filled to bring it up to formation level.

Slopes of Cut and Fill

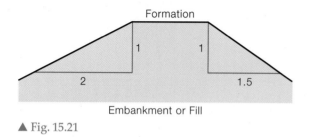

▲ Fig. 15.21

As mentioned earlier, the embankment or fill slopes away from the road at an even angle. The steeper the angle the less actual fill material will be needed. However, the embankment becomes less stable as it gets steeper. A similar argument can be used for the cut. Steep angles involve less excavation but are more likely to collapse. The slope is expressed as a ratio 1:2 or an angle. The ratio refers to vertical height:width. The left side of Fig. 15.21 has a slope of 1:2 and the right side has a slope of 1:1.5.

Fig. 15.22 shows ground contours at 5 m vertical intervals. AB is the line of a proposed roadway. The road is to have the following specifications:

(i) Formation width 16 m.

(ii) Formation level 75 m.

(iii) Side slopes for cuttings 1:1.

(iv) Side slopes for embankments 1:1.5.

Show the earthworks needed to accommodate the roadway.

(1) Draw the sides of the formation parallel to the line AB.

(2) The formation level is at 75 m so therefore the 75 m contour will have neither cut nor fill.

(3) The slope for cutting is 1:1. For every 1 m rise in the cut one moves 1 m from the road. The contours are at 5 m intervals, so to get a 5 m rise in the cut a move 5 m away from the road is needed. The road side is at 75 m level. A line 5 m away and parallel represents 80 m on the cut, 10 m away and parallel to the side of the road represents 85 m on the cut. Draw in the cut lines as shown. Where they intersect the contour lines, locate points on the cut outline. Draw in the cut.

(4) The fill is constructed in the same way. The slope for fill is 1:1.5. For a 5 m fall in the embankment level, a distance of 1.5 × 5 m = 7.5 m must be travelled away from the road. Draw in the embankment lines parallel to the roadside and 7.5 m apart as shown. As you move out from the road you move down the bank, the level drops. Where the fill lines and the contour lines cross give points on the embankment line.

(5) Draw in the symbols for cut and fill as shown.

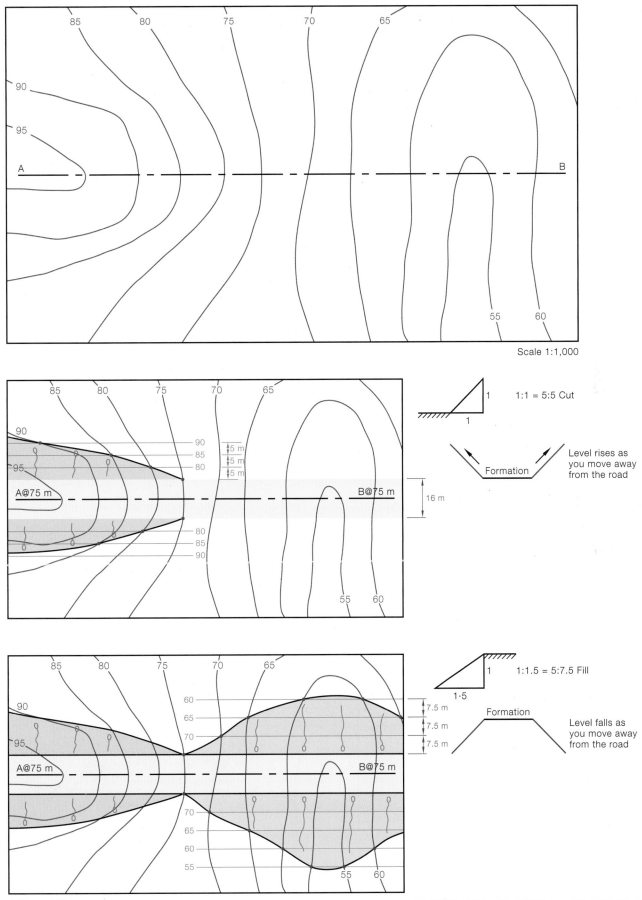

Scale 1:1,000

1:1 = 5:5 Cut

Level rises as you move away from the road

1:1.5 = 5:7.5 Fill

Level falls as you move away from the road

▲ Fig. 15.22

See worksheets 15.6 and 15.7

Figure 15.23 shows ground contours at 4 m vertical intervals. ABCD is the centre line of a proposed roadway with the centre for the curve at O. The road is to have the following specifications.

(i) Formation width 14 m.

(ii) Formation level 52 m.

(iii) Side slopes for cutting 1:1.5.

(iv) Side slopes for embankment 1:2.

Show the earthworks needed to accommodate the roadway.

(1) Draw in the formation.

(2) Mark the 52 m contour as it crosses the side of the formation.

(3) Cutting slope 1:1.5. With the difference between contours at 4 m this will mean a spacing between the cutting contours of 6 m (4 × 1.5). Draw in the cuttings.

(4) Embankment slope of 1:2. With the contours at 4 m intervals this will mean a spacing between the fill contours of 8 m (4 × 2). These cutting contours remain parallel to the formation even around the curve.

(5) Complete the outline of the earthworks as shown in Fig. 15.24.

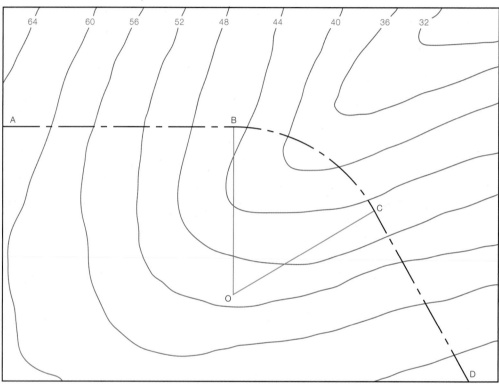

▲ Fig. 15.23   Scale 1:1,000

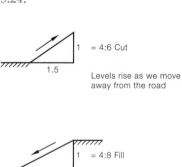

1 = 4:6 Cut

Levels rise as we move away from the road

1 = 4:8 Fill

Levels fall as we move away from the road

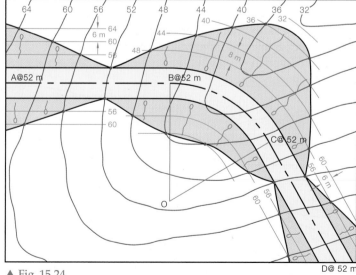

▲ Fig. 15.24

See worksheets 15.8 and 15.9

Figure 15.25 shows ground contours at 2 m vertical intervals. AB shows a proposed roadway with CDEF being a car park. The car park is level and at the same level as the road. The road and car park are to have the following specifications:

(i)   Formation width 12 m.

(ii) Formation level 110 m.

(iii) Side slopes for cutting 1:2.

(iv) Side slopes for embankment 1:2.5.

Show the earthworks necessary to accommodate the road and car park.

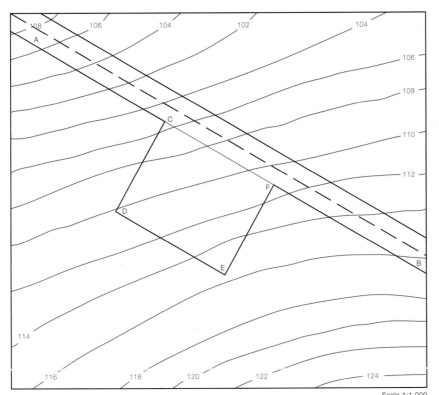

▲ Fig. 15.25

Scale 1:1,000

(1) Ignore the car park initially and find the cut and fill for the road. The slopes for cutting are 1:2 and the contours are at 2 m vertical intervals. The cutting contours are at (2 × 2 m) 4 m spacings from the side of the road. Draw the cut outline.

(2) The slopes for embankment are 1:2.5 and the contours are at 2 m vertical intervals. The fill lines are at (2 × 2.5 m) 5 m spacing from the side of the road. Draw the cut outline.

(3) Each side of the car park is treated like the side of a road. The cut and fill are plotted slightly beyond the sides.

(4) The earthworks for each side intersect each other.

(5) It should be noted that at corner, C, E and F where embankments intersect, and cuts intersect, a valley or ridge will be formed. These are indicated in Fig. 15.26.

(6) Draw in the symbols.

See worksheets 15.10 and 15.11

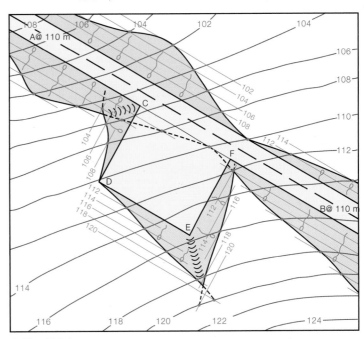

▲ Fig. 15.26

Skew Boreholes

It is possible to determine the strike, dip and thickness of a stratum of ore using only two non-parallel boreholes. The pictorial diagram, Fig. 15.27, shows two skew boreholes (skew means non-parallel, nonintersecting lines) intersecting a vein of ore. Borehole A intersects the top surface, the headwall, at A_H and exits the stratum through the footwall at A_F. Similarly borehole B enters the headwall at B_H and exits through the footwall at B_F. A straight line joining A_H and B_H will run along the headwall for its entire length. The line A_F B_F lies on the footwall. By finding a view that shows A_H B_H and A_F B_F appearing parallel, an edge view of the stratum can be seen.

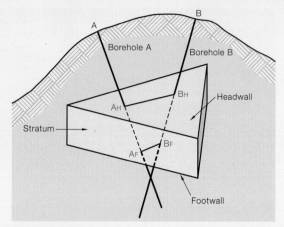

▲ Fig. 15.27

On a contour map, A and B are two points whose altitudes are 80 m and 100 m respectively. On the map, B is located 80 m east of A. A skew borehole at A is drilled in a southerly direction in plan and has an actual inclination of 45° to the horizontal plane. It reveals the top and bottom surfaces of the stratum at altitudes of 65 m and 25 m respectively. A skew borehole at B is drilled in a north-westerly direction in plan and has an actual inclination of 65° to the horizontal plane. It reveals the top and bottom surfaces of the stratum at altitudes of 80 m and 45 m. Find the strike, dip and thickness of the stratum.

Scale 1:1,000

HIGHER LEVEL

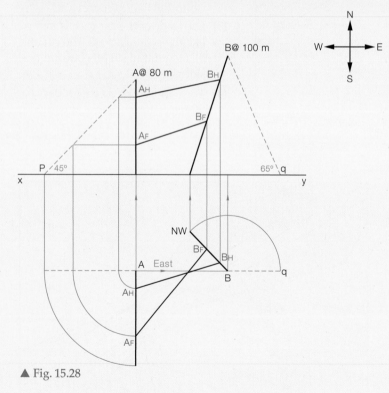

▲ Fig. 15.28

(1) Draw the xy line. In plan choose a position for borehole A. Borehole B is located 80 m east of A. It is always advisable to draw a directional compass to reduce the chance of errors.

(2) Project points A and B to elevation and measure vertically to the specified altitudes of 80 m and 100 m.

(3) Borehole A is bored at an angle of 45° to the HP and in a southerly direction. The borehole is constructed first in a westerly or easterly direction and then rotated to a southerly direction. Draw a line from A at 45° to the xy line. Where this line meets the xy line at p, project down to a horizontal from A in plan. This 'constructed' borehole can now be swung around into a southerly direction. The borehole is drawn in bold in both views.

(4) This borehole reveals the top and bottom of the stratum at altitudes of 65 m and 25 m. An altitude is a vertical measurement. Vertical distances of 65 m and 25 m above the xy line are found on the borehole giving AH and AF.

(5) A_H and A_F are found in plan by projecting the two points onto the constructional borehole, projecting to plan and rotating onto the actual borehole.

(6) The construction of borehole B is the same. It is bored at an angle of 65° in a north-westerly direction. Draw a line from B at an angle of 65° to the xy line. Where this line meets the xy line at q, project down to a horizontal from B in plan. The constructional borehole is rotated about B into a north-westerly direction and drawn in bold. Find this borehole in elevation.

(7) B_H and B_F have altitudes of 80 m and 45 m respectively. Project these heights onto borehole B in elevation and project to plan.

(8) Join A_H to B_H and also A_F to B_F. The first of these skew lines lies on the headwall and the second on the footwall.

(1) Fig. 15.29 shows that by getting a view showing $A_H B_H$ and $A_F B_F$ appearing as parallel, the strike, dip and thickness of the stratum can be found. Draw a level line in elevation from one of the points, e.g. A_H From B_H in elevation draw a line parallel to $A_F B_F$ to intersect the level line at O.

(2) From B_H in plan draw a line parallel to $A_F B_F$. This line intersects the projection line from O in elevation to find point O in plan.

(3) Join O back to A_H. View along $A_H O$ which is the strike. An auxiliary projected in this direction shows the skew lines appearing parallel and thus reveals the thickness and dip of the stratum.

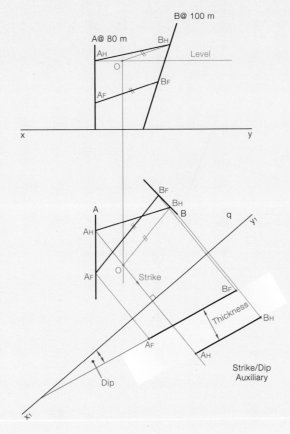

▲ Fig. 15.29

On a contour map A and B are two points whose altitudes are 70 m and 90 m respectively. On a map, B is located 90 m south-east of A. A skew borehole at A is drilled in a north-westerly direction in plan and has an actual inclination of 50° to the horizontal plane. It reveals the top and bottom surfaces of the stratum at distances of 35 m and 65 m respectively from A.

A skew borehole at B is drilled in a north-easterly direction in plan and has an actual inclination of 60° to the horizontal plane. It reveals the top and bottom surfaces of the stratum at altitudes of 70 m and 35 m respectively.

(i)   Determine the strike, dip and thickness of the stratum.

(ii) A second skew borehole from A is drilled in a southerly direction and has an actual inclination of 60° to the horizontal plane. Determine the altitude at which this borehole touches the bottom surface of the stratum and also the inclination of the borehole to the stratum.

Scale 1:1,000

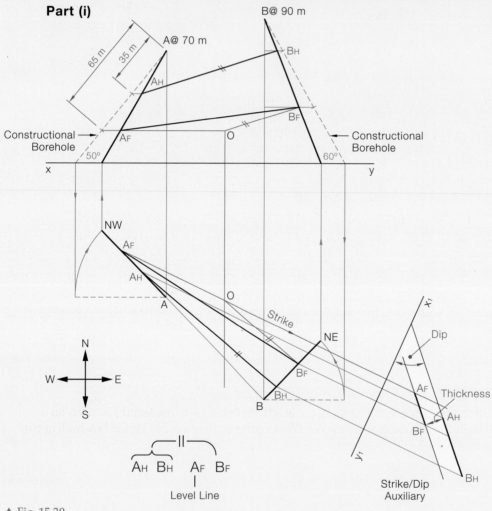

▲ Fig. 15.30

(1) Set up the problem as explained in the previous example. Points A and B are first found in plan. B is 90m away from A and at a 45° angle in a south-easterly direction.

(2) Project the two points to elevation and at the required elevation.

(3) Draw the borehole A at a 50° angle in elevation, drop it to plan and rotate to a north-westerly direction. Project the rotated borehole to elevation.

(4) This borehole reveals the top and bottom surfaces of the stratum at distances of 35 m and 65 m respectively from A. **These two distances must be measured down from A, along the constructional borehole.** This constructional borehole shows true angles and true lengths. As this borehole is rotated into

position the points move horizontally thus locating A_H and A_F on the actual borehole. These may be projected down to plan.

(5) Borehole B is found in a similar fashion. The points on the headwall and footwall are given as altitudes. These vertical heights are projected horizontally onto the actual borehole and then down to plan.

(6) $A_H B_H$ and $A_F B_F$ are treated as skew lines. The strike dip and thickness are found as explained in Fig. 15.29.

Part (ii)

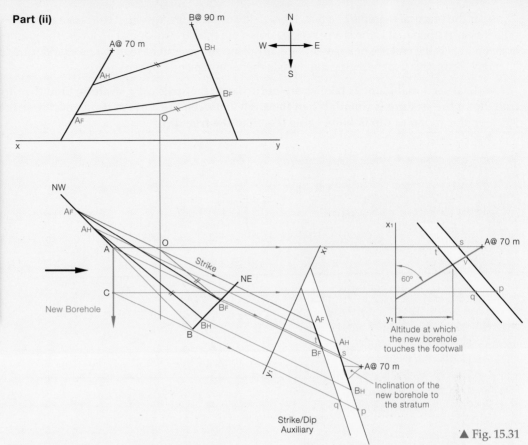

The second part of the question refers to a new borehole from A, bored in a southerly direction. In order to see this new borehole as a true length and with a true angle, it is viewed perpendicularly. A vertical section is taken along the new borehole to see the position of the stratum at that particular place.

▲ Fig. 15.31

(1) Draw the new borehole from A in plan in a southerly direction.

(2) View perpendicular to this to get the auxiliary view. Point A is projected onto this view to an altitude of 70 m.
The borehole is now drawn in the auxiliary making an angle of 60° to the horizontal plane (from question).

(3) The stratum is found by taking a vertical section along the new borehole and projecting it onto the new auxiliary. A vertical borehole is drilled from point A in plan and a second vertical borehole is drilled from a point C anywhere along the new borehole.

(4) Vertical boreholes will appear perpendicular to the horizontal plane in all elevations. Draw these vertical boreholes in the new elevation. These two vertical boreholes will hit the stratum at points s, t, p and q (Fig. 15.31). The heights of these four points are found by projecting the same vertical boreholes, A and C, onto the strike/dip auxiliary.

(5) When the points s, t, p and q have been located the vertical section through the stratum can be drawn. The required altitude and inclination can then be clearly seen.

(6) To find the true inclination of the borehole to the stratum, the length Av (which is a true length) is taken on a compass. Use this, as a radius, in the strike/dip auxiliary. With A as centre, scribe an arc to hit the headwall in two places. The inclination of the borehole can then be seen.

True Dip and Apparent Dip

The true dip of a stratum, which is what we have been finding up to this stage, is taken perpendicular to the strike. It can be taken from an edge view of the stratum plane(s) or as a vertical section taken perpendicular to the strike direction. Consider a vertical section taken at a different angle. This will show the layer(s) apparently at a lesser dip. This angle is the apparent dip.

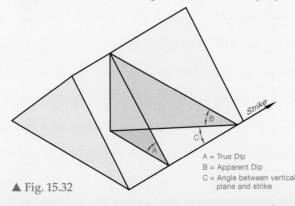

A = True Dip
B = Apparent Dip
C = Angle between vertical
plane and strike

▲ Fig. 15.32

HIGHER LEVEL

Consider the practical example of a pitched roof. If you walk directly down the roof, taking the shortest route from ridge to eaves, then that is the steepest slope down the roof. By walking at an angle, the journey will be longer but not as steep. This is the essence of apparent dip. Any plane surface can have only one true dip angle but can have multiple apparent dip angles depending at which angle the section plane is taken.

If a vertical sectional plane is taken perpendicular to the strike of a stratum, then the dip is at its maximum, the true dip of the stratum is found. When the angle between the cross-section and the strike is anything less than 90° then the apparent dip is some value less than the true dip.

On a contour map A and B are two points whose altitudes are 85 m and 110 m respectively. On the map, B is located 70 m north of A. A skew borehole at A is drilled in a south-westerly direction in plan and has an actual inclination of 55° to the horizontal plane. It reveals the top and bottom surfaces of a stratum at altitudes of 60 m and 40 m respectively. A skew borehole at B is drilled in a south-easterly direction in plan and has an actual inclination of 60° to the horizontal plane. It reveals the top and bottom surfaces of the stratum at altitudes of 90 m and 10 m respectively.

(i) Determine the strike, dip and thickness of the stratum.

(ii) Determine the apparent dip of the stratum on a vertical section through A that trends in a southerly direction.

Scale 1:1,000

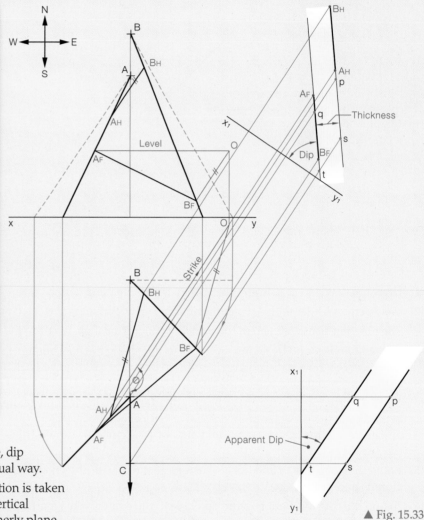

▲ Fig. 15.33

(1) Set up the problem and find the strike, dip and thickness of the stratum in the usual way.

(2) To find the apparent dip, a vertical section is taken in a southerly direction from A. Two vertical boreholes are introduced on this southerly plane, one at A and another at C.

(3) Draw a new auxiliary to show the sectional view. The vertical boreholes are projected to the strike/dip auxiliary and to this new auxiliary. Heights p, q, s and t are found from the strike/dip auxiliary and tranferred to the new auxiliary. The apparent dip can be measured from new auxiliary.

 # Earthworks for Inclined Roads

The earthwork problems that we have dealt with so far have involved level stretches of road and level car parking sites. On a variable height site it is often more practical to design a sloping road because it can often reduce the amount of earth to be moved. By closely balancing the amount of cut and fill it can mean that the material removed in the cut can be used to build up the fill.

Plotting Fill for a Sloping Road

Fig. 15.34 shows a road rising at a steep gradient. The road is to be built on a level plane. It can be seen that the amount of fill needed increases as the road rises. It can also be seen that the level lines along the embankment are parallel to each other but are not parallel to the side of the formation. They splay away from the road as it rises. The slope of the fill remains constant, so for a straight stretch of road it may be considered as a plane. This plane leans against the fill cone at the high end of the road and is tangential to it.

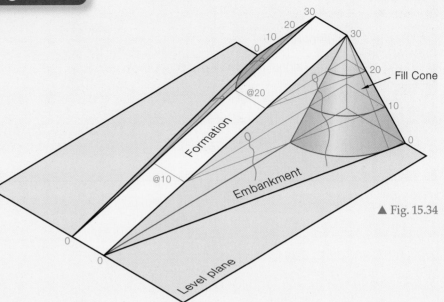

▲ Fig. 15.34

Plotting Cut for a Sloping Road

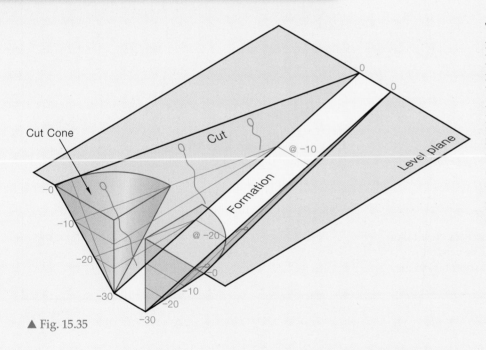

▲ Fig. 15.35

The diagram Fig. 15.35 shows a road sloping downwards into a level plane. The cutting needed increases as the road level drops. Level lines along the cutting are parallel to each other but are not parallel to the sides of the formation. They splay away from the road as it falls. The cut can be considered to be a plane when the road is straight. This plane is tangential to the cut cone. The cut cone is an inverted cone as shown.

Fig. 15.36 shows ground contours at 5 m vertical intervals. AB is the line of a proposed roadway. The road has the following specifications.

(i) Formation width is 12 m.

(ii) Formation level at A is 70 m.

(iii) Gradient A to B is 1 in 15 rising.

(iv) Side slopes for cuttings 1 in 2.

(v) Side slopes for embankments 1 in 1.5.

On the drawing supplied, show the earthworks necessary to accommodate the roadway.

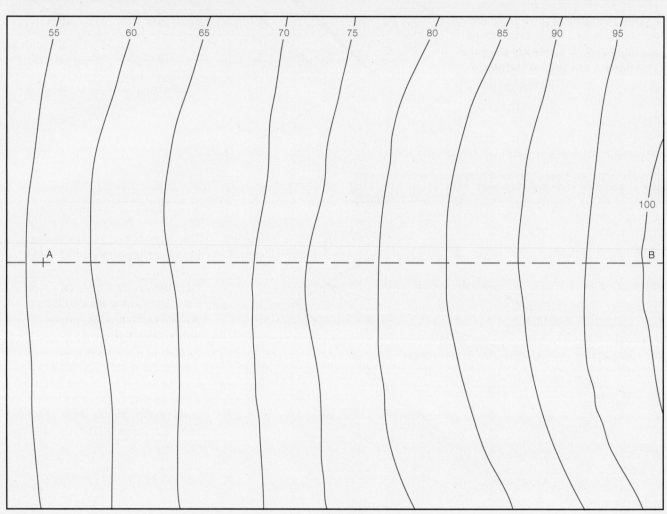

▲ Fig. 15.36

Scale 1:1,000

(1) Draw in the formation sides 6 m each side of the centre line.

(2) The road is level from side to side so the 70 m level from A is projected to the sides of the formation.

(3) The road rises at 1:15. Travelling from A to B the road rises by 1 m for every 15 m travelled on the map. For the purpose of solving these problems we are only interested in altitudes that correspond to contour levels.

Locate a point C along the road that produces a rise of 5 m or 10 m or 15 m (a multiple of 5 m). By measuring 150 m from point A, a point C is found that has an altitude 10 m greater than A.

(4) Project C to the sides of the formation. The fill cones are drawn. These appear as semicircles on the map. The radius in this example will be 15 m. **Fill cones are drawn at the high end of the formation**.

The 15 m is calculated by looking at the change in altitude and relating it to the embankment ratio. For a rise of 1 m a horizontal distance of 1.5 m is travelled away from the formation side. For a rise of 1 m a horizontal distance of 1.5 m is travelled away from the formation side.

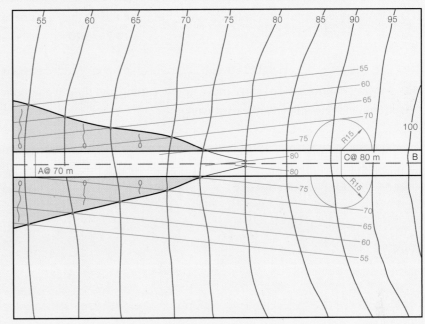

▲ Fig. 15.37

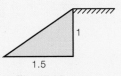

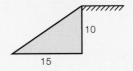

▲ Fig. 15.38

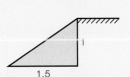

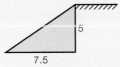

▲ Fig. 15.39

(5) Join the 70 m level on the side of the road as a tangent to the fill cone circle. This is a 70 m contour line along the embankment.

(6) Subsequent contour lines on the embankment will be parallel to this and 7.5 m apart on the map. Again, the figure of 7.5 m has been calculated from the fill ratio. The contours on the map are at 5 m intervals. To match these, the fill contours must be at 5 m intervals. A 5 m rise produces a 7.5 m horizontal spacing.

(7) Where the corresponding fill contours and map contours intersect gives points on the embankment edge.

(8) Note how the embankment point on the 80 m contour line was found to help locate the exact point where the fill edge hit the road.

Moving out from the side of the road, we move down the bank and the fill contours must drop.

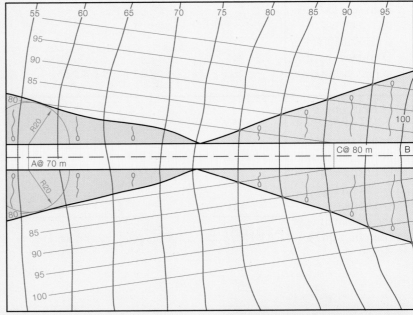

▲ Fig. 15.40

See worksheet 15.12

Cuttings

(9) The cutting cone is drawn at the low end of the formation. This cone will have a 20 m radius in plan. The 20 m is calculated by slotting the fall from C to A into the cutting ratio. 1:2 = 10:20

(10) Join the 80 m level at C as a tangent to the cut cone. This line forms the 80 m contour line on the cutting.

(11) Draw subsequent contour lines on the cutting parallel to this first line and 10 m apart.

$$1:2 = 5:10$$

Height between contours on map.   Width between cutting contours.

(12) Moving out from the road we move up the cutting and the cut contours must rise.

(13) Complete the outline of the earthworks.

Fig. 15.41 shows ground contours at 5 m vertical intervals. ABC is the line of a proposed roadway. The road has the following specifications:

(i)   Formation width is 12 m.

(ii) Formation level at A is 50 m.

(iii) Gradient A to B to C is 1 in 15 falling.

(iv) Side slopes for cutting 1 in 1.5.

(v)   Side slopes for fill 1 in 1.

On the drawing, show the earthworks necessary to accommodate the road.

---

(1) Draw in the formation sides 6 m each side of the centre line.

(2) The road is falling 1:15 from A to B to C. We ignore the bend in the road and treat the straight stretch A to B. If we travel from A, a distance of 150 m, we will locate point D and will have fallen in altitude by 10 m.

(3) The fill cone is drawn at the high end of the road at A. The radius of the cone is 10 m and the spacing between the embankment contours will be 5 m.

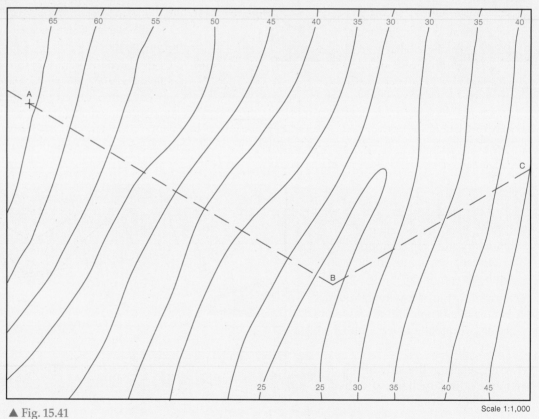

▲ Fig. 15.41

Scale 1:1,000

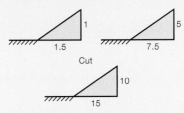

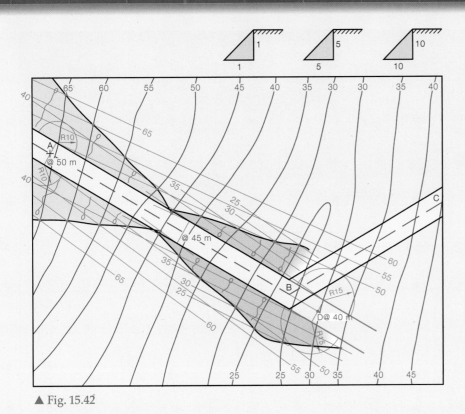

▲ Fig. 15.42

(4) The cut cone is always drawn at the lower end of the road. The cut cone will have a radius of 15 m and the spacing between the cutting contours will be 7.5 m.

Cut

▲ Fig. 15.43

(5) Draw in the cut and fill for the first section of road A to D.

(6) Rotate point D about the corner O onto the other section of road. D is at an altitude of 40 m.

(7) Locate point E at an altitude of 45 m. D and E will be 75 m apart.

(8) Set up the cut and fill cones. The fill cone will be at the high end of the road, at E, and will have a radius of 5 m. The cutting cone will be at the lower end of the road and will have a radius of 7.5 m. Both of these are calculated from the cut and fill ratios. Altitude difference between

D + E = 5 m

Fill 1:1 = 5:5

Cut 1:1.5 = 5:7.5

(9) Complete the earthworks.

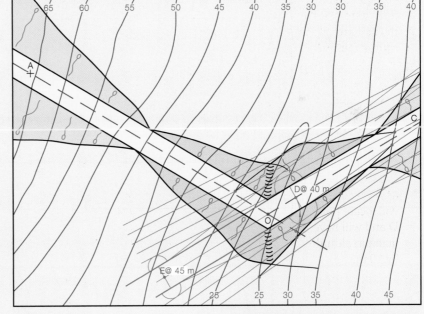

▲ Fig. 15.44

See worksheet 15.13

Fig. 15.45 shows ground contours at 5 m vertical intervals. ABCD is a proposed roadway that widens from C to D. The road has the following specification:

(i)   A to C formation width of 12 m.

(ii)   Formation level at B is 205 m.

(iii)   A to B is 1 in 10 rising, B to D is 1 in 15 rising.

(iv)   Side slopes for cutting 1 in 2.

(v)   Side slopes for embankment 1 in 1.5.

On the drawing show the earthworks necessary to accommodate the road.

(1) A to B is 1 in 10 rising. B is at 205 m. Measure towards A for 50 m to point E which will be at 200 m.

(2) Draw the cut and fill cones at B and E and deal only with this section of road. The difference in altitude between B and E is 5 m, therefore the cut cone has a radius of 10 m and the fill cone has a radius of 7.5 m.

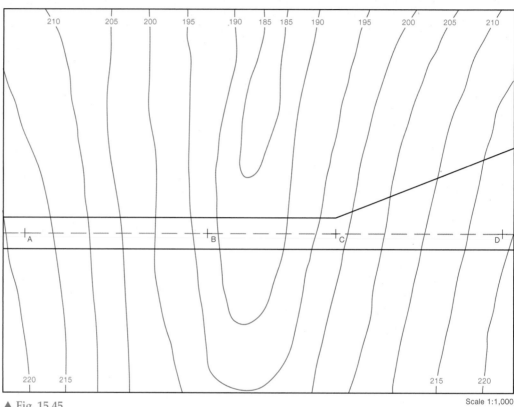

▲ Fig. 15.45

Scale 1:1,000

▼ Fig. 15.46

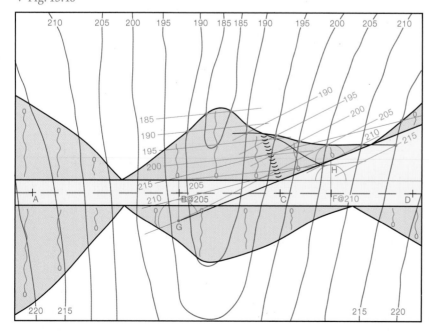

(3) The slope of the road changes at B to 1 in 15 rising. Measure from B to F for 75 m. Point F will be at a 210 m level. Set up the cut and fill cones at B and F. The cut cone has a 10 m radius. The fill cone has a 7.5 m radius.

(4) Ignore the fact that the road widens at C and draw the fill.

(5) Extend the widened road edge to point G which is in line with point B. Point G will be at 205 m level. Also project point F to the side of the widened road at H. H is at 210 m level. Treat GH as a separate road and find the outline of the earthworks.

(6) The cut cone at G will be 10 m radius, the fill cone at H will be at 7.5 m radius. The spacing between the cut contours is 10 m and the spacing between the fill contours is 7.5 m.

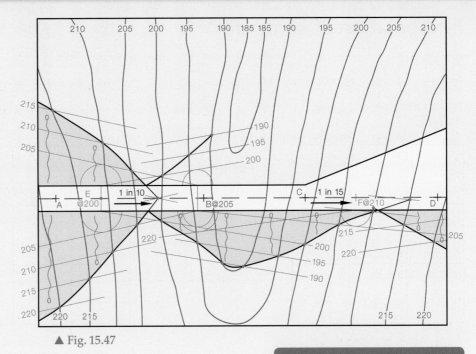

▲ Fig. 15.47

See worksheet 15.14

Activities

Profiles

Q1. To a scale of 1:1,000 redraw the portion of the map shown in **Fig. 15.48**.

   (i) Draw a profile of the line AB.

   (ii) Determine the gradient of the slope at C in an easterly direction.

   (iii) If a vertical mast 20 m high stands at point A, is it visible from point B on the ground?

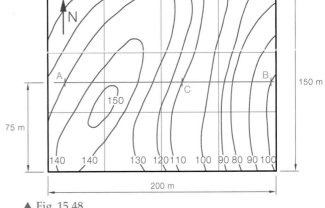

▲ Fig. 15.48

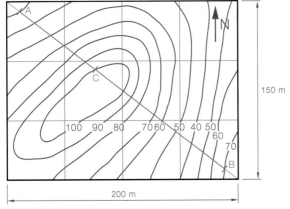

▲ Fig. 15.49

Q2. To a scale of 1:1,000 redraw the portion of the map shown in **Fig. 15.49**.

   (i) Find the profile of the line AB.

   (ii) Determine the gradient at point C in the AB direction.

   (iii) How tall does a vertical object at C need to stand in order to be seen from point B?

Interpolation of contours

Q3.   Plot the contours for the grid levels shown in **Figures 15.50** and **15.51**. Scale 1:1,000.

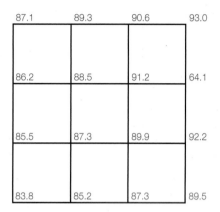

50 m grid squares
Contour interval required = 2 m   ▲ Fig. 15.50

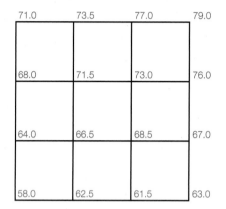

50 m grid squares
Contour interval required = 5 m   ▲ Fig. 15.51

Mining strike and dip

Q4.   Explain the following mining terms:
    (i) strike,   **(ii)** dip,   **(iii)** stratum,   **(iv)** headwall,
    (v) footwall,   **(vii)** thickness.   **(vi)** outcrop,

Q5.   The maps shown in **Figures 15.52** and **15.53** show ground contours at 10 m vertical intervals. Also shown are outcrop points A, B and C on a stratum of ore. Redraw the maps to a scale of 1:1,000 and find the strike and dip of the stratum.

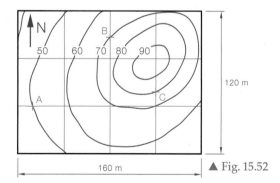

▲ Fig. 15.52

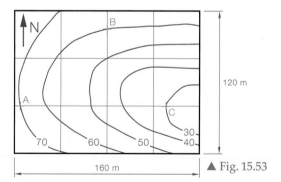

▲ Fig. 15.53

Q6. Figures 15.54 and 15.55 show ground contours at 10 m vertical intervals. Points A, B and C are outcrop points on a stratum of ore. Redraw the maps to a scale of 1:1,000.

    (i)   Find the strike and dip of the stratum.

    (ii)   Determine the outline of the outcrop between A and C and between C and B.

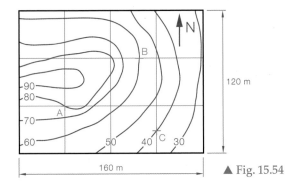

▲ Fig. 15.54

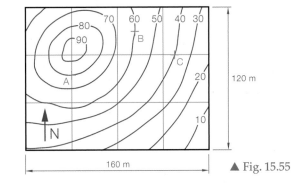

▲ Fig. 15.55

Q7. The maps shown in **Figures 15.56** and **15.57** show ground contours at 10 m vertical intervals. Vertical boreholes at A, B and C strike a stratum at altitudes of 90, 60 and 50 m respectively. Redraw the maps to a scale of 1:1,000.

    (i)   Determine the strike and dip of the stratum.

    (ii)   Find the complete outline of the outcrop.

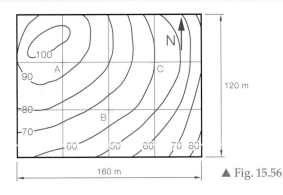

▲ Fig. 15.56

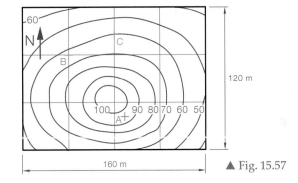

▲ Fig. 15.57

Q8. Figures 15.58 and 15.59 show ground contours at 10 m vertical intervals. Points A, B and C are outcrop points on the headwall of a stratum of ore and D is an outcrop point on the footwall. Redraw the diagrams to a scale of 1:1,000.

    (i)   Determine the strike, dip and thickness of the stratum.

    (ii)   Find the outline of the outcrop.

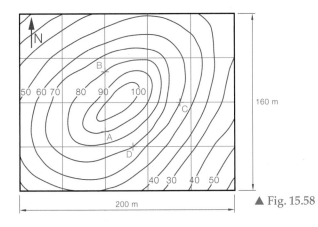

▲ Fig. 15.58

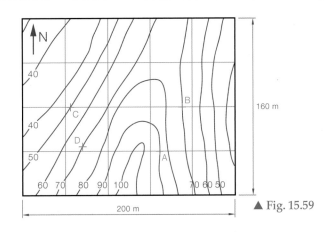

▲ Fig. 15.59

Earthworks

Q9. Figures 15.60 and 15.61 show ground contours at 5 m vertical intervals. AB is the line of a proposed roadway. The road is to have the following specifications. Redraw the maps to a scale of 1:1,000.

    (i)   Formation width 14 m.

    (ii)   Formation level 85 m.

    (iii)   Side slopes for cutting 1:1.5, side slopes for embankment 1:2.

Show the earthworks necessary to accommodate the roadway.

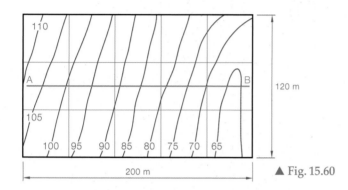

▲ Fig. 15.60

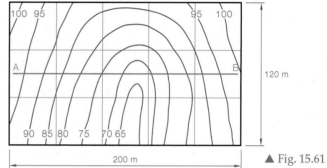

▲ Fig. 15.61

Q10. Figure 15.62 shows ground contours at 2 m vertical intervals. ABCD is the centre line of a proposed roadway with the centre for the curve at point O. The road is to have the following specifications:

    (i)   Formation width 14 m.

    (ii)   Formation level 40 m.

    (iii)   Side slopes for cutting 1:2, side slopes for embankment 1:2.5.

Redraw the given map to a scale of 1:1,000 and show the earthworks necessary to accommodate the roadway.

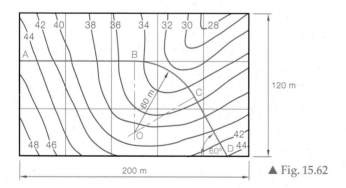

▲ Fig. 15.62

Q11. The map shown in **Figure 15.63** shows ground contours at 4 m vertical intervals. AB shows a proposed roadway with CDEF being a car park. The car park and road are at the same level. The road and car park are to have the following specifications:

(i) Formation width 12 m.

(ii) Formation level 100 m.

(iii) Side slopes for cutting 1:1.5, side slopes for embankment 1:1.

Redraw the map to a scale of 1:1,000 and show the earthworks necessary to accommodate the road and car park.

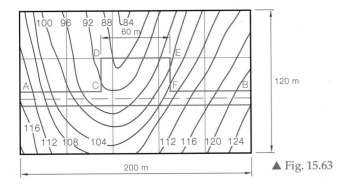

▲ Fig. 15.63

Mining: skew boreholes

Q12. On a contour map A and B are two points whose altitudes are 105 m and 80 m respectively. On the map B is located 120 m north-east of A. A skew borehole at A is drilled in a south-westerly direction in plan and has an actual inclination of 60° to the horizontal plane. It reveals the top and bottom surfaces of the stratum at distances of 30 m and 65 m respectively from A.

A skew borehole at B is drilled in a southerly direction in plan and has an actual inclination of 50° to the horizontal plane. It reveals the top and bottom surfaces of the stratum at altitudes of 50 m and 35 m respectively.

(i) Determine the dip, strike and thickness of the stratum.

(ii) Another skew borehole at B is drilled in a south-westerly direction in plan and meets the bottom surface of the stratum at a distance of 110 m from B. Determine the inclination of this borehole to the horizontal plane.

Scale 1:1,000.

Q13. On a contour map, A and B are two points whose altitudes are 115 m and 120 m respectively. On the map, B is located 125 m north-east of A. A skew borehole at A is drilled in a northerly direction in plan and has an actual inclination of 60° to the horizontal plane. It reveals the top and bottom surfaces of the stratum at altitudes of 105 m and 40 m respectively.

A skew borehole at B is drilled in a south-westerly direction in plan and has a true inclination of 50° to the horizontal plane. It reveals the top and bottom surfaces of the stratum at altitudes of 85 m and 65 m respectively.

(i) Determine the strike, dip and thickness of the stratum.

(ii) Another skew borehole at B is drilled in a southerly direction in plan. The length of the borehole as it goes through the stratum is 20 m. Determine the altitude at which this borehole hits the bottom surface of the stratum.

Scale 1:1,000.

Apparent Dip

Q14. On a contour map, A and B are two points whose altitudes are 95 m and 105 m respectively. On the map, A is located 65 m north of B. A skew borehole at A is drilled in a north-easterly direction in plan and has an actual inclination of 60° to the horizontal plane. It reveals the top and bottom surfaces of the stratum at altitudes of 65 m and 35 m respectively.

A skew borehole at B is drilled in a north-westerly direction in plan and has a true inclination of 40° to the horizontal plane. It reveals the top and bottom surfaces of the stratum at altitudes of 85 m and 15 m respectively.

   (i)   Determine the strike, dip and thickness of the stratum.

   (ii)   Determine the apparent dip of the stratum in a westerly direction.

Scale 1:1,000.

Earthworks

Q15. **Figure 15.64** shows ground contours at 5 m vertical intervals. AB is the line of a proposed roadway. To a scale of 1:1,000, redraw the maps and show the earthworks necessary to accommodate the roadway.

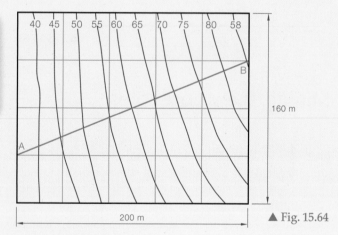

▲ Fig. 15.64

Formation width 12 m
Formation level at A 70 m
Gradient A to B is 1 in 15 falling
Side slopes for cutting 1 in 1.5
Side slopes for embankment 1 in 1

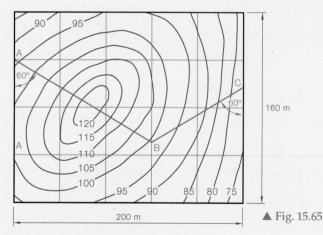

▲ Fig. 15.65

Formation width 12 m
Formation level at A 100 m
Gradient A to B to C 1 in 15 falling
Side slopes for cutting 1 in 1.5
Side slopes for embankment 1 in 2

Q16. **Figure 15.65** shows ground contours at 5 m vertical intervals. ABC is the line of a proposed roadway. To a scale of 1:1,000, redraw each map and show the earthworks necessary to accommodate the roadway.

Q17. Figure 15.66 shows ground contours at 5 m vertical intervals. ABC is a roadway which widens into a car parking area. Redraw the map to a scale of 1:1,000 and show the earthworks necessary to accommodate the road and car park.

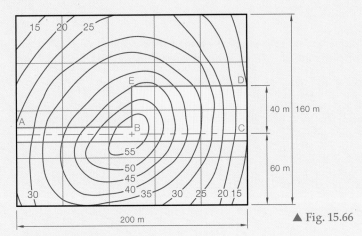

▲ Fig. 15.66

Formation width A to B 12 m
Formation level at A 40 m
Gradient from A to C 1 in 20 rising
From B to C the road widens as shown
Side slopes for cutting 1 in 1.5
Side slopes for embankment 1 in 2

16 Surface Geometry

Dihedral Angle

The angle between two planes is a dihedral angle. We have already looked at finding dihedral angles in chapter 8, The Oblique Plane. The dihedral angle is the smallest angle that can be measured between the planes and is measured perpendicular to each plane and perpendicular to the line of intersection. The dihedral angle is often needed in roof construction, hopper construction and other fabrications involving plane surfaces.

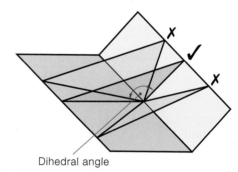

Dihedral angle

▲ Fig. 16.1

Finding the Dihedral Angle

1. Point View Method

Draw a line on a plane, e.g. a sheet of paper, and view along the length of the line so that we see the line as a point. When the line is seen as a point, the plane that it is resting on appears as an edge view.

To get the edge view of a plane you must find the point view of any straight line on that plane.

When two planes intersect, the line of intersection will be a straight line and this straight line rests on both planes at the same time. A point view of the line of intersection will show both planes as edge views and will therefore show the dihedral angle between the two planes.

To get the dihedral angle between two planes, get the point view of the line of intersection of the planes.

> Fig. 16.2 shows the plan and elevation of a solid with an equilateral triangular base. Find the dihedral angle between surfaces P and Q.

Using the theory outlined above we need to get a point view of line bO.

(1) Identify the line of intersection between the planes, line bO.

(2) Find the true length of bO. This is done by projecting an auxiliary viewing perpendicular to bO in plan. x_1y_1 will therefore be parallel to the line of intersection in plan. The view projected from the plan will be an auxiliary elevation and as such will have heights equal to the front elevation.

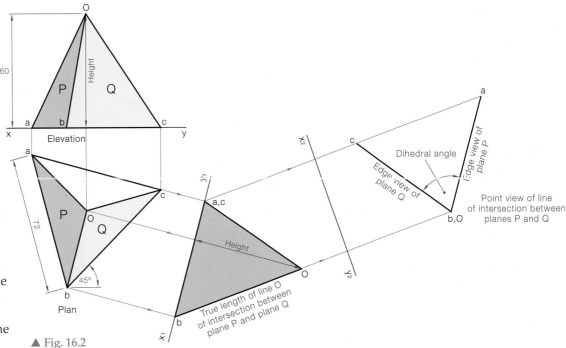

▲ Fig. 16.2

(3) The final stage is to view along the true length found in step (2). Extend on line bO and project the other points in this direction. Draw x_2y_2 perpendicular to this line of sight, i.e. perpendicular to the true length. Being a second auxiliary plan the distances are taken from x_1y_1 back to the plan. The line of intersection appears as a point, the planes appear as lines and the dihedral angle is displayed clearly.

2. Rebatment Method

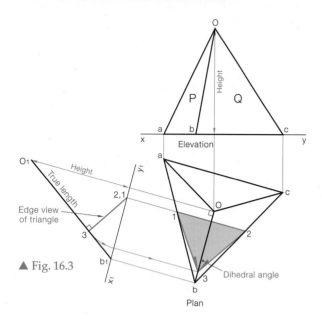

▲ Fig. 16.3

This method is perhaps more difficult to understand but is much neater. If we introduce a cutting plane to cut through the line of intersection, bO, perpendicularly, the triangle that it produces underneath the planes contains the dihedral angle. If we can rebat this plane onto the horizontal plane we will see its true shape and angles in plan.

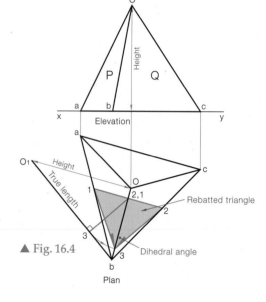

▲ Fig. 16.4

(1) Ob is the plan of the line of intersection. Find the true length of this line by using an auxiliary elevation. Draw x_1y_1 parallel to the line of intersection in plan. In the auxiliary, point b rests on x_1y_1 and point O_1 is the 'height' above x_1y_1.

(2) In the auxiliary, draw the edge view of the triangle 1,2,3 perpendicular to the true length.

(3) Rebat or hinge the triangle about edge 1,2 so that it rests on the x_1y_1 and project back to the line of intersection in plan.

(4) Join up the triangle 1,2,3 in plan. This is the true shape of the triangle and therefore shows true angles. Angle 3 is the dihedral angle between planes P and Q.

(5) Fig. 16.4 shows exactly the same method except that the auxiliary is drawn in on the plan and gives a neater result.

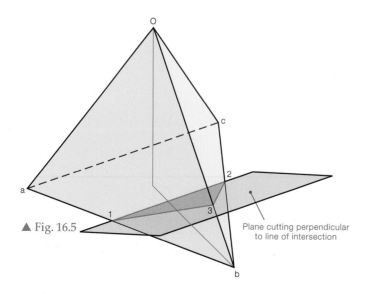

▲ Fig. 16.5

Plane cutting perpendicular to line of intersection

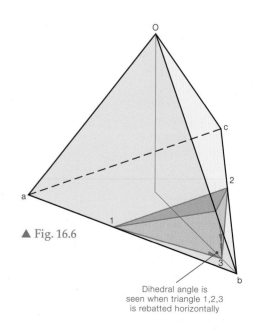

▲ Fig. 16.6

Dihedral angle is seen when triangle 1,2,3 is rebatted horizontally

Roof Geometry

Roof geometry provides a very practical application of plane geometry, development of surfaces and dihedral angles. There is nothing new in this section, rather it is the application of what has already been learned.

Fig. 16.7 shows the outline plan of a roof. Surfaces A and B have a pitch of 45°. Surface C has a pitch of 40° and surface D has a pitch of 60°.

(i)   Draw the plan and elevation.

(ii) Develop surfaces B, C and D.

(iii) Find the dihedral angle between surfaces B and D.

Scale 1:100

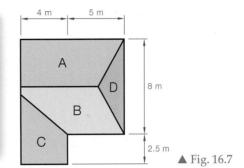

▲ Fig. 16.7

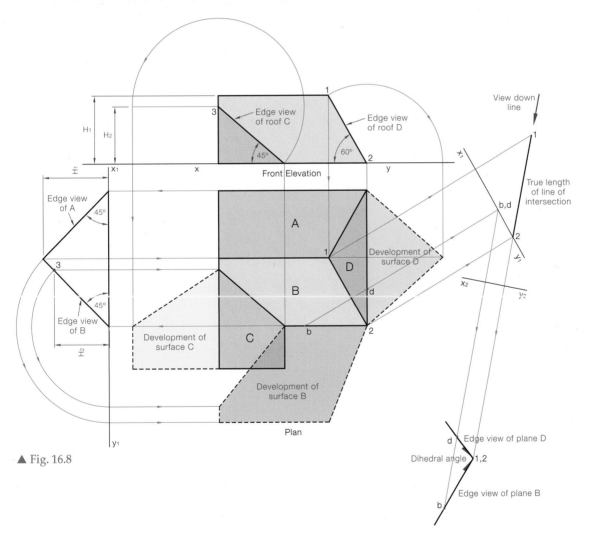

▲ Fig. 16.8

(1) Auxiliary views are used extensively in solving roof geometry questions. Edge views of planes A and B are found by using an auxiliary elevation. The auxiliary shows the true pitch of these planes, 45° (from the question). The height, H_1, for the elevation is found here.

(2) Draw the elevation which will show planes C and D as edge views and again their true pitch will be seen, 40° and 60° respectively. H_2, the height of roof C, is found here. Point 1 is projected to plan and surface D is drawn in plan.

(3) H$_2$, the height of roof C, is stepped up on the auxiliary which shows roof A and B as edge views. Point 3 is found and projected to plan.

(4) Develop the surfaces by rebatting the planes where they are seen as edge views. Planes C and D are rebatted in the front elevation and surface B is rebatted in the auxiliary elevation. The planes in each case are folded until they are horizontal and the developments are found in plan.

(5) The dihedral angle is constructed using the point view method and is found as explained earlier.

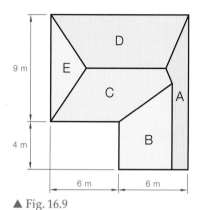

Fig. 16.9 shows the plan of a roof. Surfaces C and D have a pitch of 50°. Surface A has a pitch of 70°, surface B has a pitch of 40° and surface E has a pitch of 60°.

(i)   Draw the plan and elevation of the roof.
(ii) Develop the surfaces A and C.
(iii) Find the dihedral angle between surfaces A and D.
(iv) Find the dihedral angle between surfaces B and C.

Scale 1:100

▲ Fig. 16.9

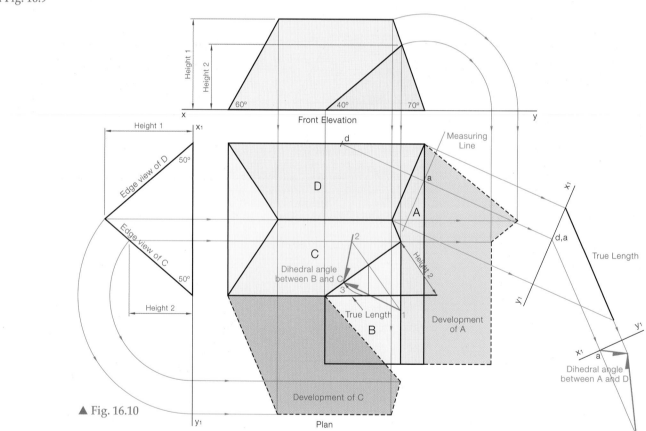

▲ Fig. 16.10

The problem is solved using edge views of the roof surfaces, either using auxiliary views or the front elevation. As we have learned earlier, **an edge view of a plane is found by viewing along a line which is seen as a true length on the plane**. In most cases we use a horizontal line and view along its length in plan. When we see the planes as edge views we can use the pitch angle given in the question. The two dihedral angles are found using the two methods outlined earlier, point view method and rebatted triangle method.

The surfaces C and B form a valley. When forming the triangle that will define the dihedral angle, triangle 1,2,3, it is essential that corners 1 and 2 are level with each other.

See worksheets 16.1 and 16.2

Intersecting Ductwork and Pipework

This section deals with the intersecting of ductwork and the subsequent development of the surfaces. We also look at the intersection of pipework. This work is used extensively in the sheet metalwork industry where unusual jointing pieces and connectors would be made up as one-offs. The material in this section is very closely linked to chapter 10, Developments and Envelopments.

A rectangular section duct is to intersect a square section duct at an angle of 45° as shown in Fig. 16.11. Find the surface development of each ducting piece.

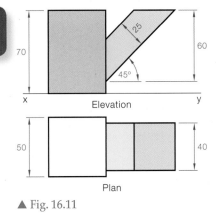

▲ Fig. 16.11

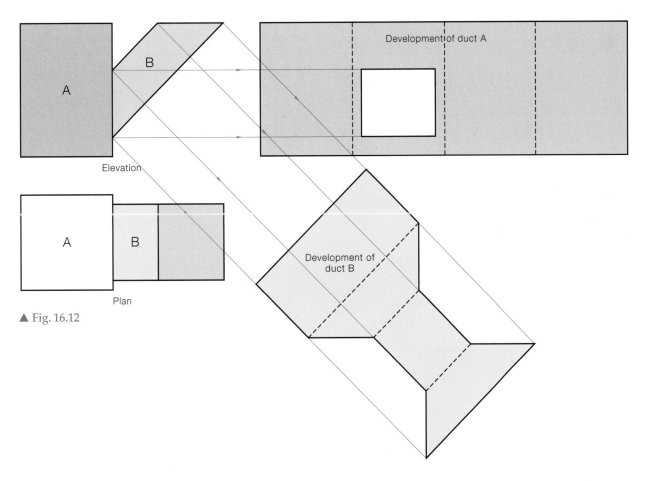

▲ Fig. 16.12

A square sectioned duct of 50 mm side is being intersected by a rectangular sectioned duct of sides 32 mm × 50 mm. The ducts meet at an angle of 60°. Find the complete surface development of both ducting pieces in Fig. 16.13.

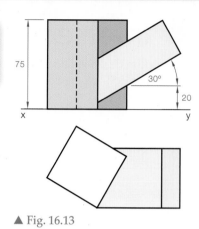

(1) The line of intersection is found first. The points where duct B joins into duct A can be seen in plan and are projected up to elevation. The line of intersection will be made up of straight lines as the intersecting ducts are planar.

(2) The development of each duct piece is obvious from Fig. 16.14.

▲ Fig. 16.13

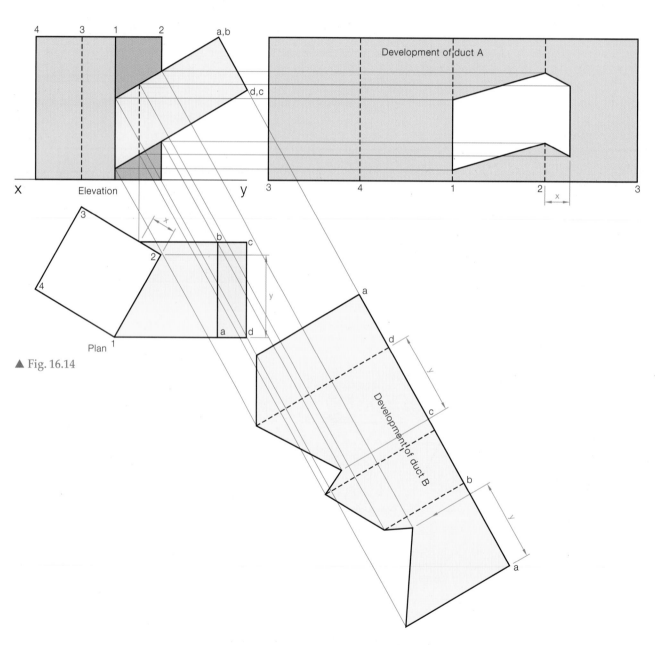

▲ Fig. 16.14

Joining Pipes and Ducts of Equal Diameter

The elevation of an elbow joint for a circular duct is shown in Fig. 16.15. Find the development of the part of the duct marked A.

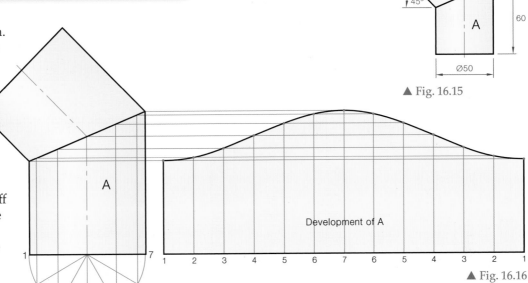

▲ Fig. 16.15

(1) Set up the elevation. There is no need to draw a plan.

(2) Draw the half-duct as shown and divide into six equal parts. Index the points.

(3) Project the base of the front elevation to the right. Step-off twelve steps to give the circumference. Draw a vertical line from each step.

(4) From the semicircle, project the generators. The length of each generator is projected across to the development.

Development of A

▲ Fig. 16.16

The elevation of a double elbow joint for a circular duct is shown. Develop the surface of the section marked A, as in Fig. 16.17

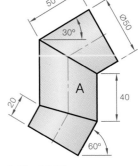

▲ Fig. 16.17

(1) In this case the circular section of the duct is drawn in the elevation. It is divided into twelve equal parts and the generators drawn through the divisions.

(2) The construction is as shown in the previous example.

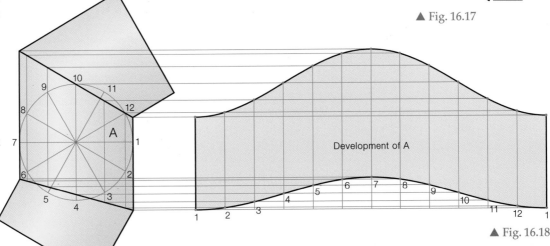

Development of A

▲ Fig. 16.18

See worksheets 16.3 and 16.4

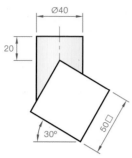

▲ Fig. 16.19

A circular duct pipe intersects a square duct pipe as shown.
(i)   Draw a front elevation and end view showing the line of intersection.
(ii)   Develop the surface of the cylindrical duct.
(iii) Show the true shape of the hole to be cut in the square duct, see Fig. 16.19.

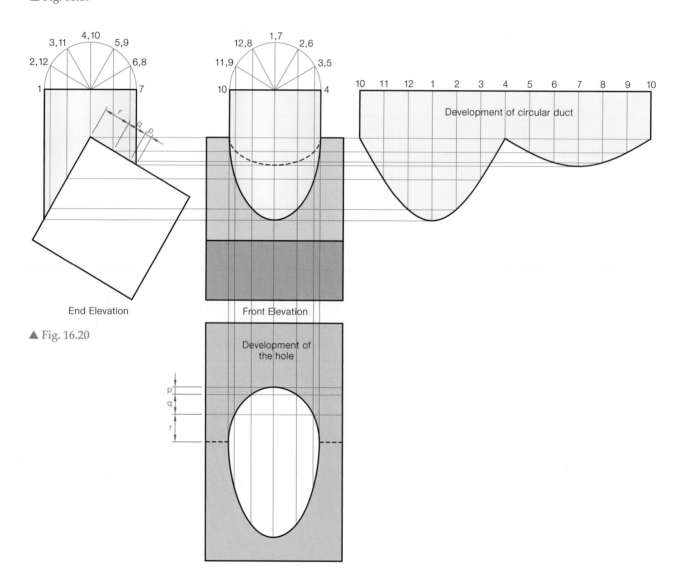

▲ Fig. 16.20

(1) Find the line of intersection in the usual way. Note how the indexing of the semicircle changes between the front elevation and the end elevation.

(2) The development of the circular duct is done in the same way as in the previous example.

(3) The true shape of the hole to be cut in the square duct is found by developing the two surfaces that it straddles. The complete sides are developed first. Distances p, q and r are taken from the end view which shows the true length of the sides of the square duct. Generators are extended down from the front elevation. Similar construction for the other side of the square duct.

See worksheet 16.5

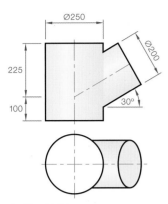

The diagram shows the plan and elevation of two intersecting air-conditioning ducts. The ducts intersect at an oblique angle, see Fig. 16.21.

(i)   Draw the given plan and elevation of the ducting, showing the line of intersection.

(ii) Project an end elevation.

(iii) Develop the oblique duct and show the true shape of the hole.

Scale 1:5

▲ Fig. 16.21

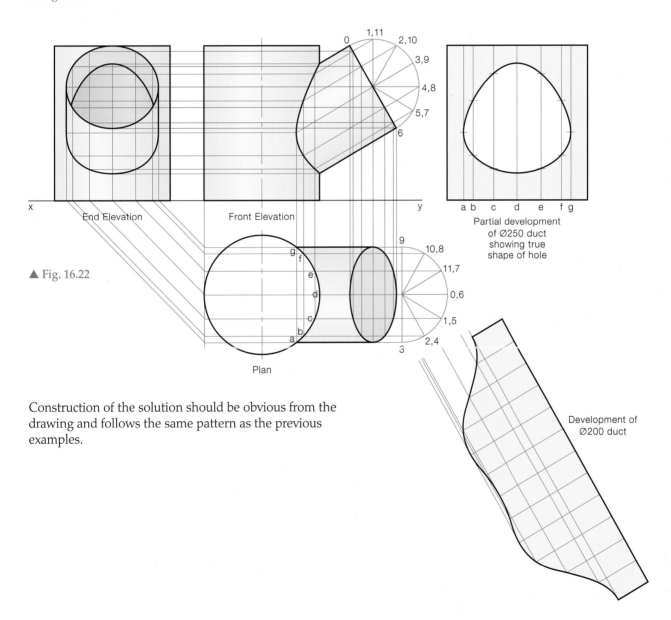

▲ Fig. 16.22

Construction of the solution should be obvious from the drawing and follows the same pattern as the previous examples.

The plan and incomplete elevation of two ducts intersecting is shown. One duct is circular in cross-section, while the other is square in cross-section, see Fig. 16.23.

(i) Find the line of intersection between the two ducts and project an end view.

(ii) Develop the surface of the square duct.

Scale 1:5.

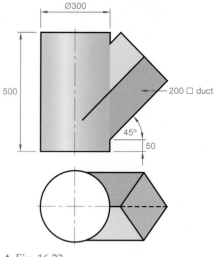

▲ Fig. 16.23

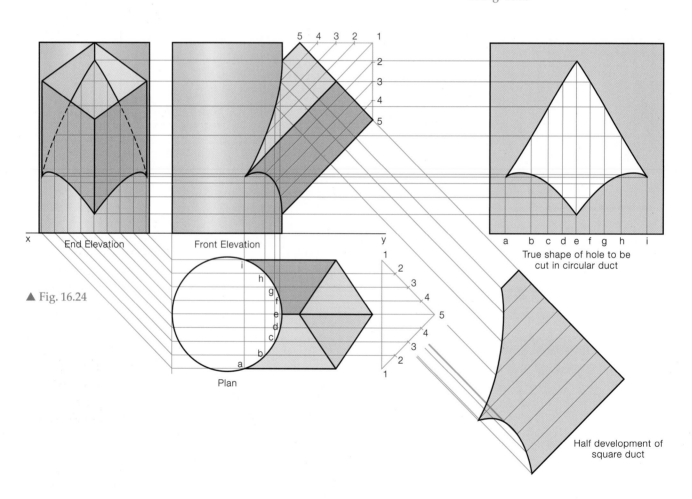

▲ Fig. 16.24

Transition Pieces

A transition piece is one that connects differently shaped openings, differently sized openings and differently angled openings, or any combination of these. In most cases the transition piece is composed of plane surfaces and conical surfaces. Transition pieces are widely used in ducting systems used in ventilation, heating, air conditioning, etc.

The development of transition pieces is done by triangulation. This is simply a method of dividing a surface into a number of triangles and using these triangles to build up the development. Triangles are used because if its sides are of a given length, it can only be one shape. A triangle can also be easily reproduced by using the compass.

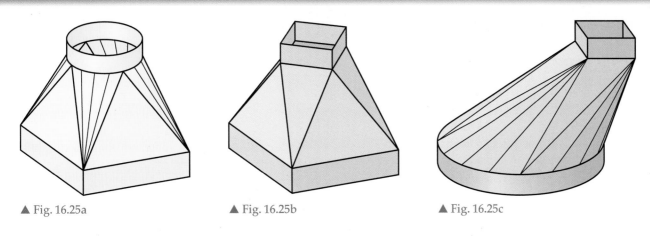

▲ Fig. 16.25a   ▲ Fig. 16.25b   ▲ Fig. 16.25c

To determine the development of a funnel piece between two rectangular ducting pieces, see Fig. 16.26.

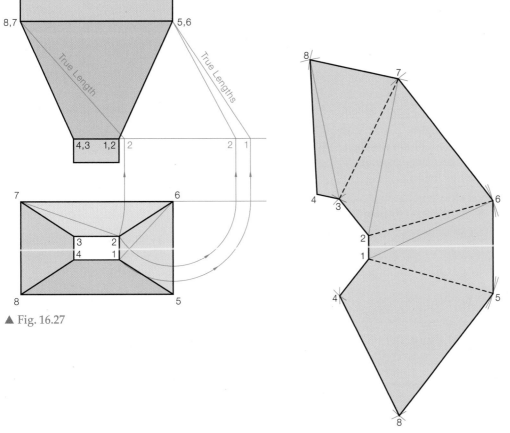

▲ Fig. 16.26

▲ Fig. 16.27

(1) Draw the plan and elevation as given. Index the corners.

(2) Find the true length of the sloping edges. In the diagram we find the true length of 2,6 by rotating point 2 about corner 6 until the line appears horizontal in plan.

This line when projected to elevation will appear as a true length.

(3) Edges 1,5 and 4,8 and 3,7 will be equal in length to 2,6.

(4) Start the development with edge 1,2 which is a true length in plan.

(5) With the true length of 2,6 and centre 2 swing an arc.

(6) With true length of diagonal 1,6 and centre 1 swing another arc. The two arcs cross locating point 6.

(7) Point 5 is found using the true length of 5,6 (from plan) and the true length of 1,5 (equal to 2,6).

(8) The complete development is built up using triangulation in this way. As a check on the development, lines parallel on the surface must also be parallel on the development. Edge 1,2 must be parallel to edge 5,6 on the development.

Alternative Method

▼ Fig. 16.28

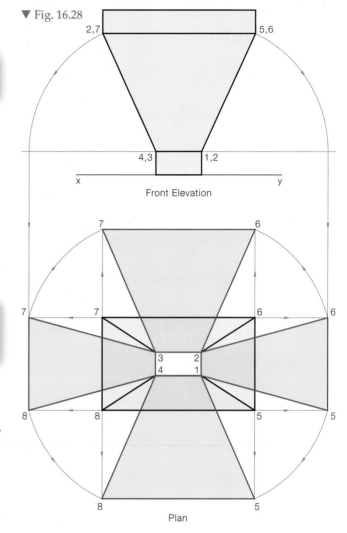

Using the same measurements as in Fig. 16.26 find the development of the funnel piece using rebattment.

(1) The two sides 3,4,8,7 and 1,2,6,5 are folded down in elevation and projected to plan.

(2) The development of these two sides can be found in plan.

(3) The other two sides are found by using the information that the seam length must be equal for two adjoining edges.

Given the plan and elevation of a sheet metal hopper. Find the complete development of the surfaces. Fig. 16.29.

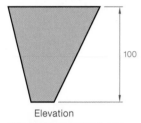

(1) Draw the given plan and elevation. Index all corners.

(2) All horizontal edges appear as true lengths in plan. The true length of the sloping edges and the diagonals must be found.

(3) Start the development with one of the top edges of the hopper, e.g. 1,4.

▲ Fig. 16.29

(4) Find the corner 8 next by swinging the true length of diagonal 1,8 from point 1, and by swinging a second arc, the true length, of 4,8 from corner 4.

(5) All other points are found using triangulation and the true lengths found in elevation.

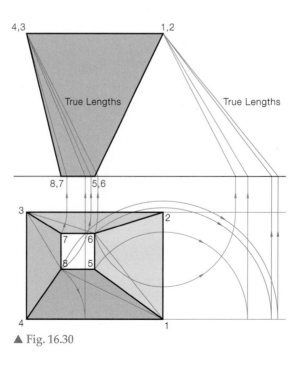

▲ Fig. 16.30

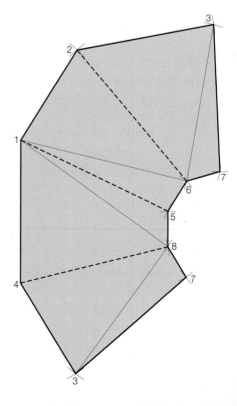

To develop the surface of a transition piece connecting two circular pipes.

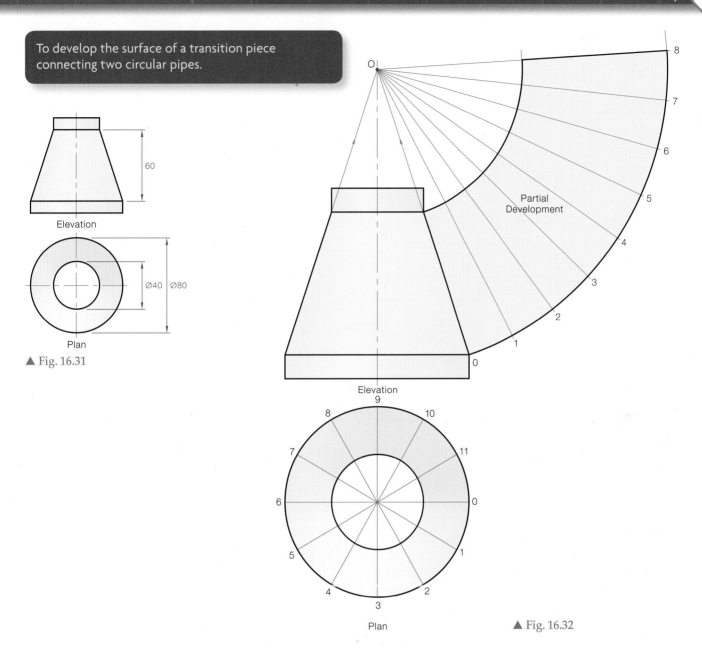

60

▲ Fig. 16.31

Ø40   Ø80

Elevation

Plan

Partial
Development

Elevation

Plan

▲ Fig. 16.32

(1) The centres of the inlet and outlet pipes lie on the same axis and therefore the transition piece will be conical. The sides of the elevation are extended to meet, giving the apex of this conical piece.

(2) The development is now completed as for a truncated cone. Divide the plan into twelve equal divisions. In elevation, having centre at O, the apex, swing an arc from the top and bottom of the truncated cone.

(3) Step-off the twelve equal divisions from plan around this arc. Join these points to the apex to complete the development.

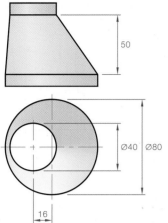

To develop the surface of a transition piece connecting two circular pipes whose axes are not aligned, see Fig. 16.33.

Even though the transition piece may look like an oblique cone it can be shown that generators on its surface do not meet at a single point when extended. The surface is warped and can only be developed approximately by triangulation.

(1) Draw the plan and elevation and divide both circles into twelve equal parts.

(2) Draw the generators in plan and elevation.

(3) Draw the diagonals which will divide the surface into triangles.

▲ Fig. 16.33

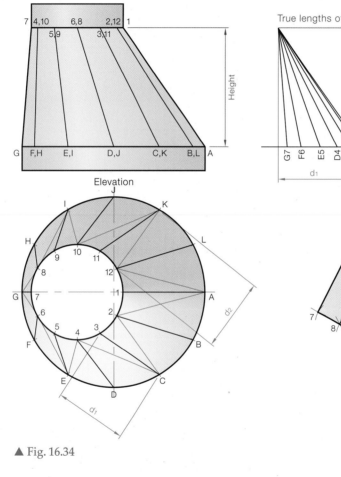

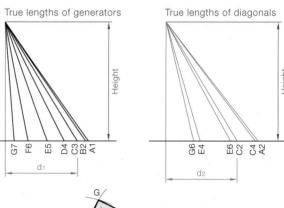

Elevation

▲ Fig. 16.34

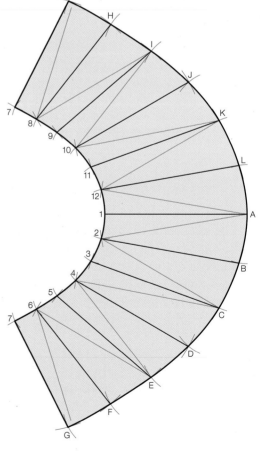

(4) The true lengths of the twelve generators and the twelve diagonals must now be found and are probably best found on a separate diagram.

(5) The development may now be built up using the true lengths and the compass as explained before.

Note: The true lengths of the generators and the diagonals are found on separate diagrams for clarity. In each case the true length is found by using the apparent length of the line in plan and the height of the line in elevation to create a right-angled triangle. The hypotenuse of the triangle is the true length.

To develop the surface of the transition piece connecting ducting of square section and rectangular section, see Fig. 16.33.

This development could be solved by rebatment or by triangulation. It will be solved by triangulation in this example.

When finding the true lengths, care must be taken that the correct heights are used.

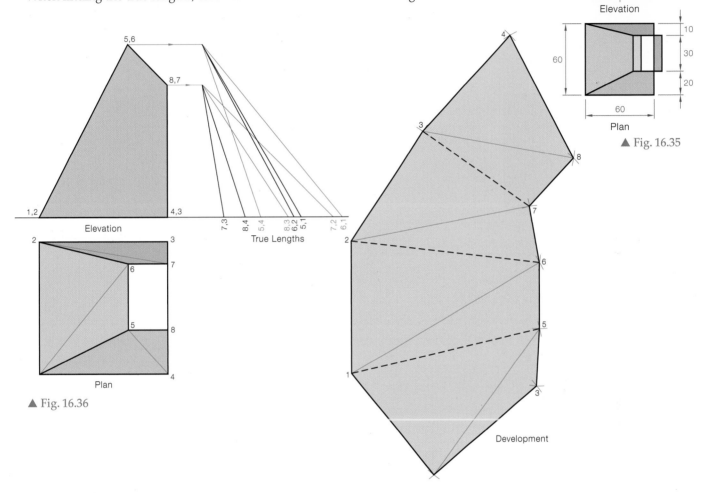

Elevation

Plan

▲ Fig. 16.35

Elevation

True Lengths

Plan

▲ Fig. 16.36

Development

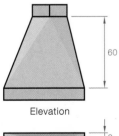

Elevation

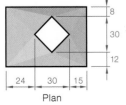

Plan

▲ Fig. 16.37

To develop the transition piece connecting a square duct and a rectangular duct. The measurements are given in Fig. 16.37.

(1) Draw the given plan and elevation.

(2) Divide the surface into triangles.

(3) Index the corners.

(4) Find the true lengths of all edges of these triangles.

(5) Complete the development in the usual way.

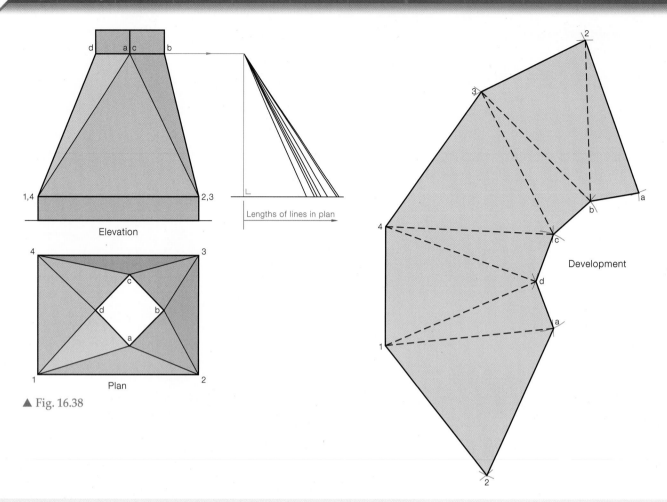

▲ Fig. 16.38

Transition Pieces: Circular to Rectilinear

To find the development of a transition piece connecting a circular pipe and a rectangular pipe on the same axis, Fig. 16.39.

The transition piece is composed of four isosceles triangles and four conical surfaces. The conical surfaces are subdivided into small triangular portions and the complete development is completed by triangulation.

(1) Divide the circle into equal divisions.

(2) Join the corners to the divisions thus forming the triangles that can be developed.

(3) Find the true lengths of lines a1, a2, a3, a4 and a5 by rotation in plan.

(4) The transition piece is symmetrical and therefore these true lengths can be used for the other three corners.

(5) Start with the isosceles triangle a1d. The length of ad is seen in plan and the true length of a1 is used to form the triangle.

(6) From point 1 on the development swing an arc equal in length to one of the divisions on the circle. From point 'a' on the development swing an arc equal to the length of a2. The two arcs cross, locating point 2 on the development.

(7) Build up the development in this way.

(8) The smaller the triangles are made on the transition piece the more accurate the development.

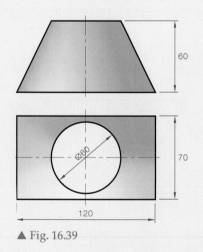

▲ Fig. 16.39

HIGHER LEVEL

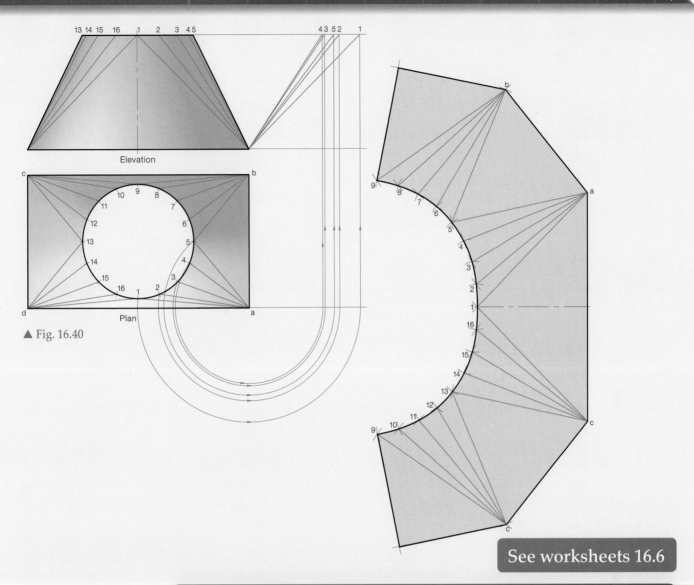

▲ Fig. 16.40

See worksheets 16.6

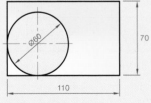

▲ Fig. 16.41

Fig. 16.41 shows a transition piece starting as a rectangle and ending as a circle. The circle is off-centre. Show the complete surface development of the surface of the transition piece.

The procedure is the same as in the previous example but is made more complex because the circle is off-centre. There are many more true lengths to be found. It should be noted that A1 and B1 will

▲ Fig. 16.42

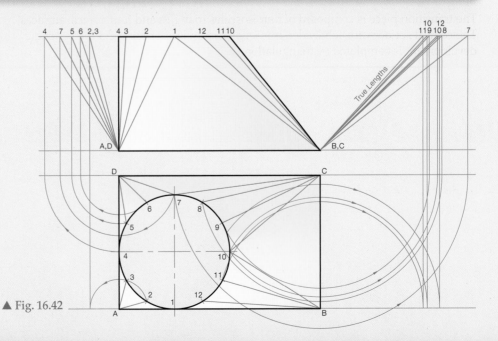

appear as true lengths in the front elevation. Elements A1 and A4 will be the same length, as will elements A2 and A3. Proper indexing is important to help keep track of which distances need to be taken.

(1) Divide the circle into a number of divisions.

(2) Divide the surface into triangles.

(3) Start with one of the larger triangles, e.g. B,C,10.

(4) Using the divisions from the circle and the appropriate true length the development is built up as before.

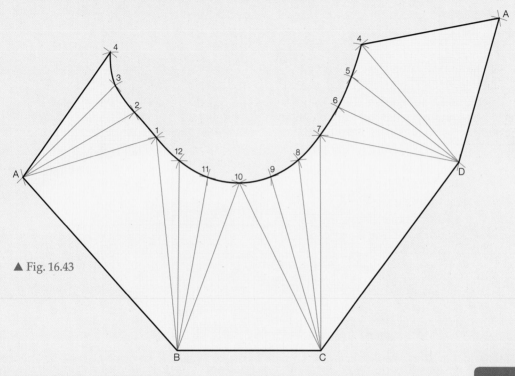

▲ Fig. 16.43

See worksheet 16.7

Fig. 16.44 shows a transition piece connecting two cylindrical pipes of different diameters and on different axes. Find a half-development of this transition piece.

This transition piece looks like a frustum of an oblique cone but it is not and must be solved by triangulation. The large pipe is shown full size in plan and an auxiliary is needed to show the true size of the inclined pipe.

(1) Draw the elevation and use the auxiliary of the small pipe to help draw the ellipse in plan.

(2) Divide up the circles and triangulate half of the transition piece.

(3) Index the sides of the triangles carefully. The true length of each of these lines must be found. Set up a right-angled triangle using the height of the element in elevation and the length of the element in plan. The hypotenuse of this triangle gives the true length.

(4) Construct the development as before.

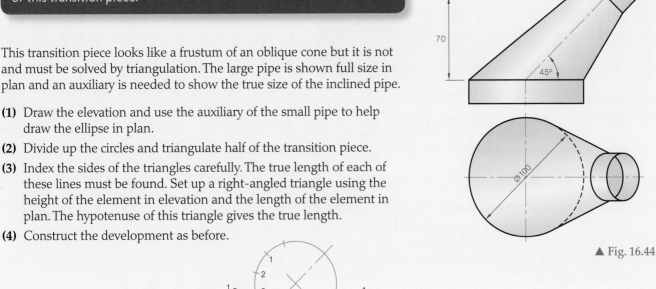

▲ Fig. 16.44

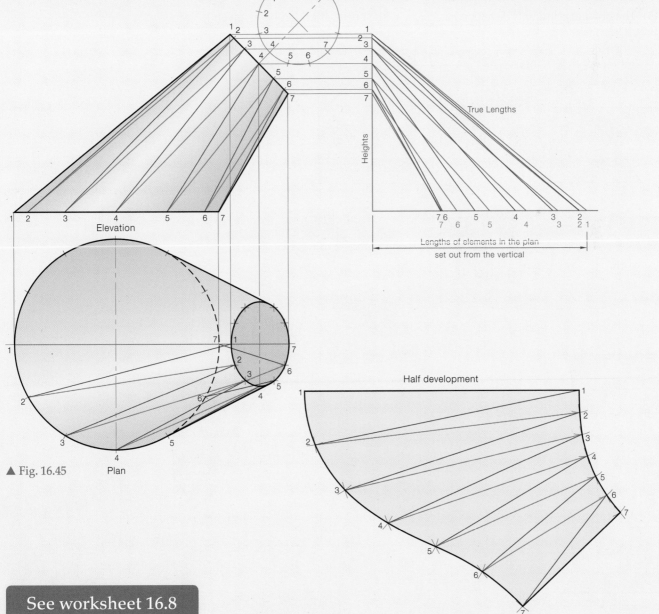

▲ Fig. 16.45   Plan

See worksheet 16.8

HIGHER LEVEL

Fig. 16.46 shows a square duct intersecting with an oblique cylindrical section of ductwork.

(i)   Draw the given views and project a plan.

(ii) Show the line of intersection in all views.

(iii) Develop the surface of the square ducting section A.

(iv) Develop the surface of the oblique cylindrical duct.

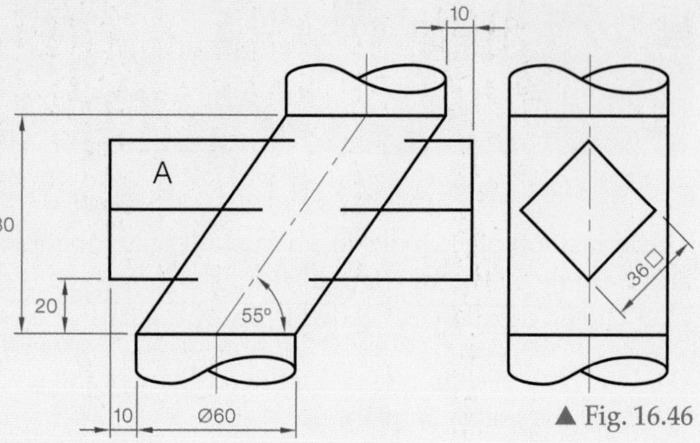

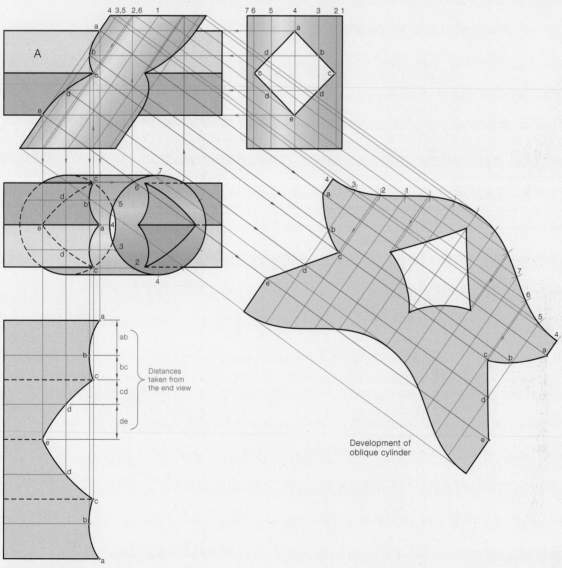

▲ Fig. 16.46

(1) The joint lines must be found first. Divide one circle in the plan into equal divisions, and from these divisions draw elements along the surface of the cylinder. Find these elements in all three views.

(2) Where the elements cross the square duct in end view locates points on the joint line.

(3) The corner 'c' can be located as shown. An element is drawn in the corner in plan to the top circle. This element is located in elevation and 'c' is projected up onto this line.

(4) The development of section A of the square duct is projected down from the front elevation. The distances between the lines in the development are taken from the end view.

(5) The oblique cylinder is developed as before with special attention being given to corner 'c'.

Development of duct section A

▲ Fig. 16.47

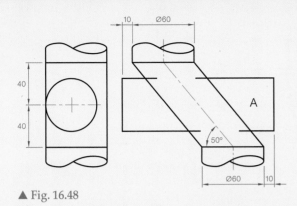

▲ Fig. 16.48

Fig. 16.48 shows a cylindrical duct intersecting an oblique cylindrical duct. The cylindrical duct is off-centre.

(i)   Draw the given views and project a plan.
(ii) Find the joint line in all views.
(iii) Develop section A of the cylindrical duct.
(iv) Develop the oblique cylindrical duct.

The development of the oblique cylinder is carried out in the usual way. The distance 'x' is found in plan and helps to locate the extra element introduced to locate point f.

The spacing of the lines in the development of section A are found using the distances between the points on the circle in end view. The gaps will vary as we move around the circle.

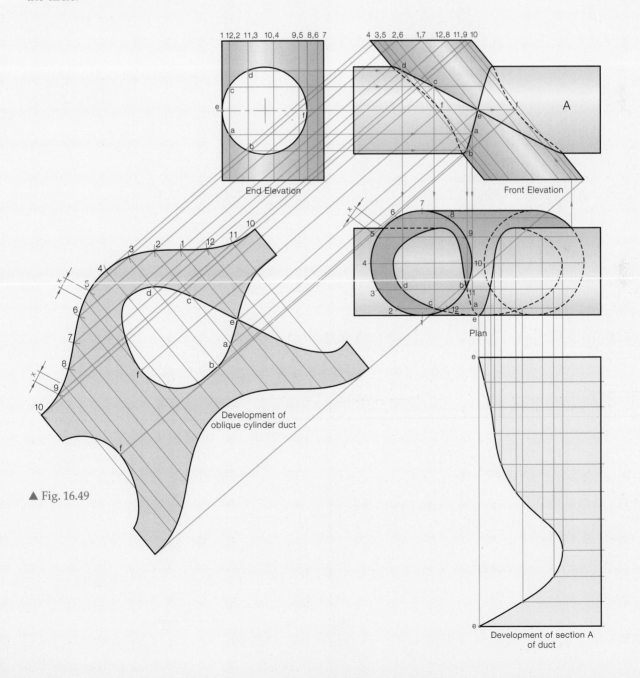

▲ Fig. 16.49

Activities

Dihedral angle

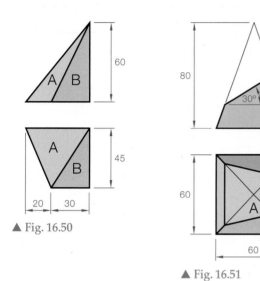

▲ Fig. 16.50

▲ Fig. 16.51

Q1 and Q2. For figures 16.50 and 16.51 draw the given plan and elevation of the solids and determine the dihedral angle between surfaces A and B using the point view method.

Q3 to Q5. For each of the following roof structures draw the given views. Determine the dihedral angle between surfaces A and B using the triangle method.

Scale 1:100

A = Pitch of 60°
B = Pitch of 45°

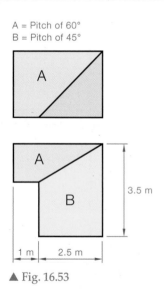

▲ Fig. 16.53

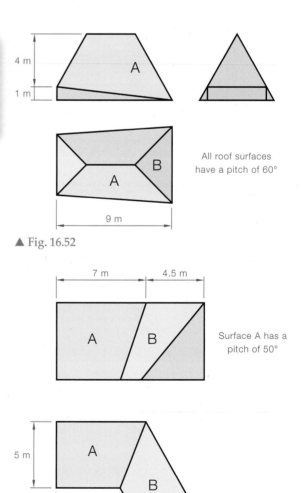

▲ Fig. 16.52

All roof surfaces have a pitch of 60°

Surface A has a pitch of 50°

5 m

A

5 m

B

60°

▲ Fig. 16.54

Q6. Fig. 16.55 shows the plan and elevation of a lean-to roof. Surface A has a pitch of 30°, surface B has a pitch of 45° and surface C has a pitch of 60°.

    (i)   Draw the plan and elevation of the roof.

    (ii)   Develop the surfaces A and B.

    (iii)   Find the dihedral angle between the surfaces A and B.

        Scale 1:100

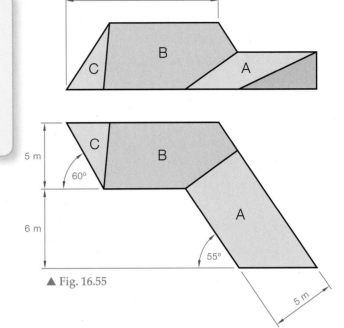

▲ Fig. 16.55

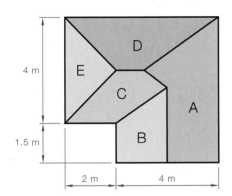

▲ Fig. 16.56

Q7. Fig. 16.56 shows the outline plan of a pitch roof. The surfaces A and B have a pitch of 50°. Surfaces C, D and E have pitches of 50°.

    (i)   Draw the given plan and project an elevation.

    (ii)   Develop the surfaces A and C.

    (iii)   Determine the dihedral angle between surfaces A and D and between surfaces B and C.

        Scale 1:50

Q8 and Q9.

The diagrams show the projections of intersecting ducts/pipes. In each case draw the given views and find the joint line in all views. Make a complete surface development of each ducting piece.

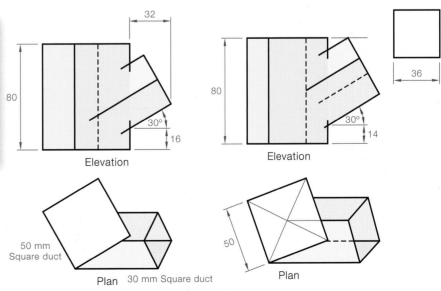

▲ Fig. 16.57　　　　　▲ Fig. 16.58

Q10, Q11 and Q12. The diagrams show end views of intersecting ducts/pipes. In each case draw the front elevation, end elevation and plan showing the joint line clearly. Develop the surface of part A and enough of the larger duct to show the true shape of the hole to be cut in it.

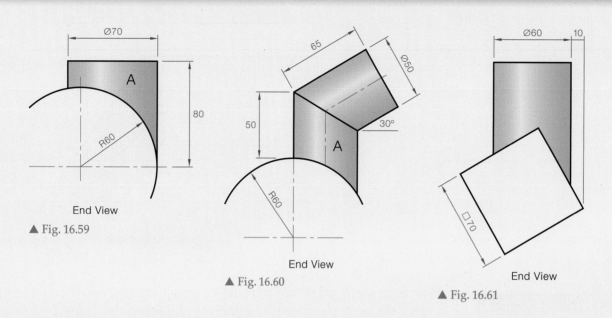

End View

▲ Fig. 16.59

End View

▲ Fig. 16.60

End View

▲ Fig. 16.61

Q13 and Q14.

Given the plan and elevation of a hopper/funnel. Draw the given views and make a complete surface development of the object.

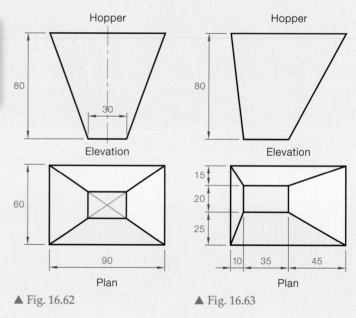

Hopper

Elevation

Plan

▲ Fig. 16.62

Hopper

Elevation

Plan

▲ Fig. 16.63

Q15 and Q16. Draw the given views and make a full surface development of the transition piece.

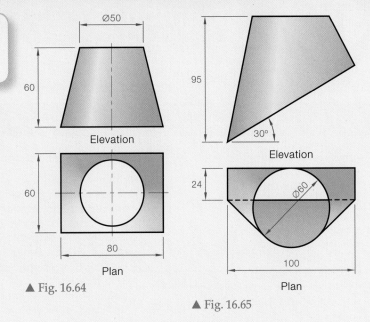

Ø50

60

Elevation

60

80

Plan

▲ Fig. 16.64

95

30°

Elevation

24

Ø60

100

Plan

▲ Fig. 16.65

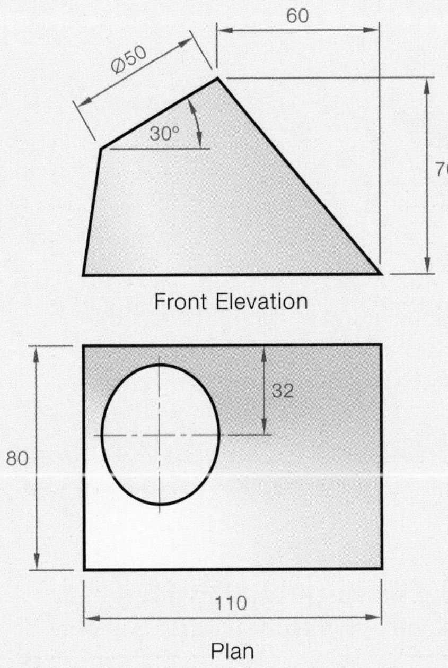

60

Ø50

30°

70

Front Elevation

32

80

110

Plan

▲ Fig. 16.66

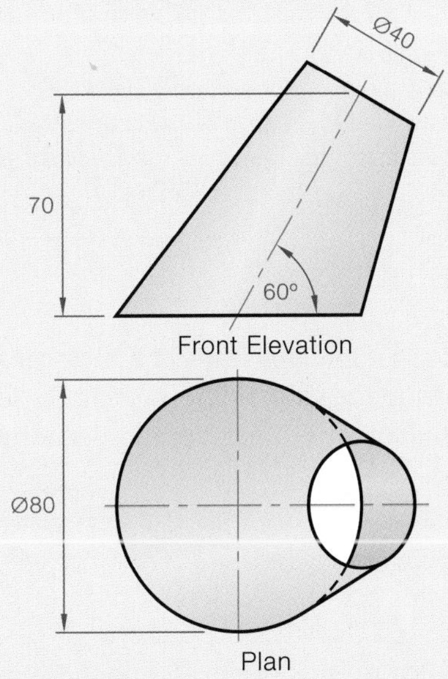

Ø40

70

60°

Front Elevation

Ø80

Plan

▲ Fig. 16.67

Q17 and Q18.

Figures 16.66 and 16.67 show projections of transition pieces. Draw the given views and produce a one-piece development of each transition piece.

Q19. Fig. 16.68 shows an oblique cylindrical duct penetrated by a square duct.

   (i) Draw the given views and project a plan.

   (ii) Find the joint line in all views.

   (iii) Make a complete surface development of the square duct.

   (iv) Make a complete surface development of the oblique cylindrical duct.

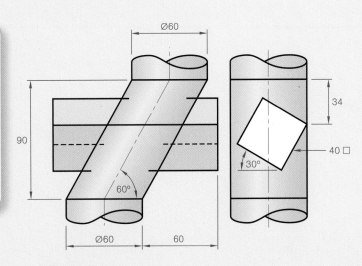

Ø60

90

60°

Ø60   60

34

30°

40 □

▲ Fig. 16.68

17 Assemblies

Syllabus Outline

Areas to be studied:
- Interpretation of exploded and assembled drawings.
- Drawings – layout and conventions.
- System of projection.
- Sectional views.
- Hatching.
- Dimensioning.
- Joining methods.
- Machine surface and texture symbols.
- Modelling assemblies in 3-D CAD.

Learning Outcomes

Students should be able to:

Higher and Ordinary levels
- Understand product assembly drawings.
- Interpret assembly drawings.
- Draw assembled views from drawings of a small number of single components.
- Draw the views essential to the representation of an assembly.
- Draw single-plane sectional views.
- Hatch sectioned parts in each view.
- Fully dimension drawings.
- Measure components to be drawn and relate the model/drawing to the artefact.
- Generate CAD models of assemblies.
- Apply balloon detailing.
- Use abbreviations and symbols.

Higher Level only
- *Draw a number of sectional views.*
- *Draw views that have been sectioned.*
- *Indicate on the drawing a surface finish as appropriate.*
- *Indicate methods of assembly.*

The understanding of machine and flat-pack assembly drawings is a necessary skill for many household and other common products. This chapter hopes to develop the skill of interpreting these types of drawing as well as the skill of producing them. The student will become familiar with dimensioning, sectioning, hatching and joining as well as the use of appropriate symbols and abbreviations.

 ## Working Drawings

A set of working drawings includes the **detail drawings** of the component parts and the **assembly drawing** which shows these parts in their correct position relative to each other. Working drawings will also include a **parts list**, brief **annotations** and **dimensions**.

Detail Drawings

A detail drawing gives all relevant information about a component. Details of one part or a number of small parts may be given on each sheet. Detail drawings usually show orthographic views, are fully dimensioned and show materials, finishes, tolerances and notes on manufacture. When several details are drawn on one sheet, careful consideration must be given to spacing. Ample space must be allowed around each component to allow for dimensions and notes. The same scale should be used for all details on a single sheet, if possible. When this is not practical the scale for each detail should be clearly noted under each component.

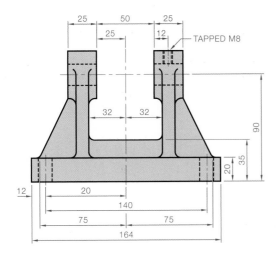

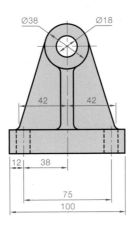

| Part Number 1 |
| Conveyor Bracket |
| Aluminium |
| Thickness of all ribs 10 mm |
| All fillets Radii 5 mm |

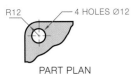

PART PLAN

▲ Fig. 17.1

Assembly Drawing

As stated earlier, an assembly drawing shows the assembled parts in their functional positions. The views selected show how the parts fit together in the assembly and suggest the function of the entire unit. The assembly drawing does not attempt to describe the shapes of the individual parts but rather the relationship between the parts. The information on each of the parts can be found by referring to the **detail drawing**.

The views selected should be the minimum views or partial views that will show how the parts fit together. The views usually take the form of sectional views as these show more clearly how parts fit into each other or overlap each other. As a result of using sectional views, it is very rare to include hidden detail. If the clarity of the assembly can be improved by using hidden lines, then they should be used.

Dimensioning of an assembly is not necessary because all the parts have been fully dimensioned in the detail drawings. When dimensions are given, they are limited to some function of the object such as the maximum opening between the jaws or the maximum movement of a piston.

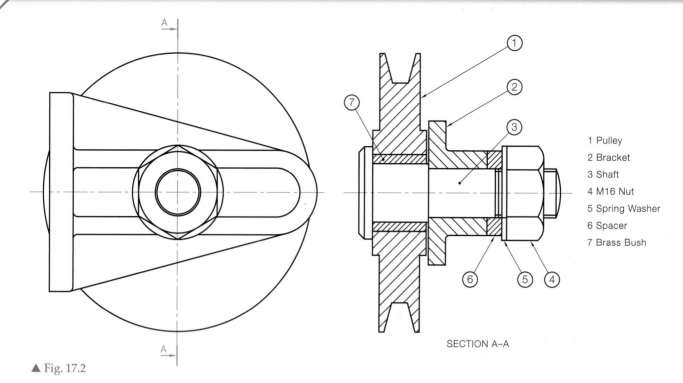

▲ Fig. 17.2

1 Pulley
2 Bracket
3 Shaft
4 M16 Nut
5 Spring Washer
6 Spacer
7 Brass Bush

SECTION A–A

Parts are identified in an assembly drawing by using numbers or letters which refer back to a parts table and the detailed drawings. Circles containing the part numbers are placed beside the parts with leaders ending with arrowheads touching the part. The circles should be placed in orderly, horizontal or vertical rows and should not be scattered over the sheet. The leaders should not cross each other and should be parallel or almost so. Fig. 17.2 shows an assembly drawing with parts list and identification numbers.

 # Sectioning Assemblies

In sectioning assemblies it is important that the sectioning aids in the identification of the individual parts. Figures 17.3a, 17.3b and 17.3c show some of the principles involved when sectioning. The large area is sectioned at 45° in Fig. 17.3a. Spacings between lines should be even and judged by eye. The second large component in Fig. 17.3b is sectioned at 45° in the opposite direction. Care should be taken that the section lines do not meet on the intersection line. Additional components in Fig. 17.3c are sectioned at 30°, 60° or an odd angle. Section lines are placed closer together in smaller areas.

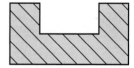

▲ Fig. 17.3a

Some parts of an assembly section are not hatched even though they may lie on the section plane. It is standard practice to show these unsectioned or in the round. Components not to be sectioned:

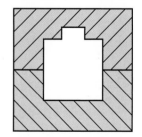

(1) Bolts	**(2)** Nuts	**(3)** Washers
(4) Rivets	**(5)** Shafts	**(6)** Keys
(7) Screws	**(8)** Pins	**(9)** Gear teeth
(10) Spokes	**(11)** Ribs	

▲ Fig. 17.3b

Sectioning of thin parts such as gaskets and sheet metal parts is both difficult and ineffective. Such parts should be shown in solid black.

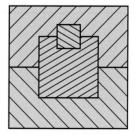

▲ Fig. 17.3c

Sectioning Holes, Tapped Holes, Set Screws, Nuts, Bolts, Washers and Rivets

Section through a drilled hole

▲ Fig. 17.4a

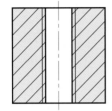

Section through a tapped hole. The sides of the hole formed by the tapping size drill are drawn dark.

▲ Fig. 17.4b

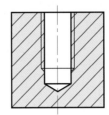

Section through a blind tapped hole. Note the section lines cross the thread to the sides of the hole.

▲ Fig. 17.4c

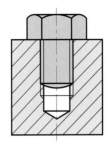

Section through a blind tapped hole with a set screw. Note the section lines are not drawn through the bolt screw thread.

▲ Fig. 17.4d

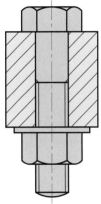

Even though the section cuts through the nut, bolt and washer they are shown in the round

▲ Fig. 17.4e

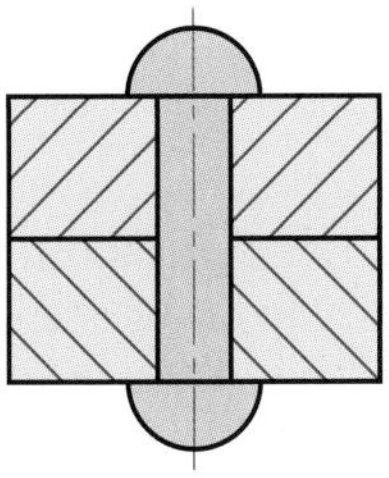

Section through a rivet. The rivet is drawn in the round.

▲ Fig. 17.4f

Sectioning Ribs

To avoid a false sense of solidity, ribs, webs, gear teeth and other thin surfaces are not sectioned even though the section plane passes through their centre plane. Fig. 17.5 shows section plane B–B passing though the rib. Yet the rib is not hatched. When the section plane cuts across a rib or any thin member, then it is sectioned. Fig. 17.5 shows section plane A–A cutting crosswise through the rib and producing a hatched rib.

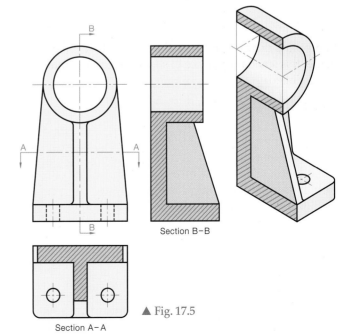

Section B–B

Section A–A

▲ Fig. 17.5

Sectioning Spokes

Spokes, like ribs, are not sectioned. Fig. 17.6 shows a partial view of a valve wheel showing only those features that are needed for minimum representation. No further information is given by drawing the full elevation so only a small portion of it needs to be drawn.

Drawing Conventions

There are many drawing conventions used to help reduce the amount of drawing needed for a particular project yet not compromising on the amount of information provided. As a general rule, drawing repetitive details is avoided and every effort must be made to provide maximum information with minimum drawing.

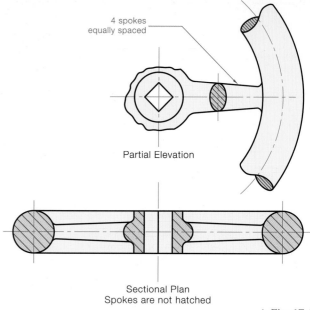

4 spokes equally spaced

Partial Elevation

Sectional Plan
Spokes are not hatched

▲ Fig. 17.6

Symmetrical Parts

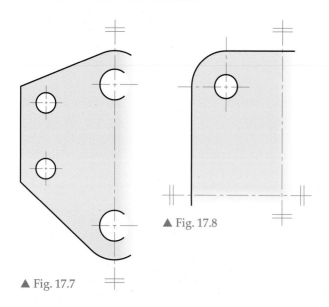

For symmetrical parts about one axis (Fig. 17.7) it is only necessary to draw one side of the shape. The line of symmetry is indicated by placing two parallel lines at each end of it. It is important that the outline is extended slightly past the symmetry line. Fig. 17.8 shows a metal plate with two axes of symmetry. Only a quarter of the plate needs to be drawn.

▲ Fig. 17.8

▲ Fig. 17.7

Repetitive Information

Repeated drawing of identical features is avoided by drawing one object and indicating the position of the others by using centre lines, Fig. 17.9. When holes, bolts and rivets etc. form a pattern, enough centre lines are drawn to establish that pattern (Fig. 17.10). Detailing of a small area of a pattern is often sufficient. Enough of the pattern needs to be drawn to show that it is repetitive.

The shaft support needs only to be drawn once with bolt centre lines shown to locate second bracket.

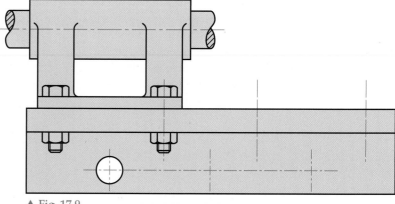

▲ Fig. 17.9

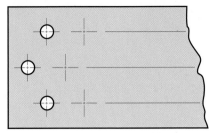

▲ Fig. 17.10

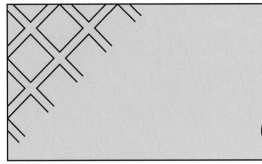

▲ Fig. 17.11

For a regular pattern of holes, rivets etc. only the number necessary to establish the pattern are drawn. An accompanying note will provide sufficient information.

For repetitive patterns such as knurling, chequered plate, perforated sheet, etc. it is sufficient to draw the pattern in a small area. A note indicating that the pattern covers a larger area will reduce the amount of drawing.

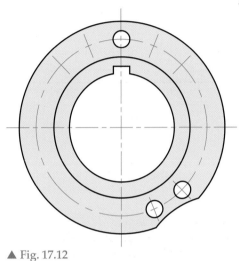

▲ Fig. 17.12

When a special feature such as a keyway or a notch is near to a repetitive feature then the repetitive feature should be drawn in full. Fig. 17.12 shows an example. The repetitive feature, the holes, are drawn in full adjacent to the keyway and the notch.

Conventions for Breaks

In order to shorten a view of an elongated object, it is recommended to use breaks. This often allows the object to be drawn to a larger scale.

If the full object were to be drawn it might have to be scaled down to fit on the sheet.

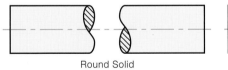

Round Solid

▲ Fig. 17.13a

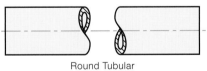

Round Tubular

▲ Fig. 17.13b

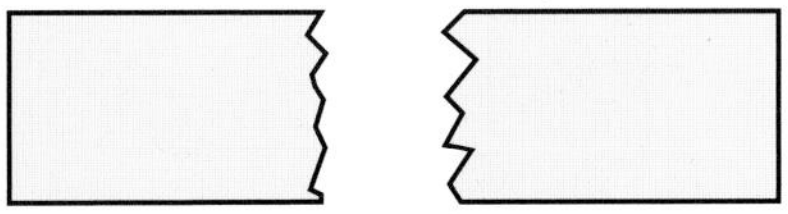

Square/Rectangular

▲ Fig. 17.13c

Conventions for Knurling

A knurl is a roughening of a cylindrical surface, usually to give a better handgrip for tightening/loosening a thread. There are two basic types, straight knurling and diamond knurling. These are shown in Figures 17.14a and 17.14b.

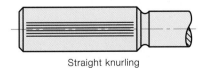

Straight knurling

▲ Fig. 17.14a

Diamond knurling

▲ Fig. 17.14b

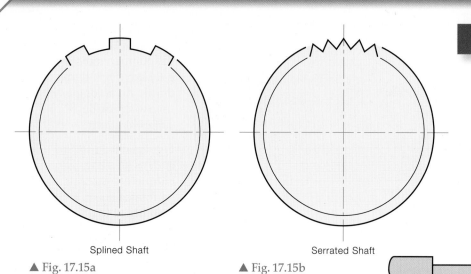

Splined Shaft

▲ Fig. 17.15a

Serrated Shaft

▲ Fig. 17.15b

Shafts

In many cases a shaft will be machined to produce splines or serrations along its length or partially along its length. This machining is to help the shaft transfer torque to another part.

▲ Fig. 17.16a

▲ Fig. 17.16b

Squared Shaft

The end of a cylindrical shaft will often be shaped to produce a square section to receive a handle or adjustment wheel.

Shaft-fixing Devices: Keys and Keyways

One way of preventing a part from slipping on a shaft is to machine a slot, a keyway, into both pieces and to fit a third piece, the key, into this slot. The key ensures there is no relative movement between the two pieces. Figures 17.17a, 17.17b and 17.17c show a number of different types of key and keyway.

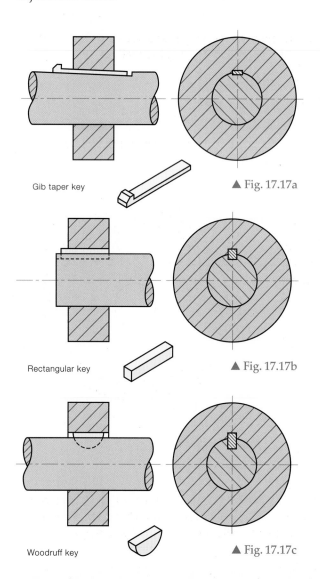

Gib taper key

▲ Fig. 17.17a

Rectangular key

▲ Fig. 17.17b

Woodruff key

▲ Fig. 17.17c

Bearings

These are used to help to reduce friction. There are two basic types – ball bearings and roller bearings. Fig. 17.18 shows pictorials of each type. The hardened steel balls or rollers are held between an inner and outer ring. These rings are called races. Bearings are often sealed units containing the balls/rollers and a lubricant. Roller bearings are used where heavy loading occurs.

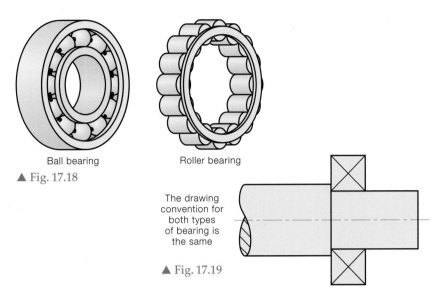

Ball bearing   Roller bearing

▲ Fig. 17.18

The drawing convention for both types of bearing is the same

▲ Fig. 17.19

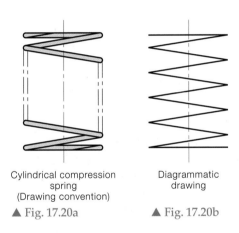

Cylindrical compression spring
(Drawing convention)

▲ Fig. 17.20a

Diagrammatic drawing

▲ Fig. 17.20b

Springs

There are many spring shapes and sizes but they all fit into three categories according to function:

(1) compression,

(2) tension,

(3) torsion.

A few coils are drawn at either end, or the diagrammatic representation may be used.

Spur Gears

A working drawing of a spur gear is shown in Fig. 17.21. It is not necessary to show individual teeth on the drawing. The addendum and the root circles are drawn as solid circles with the pitch circle as a chain line.

In section, the teeth are not sectioned as this would give a false sense of solidity.

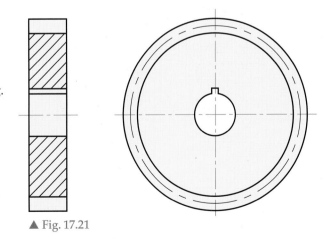

▲ Fig. 17.21

Drawing Standard Bolts

Standard bolts and nuts are not shown on detail drawings but appear regularly on assembly drawings. The conventional way of drawing nuts and bolts is based on the body diameter as shown in Fig. 17.22a. The method for finding the centres for the curves on the bolt head is shown in Fig. 17.22b. Points C_1, C_2 and C_3 are all found with the 60° set-square.

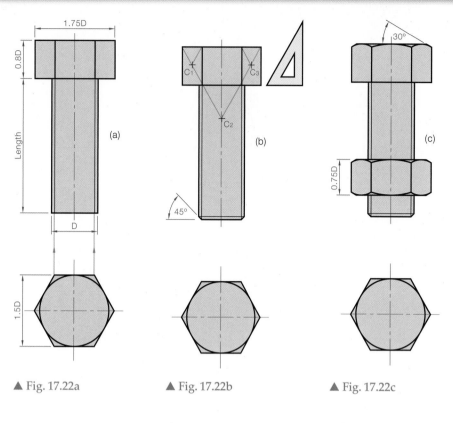

▲ Fig. 17.22a   ▲ Fig. 17.22b   ▲ Fig. 17.22c

The inner thread lines are in line with the two inner edges of the hexagonal head. In general, bolt heads and nuts should be drawn across corners in all views, regardless of projection. This is a violation of projection rules but there are good reasons for it:

(1) It avoids confusion between hexagonal-head bolts and square-head bolts.

(2) It shows the clearance of both bolt heads and nut, in all views.

(3) It is faster to use the same construction in all views.

Bolt heads and nuts should only be drawn across the flats for a very special reason. Fig. 17.23 shows the construction convention used in such a view.

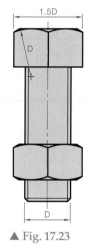

▲ Fig. 17.23

Abbreviations and Their Uses

When producing engineering drawings there are many terms and expressions that need to be included on the drawings. Some of these are used frequently enough to justify the use of abbreviations. Many of these have been standardised.

Abbreviation	Explanation	Diagram
A/C	Across corners	
A/F	Across flats	
Hex HD	Hexagon head	
ASSY	Assembly	
CRS	Centres	
CL or ¢	Centre line	
CHAM	Chamfered	

Abbreviation	Explanation	Diagram
CH HD	Cheese head screw/bolt	CH HD
CSK	Countersunk head screw or countersunk hole	CSK
C'BORE	Counterbore	C'BORE
CYL	Cylindrical	
DIA	Diameter (in a note)	
Ø	Diameter (preceding a dimension)	Ø26 R70
R	Radius. Capital letter only.	
FIG	Figure	
DRG	Drawing	
HEX HD	Hexagonal head	
INSUL	Insulated or insulation	
INT	Internal	
EXT	External	
LH	Left hand	
LG	Long	
MATL	Material	
MAX and MIN	Maximum and minimum	
No.	Number	

Abbreviation	Explanation	Diagram
PCD	Pitch circle diameter	6 x Ø8 hole equally spaced on 60 PCD / 4 x Ø6 holes equally spaced on 35 PCD
REQD	Required	
RH	Right hand	
RD HD	Round head	RD HD
SCR	Screwed	
SH	Sheet	
SK	Sketch	
SPEC	Specification	
SQ	Square (in a note)	
	Square preceding a dimension	□40
STD	Standard	
U'CUT	Undercut	U'CUT
NTS	Not to scale	
RPM	Revolutions per minute	
FIM	Full indicated movement	

Drawings: Layout and Conventions

Title Block

Each sheet must have a title block, generally in the lower right corner. This title block will contain essential information for the identification and interpretation of the drawing. The actual layout of the title block does not matter and may be stamped on, pre-printed or drawn by hand. The following information would generally be given in the title block:

- name of firm,
- name of the object represented or assembly,
- drawing number,
- scale,
- date,
- signature(s),
- projection symbol,
- copyright clause.

As well as this information a whole body of additional information may be included such as material, quantity, treatment/hardness, finish, surface texture, screw thread forms, etc.

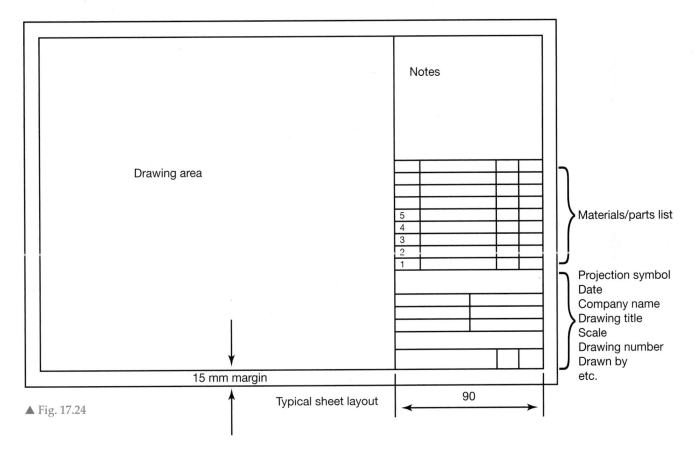

▲ Fig. 17.24

Parts List

A parts list consists of an itemised list of the parts shown on a detail drawing or an assembly drawing. The list should contain the part number, a descriptive title, quantity needed, material used, as well as other information as deemed necessary. The parts should be listed in order of size or importance. The main castings or forgings are listed first; parts cut from cold-rolled stock are second; and standard parts such as bolts, washers and bushing are third. If the parts list is placed as shown in Fig. 17.25 then the order of parts should be from the bottom upwards so that new parts may be added to the list later if necessary.

No.	Part name	REQD	MATL
5	Pin	1	STEEL
4	Pulley	1	CI
3	Hook	1	STEEL
2	Trunnion	1	CI
1	Bracket	1	CI

▲ Fig. 17.25

Standard parts such as bolts, screws and bearings are not drawn, but are listed in the parts list.

Lines and Linework

All lines of a similar type should be consistently dense and bold throughout a drawing. Particular care should be taken with revisions of the drawing so that the new lines are not at variance with existing linework. The table below shows line types and their application.

Type of line	Example	Application of line
Thick continuous	———————	Visible outlines and edges.
Thin continuous	———————	Dimensions and leader lines, hatching, fictitious outlines and edges, outlines of revolved sections.
Short dashes (thin)	– – – – – – –	Hidden outlines and edges.
Chain (thin)	— · — · — · —	Centre lines, pitch circles, extreme positions of moving parts.
Chain (thin but thickened at ends and change of direction)	— · — · —	Cutting planes.
Continuous irregular (thin)	∼∼∼∼∼	Limits of partial views and sections where the line is not an axis.
Thick continuous	— · — · —	A surface that must meet special requirements.

As a general rule, all chain lines should start and finish with a long dash. Centre lines should cross each other at solid portions of the line and should extend only a short distance beyond the feature. Centre lines should not continue through the spaces between views.

Lettering

Characters should be uniform and, most important, legible. They should be of open form and free from serifs and other embellishments. Particular care must be taken with figures because, unlike letters, they rarely fall into patterns and must be read individually. The use of capital letters is preferred to lower case as they are less congested and, even when reduced in size, are less likely to be misread.

System of Projection

The system of projection used on the drawing must be clearly indicated by using the projection symbols.

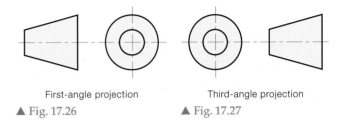

First-angle projection
▲ Fig. 17.26

Third-angle projection
▲ Fig. 17.27

 # Dimensioning

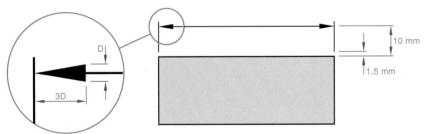

▲ Fig. 17.28

A dimension line is a thin, solid, dark line which ends with arrowheads. The dimension line indicates the direction and extent of a measurement. The dimension nearest the object should be spaced about 10 mm away from the object outline. The extension lines 'extend' from the point on the drawing to which the dimension refers. A gap of about 1.5 mm should be left between the extension line and its reference point and it should continue slightly past the arrowhead. The arrowheads should be uniform in style and size throughout the drawing. Arrowheads should be drawn freehand and have a length and width in a ratio of 3:1.

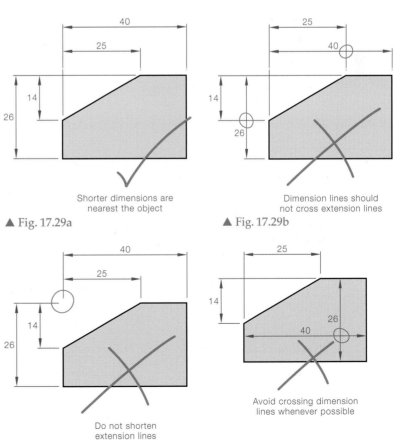

Shorter dimensions are nearest the object
▲ Fig. 17.29a

Dimension lines should not cross extension lines
▲ Fig. 17.29b

Do not shorten extension lines
▲ Fig. 17.29c

Avoid crossing dimension lines whenever possible
▲ Fig. 17.29d

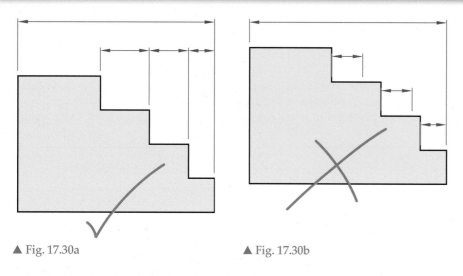

▲ Fig. 17.30a   ▲ Fig. 17.30b

Fig. 17.30a shows how dimensions should be lined up and grouped together. The dimensioning shown in Fig. 17.30b does not show good practice.

Fig. 17.31 shows a method of dimensioning which uses a datum or reference line. By referring all dimensions to a small number of reference lines/points the accumulation of slight inaccuracies can be avoided.

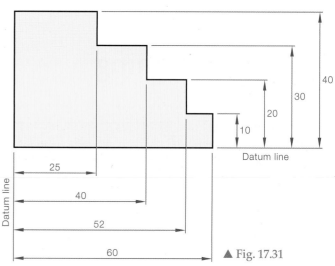

▲ Fig. 17.31

Direction of Dimension Text

There are two accepted systems used for placing dimension text:

• The unidirectional system (preferred).

• The aligned system.

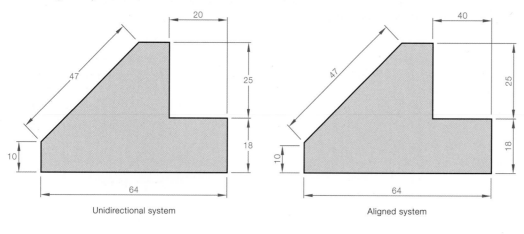

Unidirectional system   Aligned system

▲ Fig. 17.32a   ▲ Fig. 17.32b

Fig. 17.32a shows a figure dimensioned using the unidirectional system. All figures and notes are lettered horizontal on the sheet and are read from the bottom of the sheet.

Fig. 17.32b shows a figure dimensioned using the aligned system. All figures are aligned with the dimension lines so that they can be read from the bottom or the right side of the sheet.

Leaders

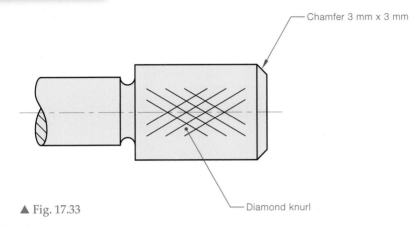

Chamfer 3 mm x 3 mm

Diamond knurl

▲ Fig. 17.33

A leader is a line leading from a note or dimension and ending with an arrowhead or a dot touching a part. Arrowheads should always terminate on a line such as the edge of a hole, while dots should be within the outline of the object, Fig. 17.33. The leader line itself should generally be inclined and should start from the beginning or end of a note.

Leaders should cross as few lines as possible and should never cross each other. If there are a large number of leaders beside each other on a drawing they should be drawn parallel. When a leader points to a hole or arc it should be radial so that if extended it would pass through the centre.

Dimensioning Circles

When dimensioning holes and circles the method used depends on the circle size. Fig. 17.34 shows four different methods. Apart from the last example they are all radial.

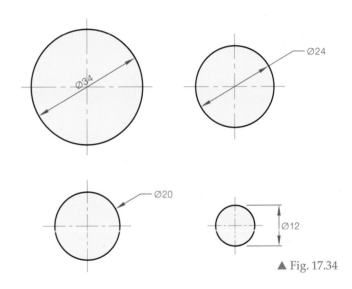

Ø34

Ø24

Ø20

Ø12

▲ Fig. 17.34

Dimensioning Arcs

Circular arcs are dimensioned in a view showing their true shapes. The centre of the arc may be indicated by using a small cross or centre lines but this is not done for small radii.

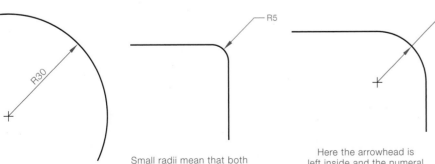

R30

R5

R15

When there is room both the numeral and arrowhead are placed inside the curve

▲ Fig. 17.35a

Small radii mean that both the arrowhead and the numeral are placed outside

▲ Fig. 17.35b

Here the arrowhead is left inside and the numeral is placed outside

▲ Fig. 17.35c

Fillets on a drawing are usually of a standard size throughout and rather than dimension each one it is customary to place a note in the lower portion of the drawing. 'FILLETS R6 UNLESS OTHERWISE SPECIFIED'.

Dimensioning Angles

One of the three methods indicated in Figures 17.36a, 17.36b and 17.36c is used depending on the space inside the angle for numerals and arrowheads.

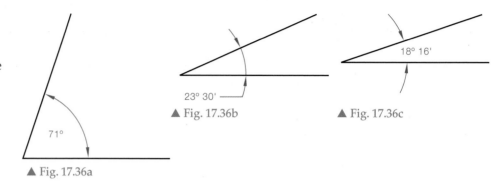

23° 30'

▲ Fig. 17.36b

18° 16'

▲ Fig. 17.36c

71°

▲ Fig. 17.36a

Chamfers and Tapers

Chamfers are dimensioned by giving the length of the offset and the angle, or in the case of a 45° chamfer, usually by note, Fig. 17.37.

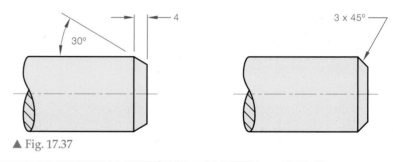

30°

4

3 x 45°

▲ Fig. 17.37

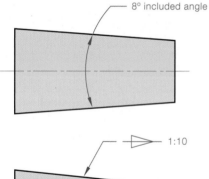

8° included angle

Tapers, which are conical surfaces on shafts or in holes, are used on machine spindles, shanks of tools, pins, etc. They are generally indicated using either of the two methods shown in Fig. 17.38.

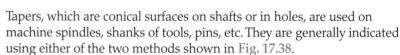

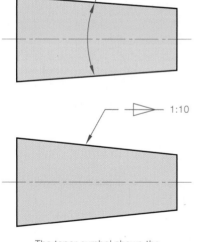

1:10

The taper symbol shows the direction of taper

▲ Fig. 17.38

Worked Examples: Sectional Views

There are many times when the interior detail of an object cannot be seen from the outside, Fig. 17.39. We get around this, as explained earlier in the chapter, by cutting the object by a plane and showing the sectional view.

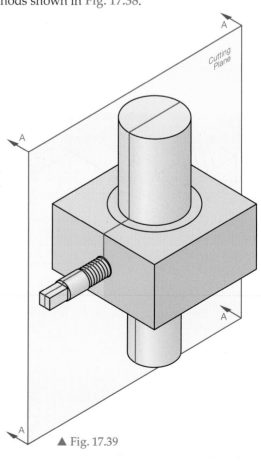

Cutting Plane

▲ Fig. 17.39

In Fig. 17.41 the cutting plane A–A slices through the object. Fig. 17.40 shows how the object looks when the front material is removed. The orthographic view of this section is shown in Fig. 17.41. The shaft is shown in the round as per normal convention. The retaining screw is drawn as shown. The sectional view gives a clear view of the inside of the object and is easy to draw. The parts are balloon-referenced.

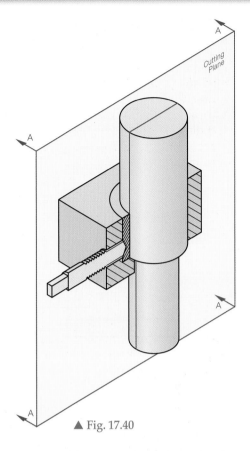

▲ Fig. 17.40

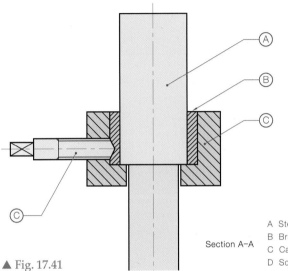

Section A–A

A Steel shaft or spindle
B Brass bush or bearing
C Cast-iron block
D Square-head retaining screw

▲ Fig. 17.41

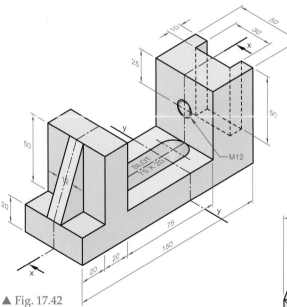

▲ Fig. 17.42

Given the isometric projection of a machine vice body in Fig. 17.42. Draw to full-size using first-angle projection.

(i)   A sectional front elevation on X–X.
(ii) A sectional end elevation on Y–Y.
(iii) A full plan.
(iv) Insert seven leading dimensions.

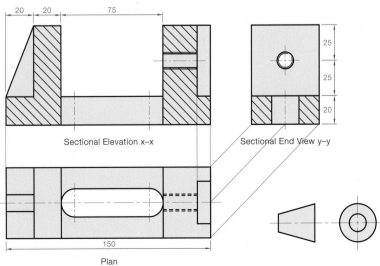

Sectional Elevation x–x

Sectional End View y–y

Plan

MACHINE VICE BODY

▲ Fig. 17.43

There are several things to note from the solution in Fig. 17.43.

(1) The rib is not hatched in the sectional elevation X–X even though the plane passes through it.

(2) The hatch lines in the sectional elevation X–X continue through the threads for the threaded hole.

(3) The projection symbol is shown.

Given the plan and elevation of a machined casting in Fig. 17.44.

(i) Draw the front elevation as shown.

(ii) Project a sectional plan from cutting plane A–A.

(iii) Project a sectional end view from cutting plane B–B. Insert the projection symbol, title and four leading dimensions.

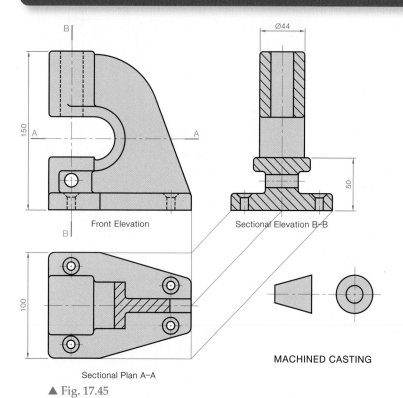

Front Elevation   Sectional Elevation B–B

MACHINED CASTING

Sectional Plan A–A

▲ Fig. 17.45

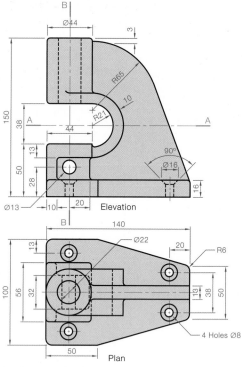

Elevation

Plan

All radii not specified to be 3 mm

▲ Fig. 17.44

In general, do not show hidden detail in sectional views.

The rib is sectioned in plan because the cutting plane cuts through it perpendicularly.

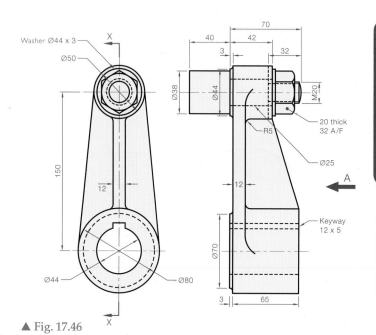

▲ Fig. 17.46

Given the projections of a CRANK AND PIN assembly.

(i) Draw an elevation looking in the direction of arrow A.

(ii) Draw a sectional end view on X–X.

(iii) Add the parts list, balloon reference the parts and include four main dimensions.

Use first-angle projection.

REF	DESCRIPTION	MATL	QTY
4	NUT	MS	1
3	WASHER	MS	1
2	PIN	MS	1
1	CRANK	CI	1

(1) The section X–X is to be viewed from the right, so therefore the sectional view is drawn on the left.

(2) In the sectional view the rib, pin, washer and nut are not sectioned.

(3) Hidden detail is generally not necessary.

(4) The keyway is not sectioned.

(5) Try to keep the leaders for the balloon references parallel and keep the balloon circles in line vertically or horizontally.

(6) The projection symbol must be drawn.

(7) The parts list is numbered from bottom to top.

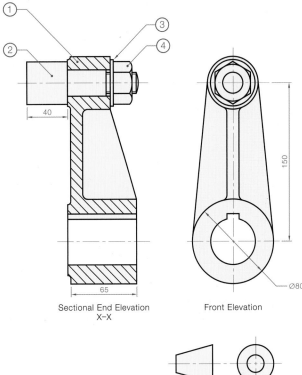

▲ Fig. 17.47

4	NUT	MS	1
3	WASHER	MS	1
2	PIN	MS	1
1	CRANK	CI	1
REF	DESCRIPTION	MATL	QTY
CRANK AND PIN			

Worked Examples: Assemblies

See worksheet 17.1

Details of a Pulley Assembly are shown in Figures 17.48a to 17.48d with the parts list tabulated.

(i) Make a sectional front elevation of the assembled parts on section plane A–A.

(ii) Project a side elevation in the direction of arrow X.

(iii) Insert the following on the drawing:

- Title: Pulley Assembly, • ISO projection symbol, • Four leading dimensions.

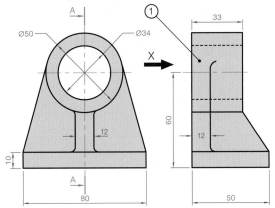

▲ Fig. 17.48a

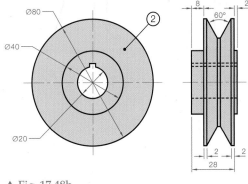

▲ Fig. 17.48b

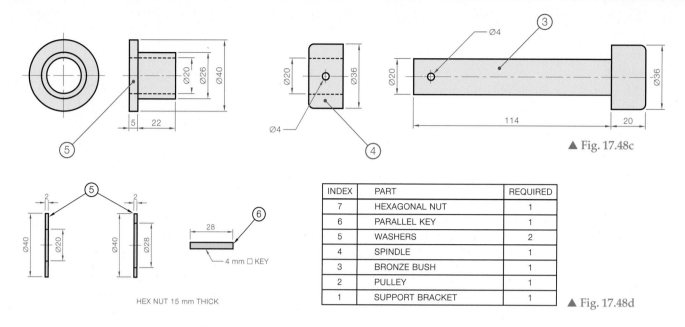

▲ Fig. 17.48c

HEX NUT 15 mm THICK

4 mm □ KEY

INDEX	PART	REQUIRED
7	HEXAGONAL NUT	1
6	PARALLEL KEY	1
5	WASHERS	2
4	SPINDLE	1
3	BRONZE BUSH	1
2	PULLEY	1
1	SUPPORT BRACKET	1

▲ Fig. 17.48d

Solution

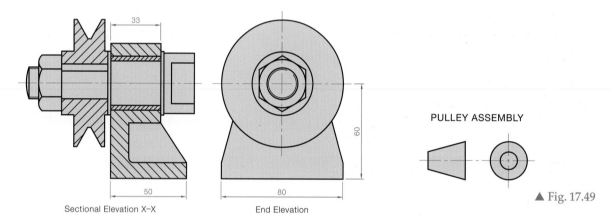

Sectional Elevation X–X

End Elevation

PULLEY ASSEMBLY

▲ Fig. 17.49

See worksheets 17.2 and 17.3

Details of a PIVOT SUPPORT are shown in Figures 17.50a to 17.50d with parts list tabulated. Make the following drawings of the assembled parts:

(i)   A sectional elevation in the direction of arrows A–A.

(ii) A sectional end elevation in the direction of arrows X–X.

(iii) A plan projected from the front elevation.

Insert the title PIVOT SUPPORT and the ISO symbol.

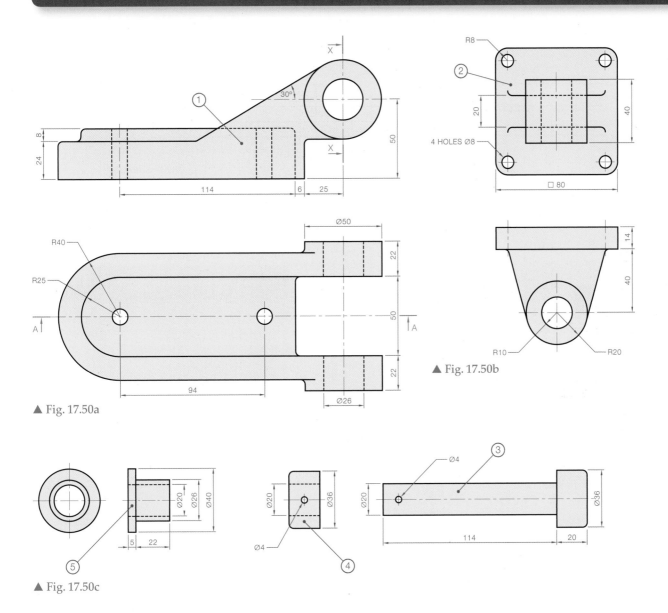

▲ Fig. 17.50a

▲ Fig. 17.50b

▲ Fig. 17.50c

INDEX	PART	REQUIRED
1	BODY CASTING	1
2	SUPPORT CASTING	1
3	PIN	1
4	COLLAR	1
5	BRONZE BUSH	2
6	SPLIT PIN	1

▲ Fig. 17.50d

Solution

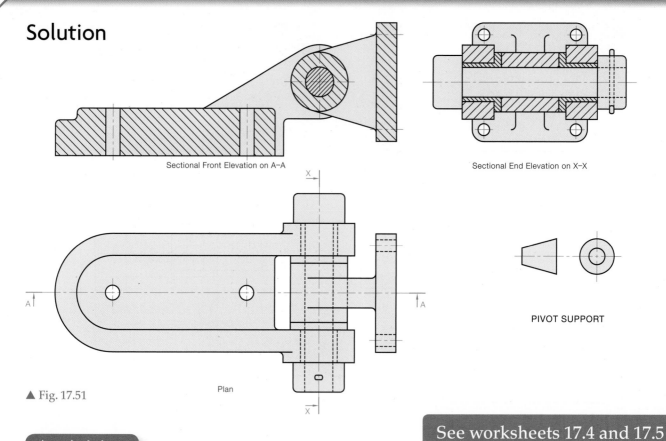

Sectional Front Elevation on A–A

Sectional End Elevation on X–X

PIVOT SUPPORT

▲ Fig. 17.51

Plan

See worksheets 17.4 and 17.5

Activities

Dimensions

Q1. Using the data below, make a fully dimensioned drawing of the machine part shown in **Fig. 17.52**.

1. Diameter 22, length 24.
2. Square 32, length 16.
3. Diameter 54, length 20, chamfer 3 × 3. Diamond knurl finish.
4. Taper: Max. diameter 40, min. diameter 24, length 40.
5. Undercut, length 3, diameter 16.
6. Included angle of 60°.

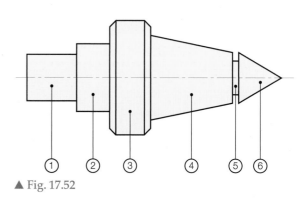

▲ Fig. 17.52

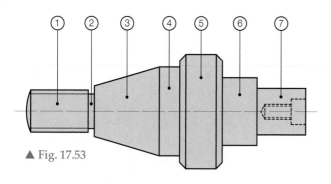

▲ Fig. 17.53

Q2. Using the data below, make a fully dimensioned drawing of the shaft shown in **Fig. 17.53**.

1. Screwthread: metric 20, pitch 2, length 30.
2. Undercut: length 3, diameter 16.
3. Taper: max. diameter 42, min. diameter 24, length 32.
4. Diameter 42, length 10.
5. Diameter 54, length 21, chamfer 3 × 3. Diamond knurl finish.
6. Diameter 32, length 17.
7. Square 22, length 24, hole threaded M7, 20 deep, counter-bored diameter 12, 7 deep.

Sectional views

Q3. A front elevation and plan of a casting are shown in **Fig. 17.54**.

    (i)   Draw a sectional elevation on plane B–B.

    (ii)   Draw a sectional plan on plane A–A.

    (iii)   An end view showing all hidden detail.

    (iv)   Insert five leading dimensions, the first-angle projection symbol and the title 'GATE SUPPORT'.

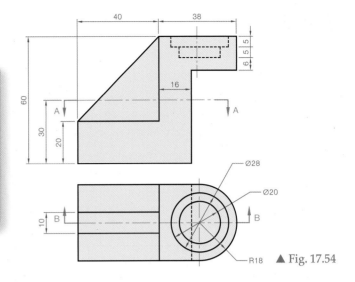

▲ Fig. 17.54

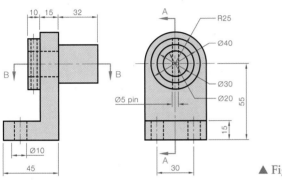

▲ Fig. 17.55

Q4. A front elevation and end view of a ring, a shaft, a pin and a bracket.

    (i)   Draw a sectional elevation on A–A.

    (ii)   Draw a sectional plan on B–B.

    (iii)   Insert four leading dimensions, the projection symbol and the title 'SHAFT SUPPORT BRACKET'.

Q5. Details of a pulley assembly are given in **Fig. 17.56**. The parts list is tabulated.

(1) Make the following drawings of the assembled parts:

    (i)   A sectional front elevation on section plane A–A.

    (ii)   A full plan projected from the front elevation.

    (iii)   An end elevation in the direction of arrow B.

(2) Insert the following on the drawing:

    (i)   Title: 'PULLEY ASSEMBLY'.

    (ii)   ISO projection symbol.

    (iii)   Five leading dimensions.

Index	Part	Required
1	Support Bracket	1
2	Shaft	1
3	Pulley	1
	Hex Nut M25	1
	Washer Ext Ø64, Int Ø42 1.5 mm thick	1
	Washer Ext Ø64, Int Ø28 2 mm thick	1

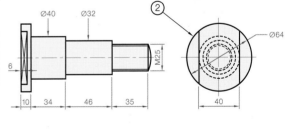

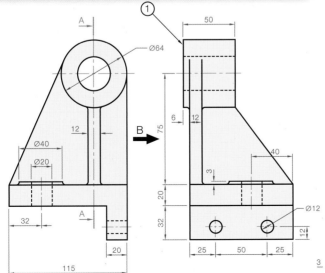

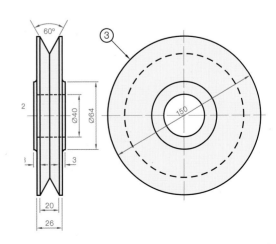

▲ Fig. 17.56

Q6. Details of a pulley hook assembly are shown in **Fig. 17.57**. The parts list is tabulated.

(1) Make the following drawings of the assembled parts:

(i) A front elevation viewed in the direction of arrow A.

(ii) A sectional side elevation on section plane B–B.

(2) Insert the following on the drawing:

(i) Title: 'PULLEY AND HOOK ASSEMBLY'.

(ii) ISO projection symbol.

(iii) Four leading dimensions.

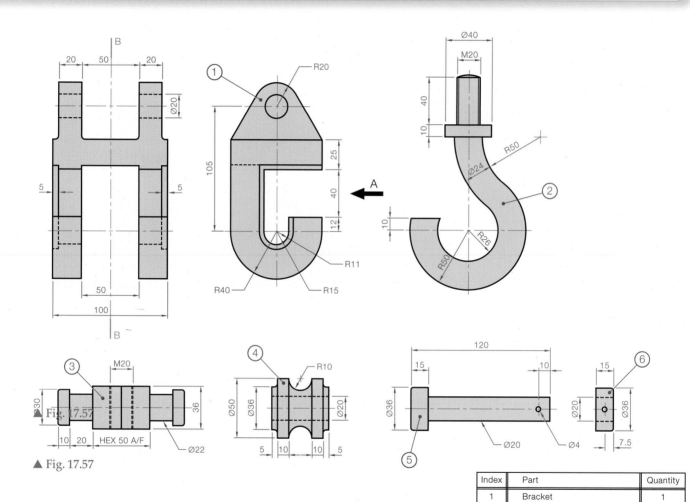

▲ Fig. 17.57

Index	Part	Quantity
1	Bracket	1
2	Hook	1
3	Trunnion	1
4	Pulley	1
5	Pin	1
6	Collar	1
7	Split Pin	1

Q7. **Details of a universal joint are shown in Fig. 17.58. The parts list is tabulated.**

(1) Make the following drawings of the assembled parts.

    (i) A sectional front elevation on section plane A–A.

    (ii) An end elevation viewed in the direction of arrow B.

(2) Insert the following on the drawing:

    (i) Title: 'UNIVERSAL JOINT'.

    (ii) ISO projection symbol.

    (iii) Four leading dimensions.

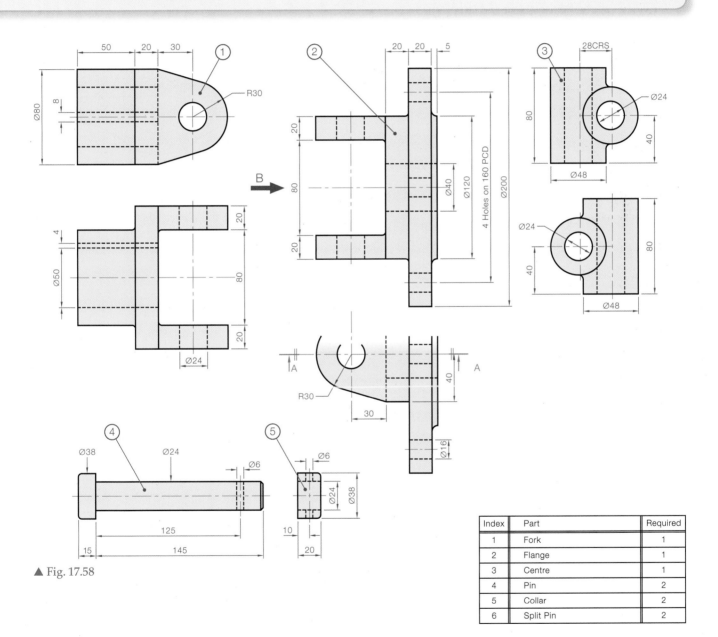

▲ Fig. 17.58

Index	Part	Required
1	Fork	1
2	Flange	1
3	Centre	1
4	Pin	2
5	Collar	2
6	Split Pin	2

Sectional Views: More Alternatives

For all the examples shown in the previous pages, single-plane sectional views have been used. There are several other useful methods of finding sectional views which we will now examine more closely.

Half Sections

These can be very useful for symmetrical objects. The cutting plane removes one quarter of the object and shows the interior of one half of the object and the exterior of the other half. The half section is at its most useful in assembly drawings where it is possible to show an internal assembly and an external construction on the same view.

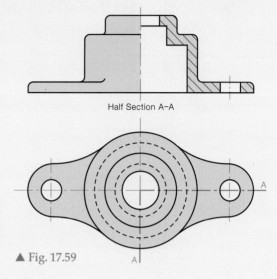

Half Section A–A

▲ Fig. 17.59

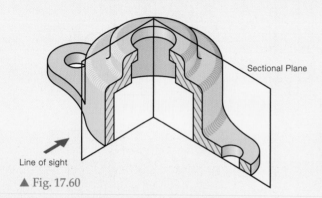

Sectional Plane

Line of sight

▲ Fig. 17.60

It can be seen from the pictorial, Fig. 17.60, that the section plane removes one quarter of the object. Half sections will often present difficulty when dimensioning and for this reason hidden lines are often included in the unsectioned half.

Broken-out Sections

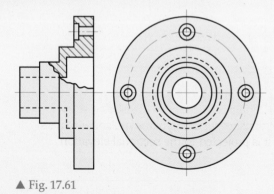

▲ Fig. 17.61

A broken-out section is used when only a small area of the object(s) needs to be sectioned in order to explain the construction. A full section or even a half section are not necessary. The edges of a broken-out section are limited by a break line. Fig. 17.61 shows an example of a broken-out section.

Successive Sections

When an object such as a bar, spoke or arm changes shape along its longitudinal axis, this change can be shown by using successive sections as shown in Fig. 17.62.

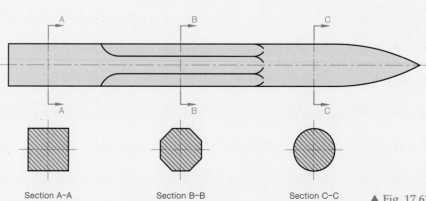

Section A–A   Section B–B   Section C–C   ▲ Fig. 17.62

HIGHER LEVEL

Revolved Sections

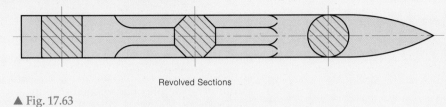

Revolved Sections

▲ Fig. 17.63

Revolved sections show the shape of the cross-section on the actual view of the part. Such sections are made by assuming a plane perpendicular to the centre line or axis and then revolving the plane through 90° about a centre line so that the true shape of the section can be seen. The section is actually superimposed on the object and all original lines covered by it should be removed.

Offset Sections

When sectioning irregular objects it is possible to show several features in section even though they do not lie in a straight line. The cutting plane is bent or offset to pass through each of the features. The sectional view produced is called an offset section. Fig. 17.64 shows an example of an offset section. It can be seen that the cutting plane in elevation is bent twice at 90° in order to pass through the centres of the two holes, one of which can be seen in elevation and the other in plan. **The bends or offsets in the cutting plane are never shown in the sectional view**.

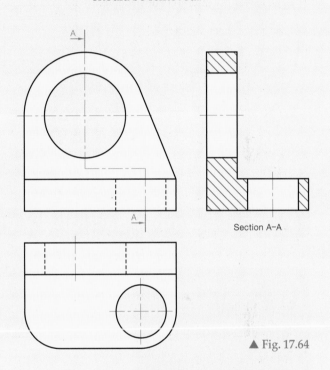

Section A–A

▲ Fig. 17.64

Aligned Sections

In an aligned section, the cutting plane is bent to pass through an angled element. The plane and section are then imagined to be revolved to align with the main direction of the cut. Fig. 17.65 shows cutting plane A–A bent to pass through the angled arm, and then rotated to a horizontal position where it is projected to the sectional elevation.

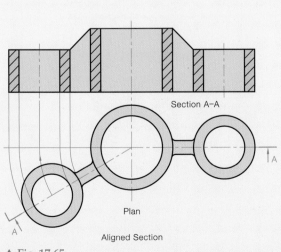

Section A–A

Plan

Aligned Section

▲ Fig. 17.65

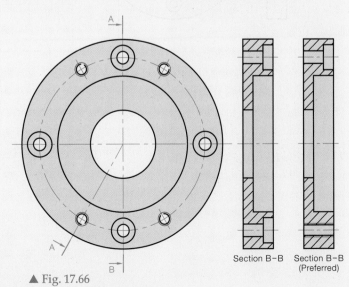

Section B–B

Section B–B (Preferred)

▲ Fig. 17.66

HIGHER LEVEL

Fig. 17.66 shows a second example of an aligned section. The cutting plane is bent to include one of the drilled and counter-bored holes and one of the threaded holes. The aligned section A–A produces a much more informative view than does section A–B which is a vertical section taken along the centre line.

For all aligned sections the angle of revolution should always be less than 90º.

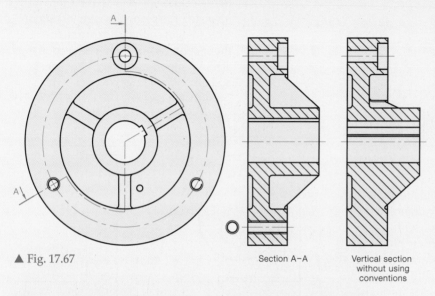

▲ Fig. 17.67

Section A–A

Vertical section without using conventions

Another example of an aligned section is shown in Fig. 17.67. The cutting plane is offset in circular arc bends to include the upper counter-bored hole, the upper rib, the keyway, the centre hole, the lower rib and one of the lower threaded holes. These features are imagined to be revolved to line up vertically and then projected to give the section.

It is now worth looking at the second section drawn. This is a vertical section through the centre without using conventions, e.g. the rib is hatched. This section is less informative, confusing and takes longer to draw.

Worked Example: Sectional Views

Figure 17.68 shows two views of a gear housing in third-angle projection.

(1) Make the following drawings in third-angle projection:

   (i) A sectional elevation on the cutting plane X–X.

   (ii) A sectional elevation on the cutting plane Y–Y.

   (iii) A sectional plan on cutting plane Z–Z.

Hidden details need not be shown.

(2) Insert the following on the drawing:

   (i) Title 'GEAR HOUSING'.

   (ii) ISO projection symbol.

   (iii) Four leading dimensions.

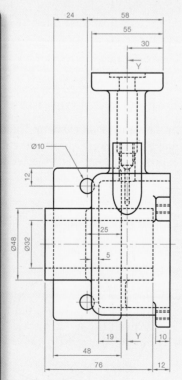

▲ Fig. 17.68

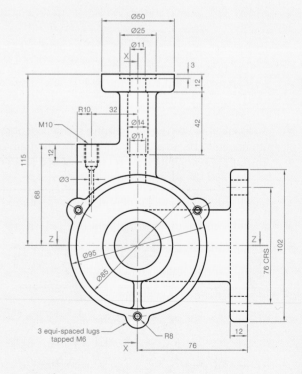

Solution

GEAR HOUSING

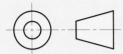

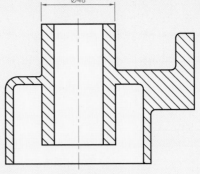

Sectional Elevation Z–Z

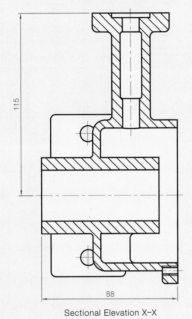

Sectional Elevation X–X

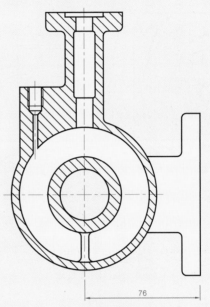

Sectional Elevation Y–Y

▲ Fig. 17.69

Worked Examples

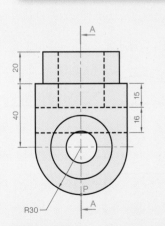

▲ Fig. 17.70

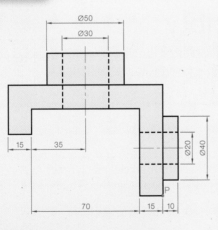

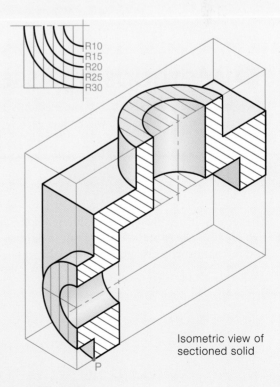

Isometric view of sectioned solid

Fig. 17.70 shows two elevations of a machine casting. Draw an isometric view of the casting, viewed on the section plane S–S, with the right-hand side removed. Make point P the lowest point of the drawing.

▲ Fig. 17.71

HIGHER LEVEL

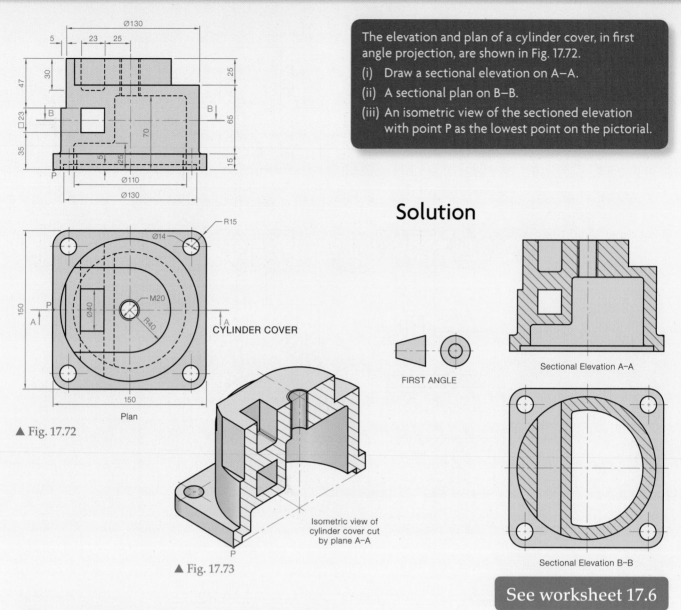

The elevation and plan of a cylinder cover, in first angle projection, are shown in Fig. 17.72.
(i) Draw a sectional elevation on A–A.
(ii) A sectional plan on B–B.
(iii) An isometric view of the sectioned elevation with point P as the lowest point on the pictorial.

Solution

CYLINDER COVER

Plan

▲ Fig. 17.72

FIRST ANGLE

Sectional Elevation A–A

Isometric view of cylinder cover cut by plane A–A

P

▲ Fig. 17.73

Sectional Elevation B–B

See worksheet 17.6

Methods of Assembly

There are many methods used to join elements of an assembly, ranging from bolts, screws and studs and rivets to folded seams and welded joints. We will look at each of these areas in a little more detail.

Bolts

The term 'bolt' usually refers to a through bolt which passes through clearance holes in two or more pieces and receives a nut to tighten and hold the parts together. The head and nut are usually hexagonal but may be square.

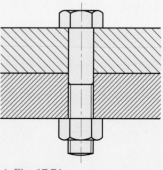

▲ Fig. 17.74

Cap Screws

Cap screws usually pass through a clearance hole in one member and screw into another which acts as the nut. A cap screw generally has a greater length of thread than a bolt. There is a large range of head types on cap screws as shown in Figure 17.75.

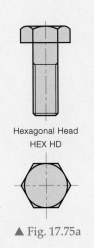 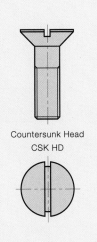   

Hexagonal Head
HEX HD

Countersunk Head
CSK HD

Pan Head
PAN HD

Round Head
RD HD

Cheese Head
CH HD

▲ Fig. 17.75a

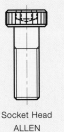 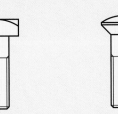 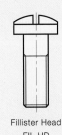

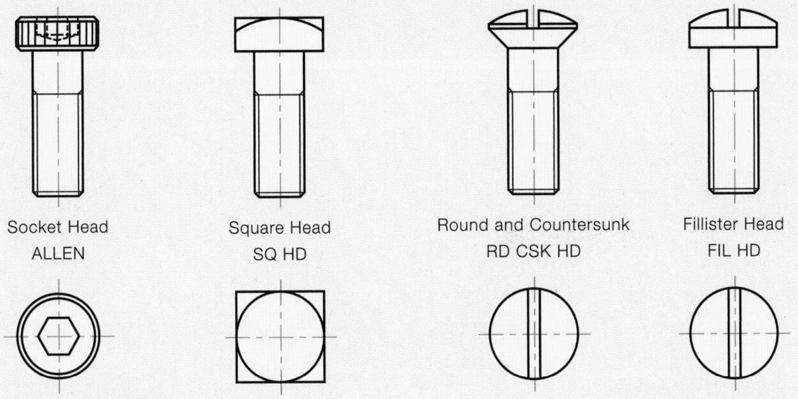

Most of the heads of the cap screws have been shown with slots to receive a flat-head screwdriver. They are also produced to accommodate other types of screwdriver.

Socket Head
ALLEN

Square Head
SQ HD

Round and Countersunk
RD CSK HD

Fillister Head
FIL HD

▲ Fig. 17.75b

Stud

A stud is a steel rod which has been threaded on both ends. The stud is usually passed through a clearance hole in one member and screwed into the other member. A nut is then tightened onto the free end as shown in Fig. 17.76. The end of the stud may have a slot or an Allen key socket to aid in its insertion into the threaded hole.

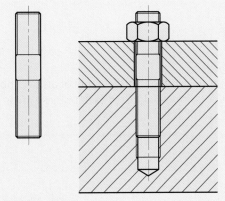

▲ Fig. 17.76

Machine Screws

Machine screws are similar to cap screws but are much smaller. They are threaded nearly to the head and are very useful for screwing into thin material.

HIGHER LEVEL

Set Screws

A set screw is used to prevent relative motion between two parts. Their most common use is to secure pulleys, etc. onto their axle shafts. The set screw is screwed into one part and its point puts pressure on the other part. If a little flat area is milled onto the shaft where the set screw is to make contact with it, then a much stronger fixing is achieved. Set screws are not able to cope with heavy loads or loads that are applied suddenly. Figures 17.77a to 17.77c show a number of set screws and some possible variations in the tip shape.

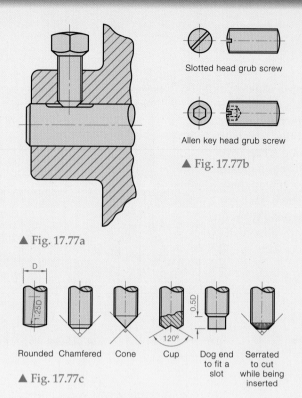

Slotted head grub screw

Allen key head grub screw

▲ Fig. 17.77b

▲ Fig. 17.77a

D

1.25D

0.5D

120°

Rounded Chamfered Cone Cup Dog end to fit a slot Serrated to cut while being inserted

▲ Fig. 17.77c

Lock Nuts and Locking Devices

There are many special nuts and devices to ensure that nuts do not work loose due to vibration during their working life. Some of the more common types are shown in Figures 17.78a to 17.78h.

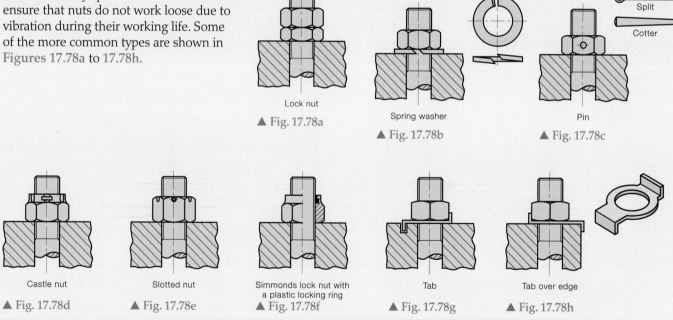

Lock nut

▲ Fig. 17.78a

Spring washer

▲ Fig. 17.78b

Split

Cotter

Pin

▲ Fig. 17.78c

Castle nut

▲ Fig. 17.78d

Slotted nut

▲ Fig. 17.78e

Simmonds lock nut with a plastic locking ring

▲ Fig. 17.78f

Tab

▲ Fig. 17.78g

Tab over edge

▲ Fig. 17.78h

Rivets

Rivets are seen as a permanent method of joining sheet metal and rolled steel together. They are made from wrought iron, soft steel, copper, brass and occasionally other metals. Each rivet has one pre-formed head; the second head is formed using a hammer and a 'dolly bar' or by machine. The process of forming the second head compresses the shank of the rivet, pushing it against the sides of the hole. A number of different rivet heads are shown in Figures 17.79a to 17.79f.

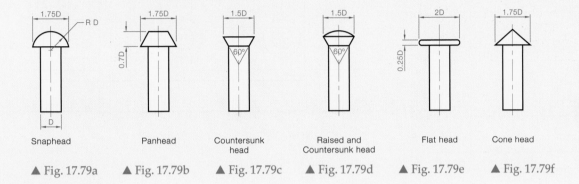

Snaphead	Panhead	Countersunk head	Raised and Countersunk head	Flat head	Cone head
▲ Fig. 17.79a	▲ Fig. 17.79b	▲ Fig. 17.79c	▲ Fig. 17.79d	▲ Fig. 17.79e	▲ Fig. 17.79f

Welding

Welding is a method of joining metals by using heat to melt and fuse them together. A filler metal is usually necessary to fill the joint. Because of the range of welded joints, a system of symbols is used to display the complete welding information on a drawing in a simple and clear manner, see Fig. 17.80.

A: Joint – the joint is shown as a butt joint regardless of the type of weld joint to be used.

B: Arrow – indicates joint line.

C: Reference line.

D: Weld symbol.

Some welding symbols are shown below in Figure 17.81.

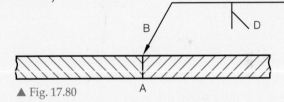

▲ Fig. 17.80

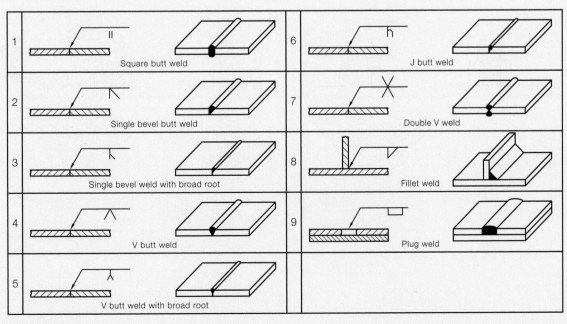

1	Square butt weld	6	J butt weld
2	Single bevel butt weld	7	Double V weld
3	Single bevel weld with broad root	8	Fillet weld
4	V butt weld	9	Plug weld
5	V butt weld with broad root		

▲ Fig. 17.81

Activities

Offset sections

Q1. **(i)** Draw the given elevations of the machined block as shown in **Fig. 17.82**.

(ii) Project an offset sectional plan A–A from the elevation.

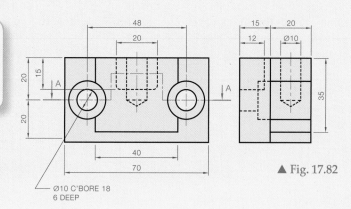

▲ Fig. 17.82

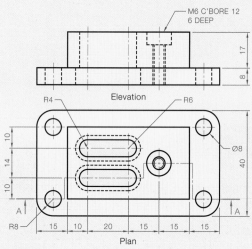

▲ Fig. 17.83

Q2. Given the plan and elevation of a shaped block in Fig. 17.83.

(i) Draw the given plan.

(ii) Project the offset section on section plane A–A.

Q3 and Q4.

In **Figures 17.84** and **17.85** you are given the plan and elevation of a shaped block.

(i) Draw the given views.

(ii) Project an aligned end view on plane A–A.

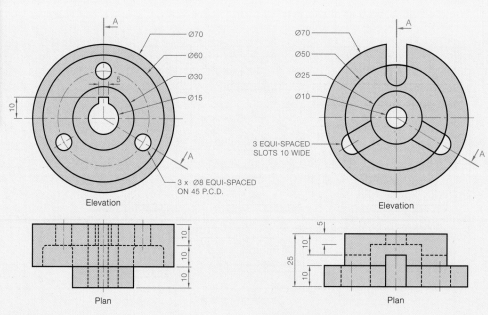

▲ Fig. 17.84   ▲ Fig. 17.85

Half sections

Q5. and Q6.

In **Figures 17.86** and **17.87** the plan and elevation of a shaped block are given.

(i) Draw the given views.

(ii) Project a halfsectional end view on cutting plane B–B.

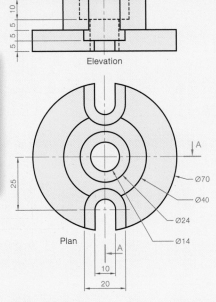

▲ Fig. 17.86

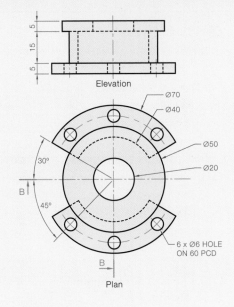

▲ Fig. 17.87

Q7.

Given two elevations of a vehicle rear hub.

(i) Draw the given front elevation.

(ii) Project a half section on cutting plane AAA.

(iii) Draw an isometric view of the half section showing a good view of the cut-out section.

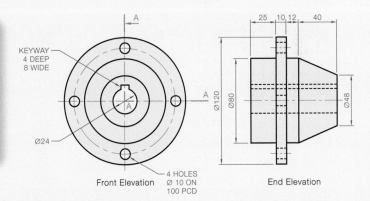

▲ Fig. 17.88

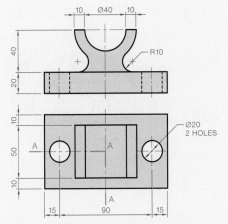

▲ Fig. 17.89

Q8.

Fig. 17.89 shows a guide shoe.

(i) Draw the given plan and project a half-sectional elevation on AAA.

(ii) Draw an isometric view of the shoe with the quadrant removed showing a good view of the cut surfaces.

Q9. Using notes and diagrams explain the difference in appearance and use of:
- bolts,
- cap screws,
- set screws.

Q10. Make neat diagrams (plan and elevation) of the following cap screws:
- Countersunk head (CSK HD).
- Round head (RD HD).
- Fillister head (FIL HD).
- Cheese head (CH HD).

Q11. Make a neat diagram of four different methods of locking a nut to ensure it does not accidentally work loose.

Q12. Make a neat diagram of the following rivet types:
- Pan head.
- Countersunk head.
- Snap head.

Q13. Make a neat diagram of a welding symbol and indicate on the symbol the important parts.

Q14. Details of a Non-return Valve are given in Fig. 17.90. The parts list is tabulated.

  (i) Draw a full sectional elevation of the assembly corresponding to the given sectional elevation of the body. The valve should be in the closed position.

  (ii) Insert:
- The title 'NON-RETURN VALVE'.
- Reference numbers to identify the parts.
- Four leading dimensions.
- ISO projection symbol.

Part No.	Name	Required
1	Body	1
2	Valve Seat	1
3	Valve	1
4	Cover	1
5	Seal	1

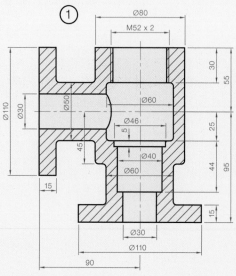

Fillet Radii R3

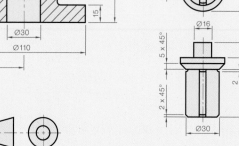

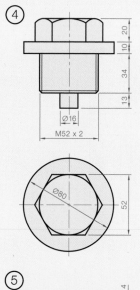

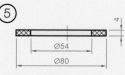

▲ Fig. 17.90

Q15. Details of a Welding Fixture are given in Fig. 17.91 with the parts list tabulated.

(i) Draw a full-size sectional elevation S–S of the assembled parts.

(ii) Insert:

- Item reference numbers.
- ISO projection symbol.
- Title 'WELDING FIXTURE'.
- Four leading dimensions.

Part No.	Description	Required
1	Body	1
2	Hinge	2
3	Jaw	2
4	Screw	2
5	Spindle	2
6	Circlip (not shown)	2

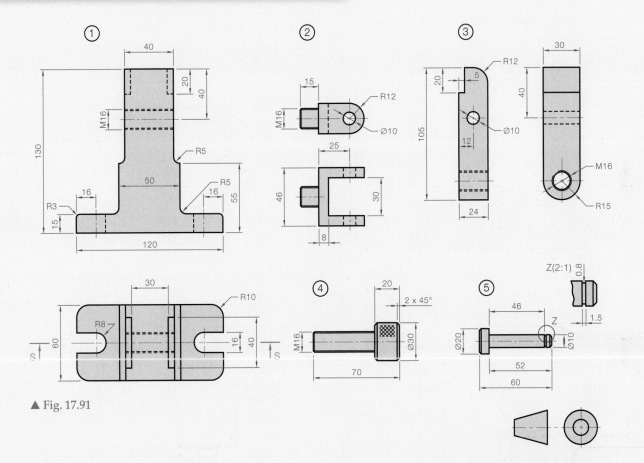

▲ Fig. 17.91

Q15. Details of a Welding Fixture are given in Fig. 17.91 with the parts list tabulated.

(i) Draw a full-size sectional elevation S–S of the assembled parts.

(ii) Insert:
- Item reference numbers.
- ISO projection symbol.
- Title 'WELDING FIXTURE'.
- Four leading dimensions.

Part No.	Description	Required
1	Body	1
2	Hinge	2
3	Jaw	2
4	Screw	2
5	Spindle	2
6	Circlip (not shown)	2

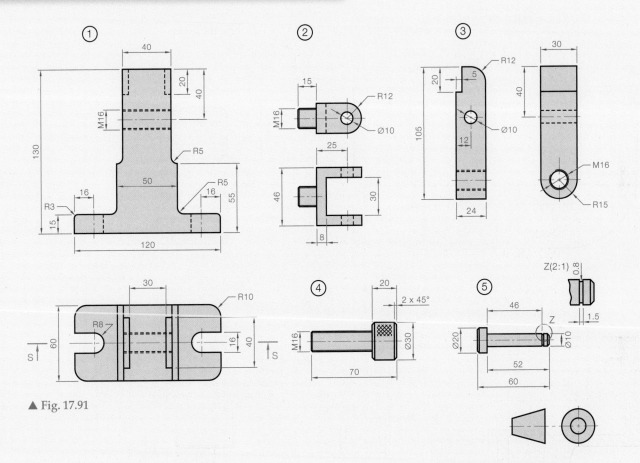

▲ Fig. 17.91

Q16. Details of a PIPE FLARING TOOL are shown in Fig. 17.92 with the parts list tabulated.

(i) Draw an elevation of the assembly showing the working parts in section and flaring a copper pipe. Pipe dimensions: outside diameter 15 mm, inside diameter 12 mm.

(ii) Balloon reference the parts and add the title 'FLARING TOOL ASSEMBLY'.

Part No.	Description	Required
1	Body	1
2	Half die	2
3	Die lock nut	1
4	Punch	1
5	Pressure screw	1
6	Handle	1

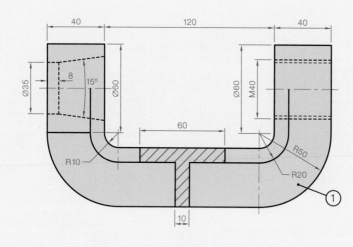

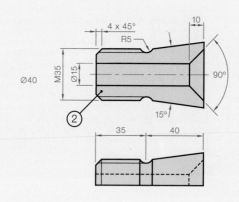

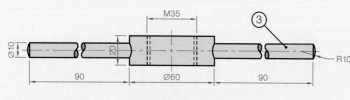

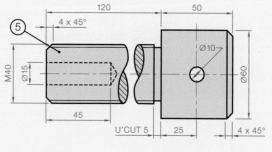

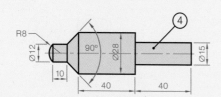

▲ Fig. 17.92